CHRONIC
PSYCHOSES

❀❀❀❀❀❀❀❀❀❀❀❀❀❀❀❀❀❀❀❀❀❀❀❀❀❀❀❀❀❀

AND
RECOVERY

Richard Sanders
Robert S. Smith
Bernard S. Weinman

FOREWORD BY JAMES W. OSBERG

CHRONIC PSYCHOSES

AND RECOVERY

An Experiment in
Socio-Environmental Treatment

Jossey-Bass Inc., Publishers
615 Montgomery Street · San Francisco · 1967

CHRONIC PSYCHOSES AND RECOVERY
An Experiment in Socio-Environmental Treatment
by Richard Sanders, Robert S. Smith, and Bernard S. Weinman

Library of Congress Catalog Card Number 67–29135

Printed in the United States of America
by York Composition Company, Inc.
York, Pennsylvania

FIRST EDITION
67109

THE JOSSEY-BASS BEHAVIORAL SCIENCE SERIES

General Editors

WILLIAM E. HENRY, *University of Chicago*
NEVITT SANFORD, *Stanford University*

Foreword

Chronic Psychoses and Recovery is not only an excellent report of an evaluation of a specific rehabilitation program for the chronic mental patient but also a significant commentary on the present status of program development in the mental health field. In the recent history of the mental health movement, the findings and recommendations of the Joint Commission on Mental Illness and Health, which highlighted the imperative need for coping with the unfinished tasks of mental health, methods for management of the chronic mental health patient in the large institution or in the community are frequently left unstated and unsolved.

It should be recognized, as the authors indicate, that the chronic patients in our mental hospitals are not only people hospitalized because of psychotic dysfunction, but they are also a poorly educated, poorly trained, inadequately socialized segment of our population. The presence of psychiatric symptomatology only serves to render more complex the task of resocialization and rehabilitation. The high percentage of chronic mental patients who have been or are on welfare, the low level of their vocational and educational attainment, and, in particular, their alienation and isolation are salient characteristics of this group as significant as their mental impairment. From this point of view, chronic mental disorder can be conceptualized as *chronic social disorder,* requiring techniques of resocialization and education as essential rehabilitation techniques.

Previous studies of chronic mental patients have tended to some degree to categorize this group as if it were unitary. A major finding in this controlled comparative study of three social treatment programs is that group socialization experiences are of particular benefit to the older, longer hospitalized male schizophrenic, in contrast to the younger male or the female patient. From this point of view, hospital administrators and clinicians have available a possible specific remedial approach for a specific patient group. In addition to the implication for community-based and hospital-based programs which this study suggests, there is also a clear indication that specific programs should be devised and evaluated for the younger male and the female schizophrenic patient. Replication of this study in other settings is urgently indicated.

The social-educational approaches utilized in this endeavor, although both expanding and clarifying earlier group and interpersonal efforts, have yet to exert their full impact on programs in large mental institutions. Sullivan's concepts, the work of Maxwell Jones with character disorders, and the Cummings' studies all point to the task of effecting changes both within the organization of the institution and in its methods of program management.

The report of the research in this book effectively portrays the difficulties faced in initiating an innovative program. Problems of initiating change and overcoming resistance, while maintaining requirements of a research design, are well documented.

Treatment in the community is a dictum of today; the community mental health center program offers the possibility of effecting such a development. Whether such community-based treatment, however, will exclude the uneducated, untrained, and disturbing chronic schizophrenic will depend on the existence of generally acceptable and understandable rehabilitation approaches which can be carried out in a community setting, as well as competently trained individuals to undertake them. The current efforts of the authors to develop a training program for indigenous community members, to rehabilitate chronic patients in the community, is a most promising step. The most promising leads are those pointing in the direction of utilizing educational and rehabilitative methods and techniques for the mentally ill patient.

James W. Osberg, M.D.
National Institute of Mental Health

Preface

Chronic Psychoses and Recovery is a report of a project initiated at the Philadelphia State Hospital in 1957 and directed toward overcoming one of the hospital's major problems: the continued increase in the number of chronically institutionalized psychotic patients. This problem is not unique to the Philadelphia State Hospital. Most large mental hospitals have accumulated over the years a large population of chronic psychotics who make up a considerable proportion of all mental patients in residential care. What is done for these patients? Insulin and electroshock have been tried, but the effects have been negligible. Lobotomy is clearly not the answer. The tranquilizing drugs have made life on hospital wards somewhat less hectic, but do not effect fundamental behavioral changes sufficient to permit the release of the chronic mental patient. If the chronic mental patient is to resume a social existence, the personality and social deficits associated with the psychotic process and the deleterious effect of long-term institutionalization require special attention. A program of socio-environmental treatment seemed to offer the greatest promise of reducing the deficits and symptomatology of the chronic mental patient.

With the aid of a grant from the National Institute of Mental Health (Grant Number OM-126), the authors established an experimental socio-environmental treatment program for chronic mental patients at the Philadelphia State Hospital. The project was concerned not only with developing socio-environmental programs of potential clinical value, but also with clarifying the role of the critical variable underlying such treatment, that is to say, social interaction. It was hoped that systematic control of this variable would increase therapeutic efficiency and permit a broader application of socio-environmental treatment principles.

To determine the relevance of social interaction, three socio-environmental treatment programs requiring different degrees of interaction were designed. The effects of these treatment programs were evaluated both at completion of treatment and after three years. An additional goal was to determine what type of patient would most benefit from socio-environmental treatment; the predictor study provides some information regarding this issue.

Although this book is primarily a report of an experimental study, it is felt that a description of difficulties encountered in establishing innovative treatment programs in a large state hospital might be helpful to those preparing to initiate such programs in similar settings. Techniques for overcoming institutional resistance to change and reducing internal conflicts are discussed from the viewpoint of organizational theory and power and decision-making strategy. Since many of the problems encountered seemed to derive from the medical model prevalent in most mental hospitals, a more appropriate model for the treatment of chronic mental patients has been formulated.

Neither this book nor the study on which it is based would have been possible without the dedication of Robert S. Smith, Ph.D., who died before the manuscript was completed. Although the over-all project was a group effort, Dr. Smith's work was essential in implementing the research design, supervising and directing data collection and analyses, and designing the follow-up study. He wrote Chapter One, presenting the conceptual basis for socio-environmental treatment, and Chapters Ten and Eleven, dealing with community tenure and the prediction of clinical outcome. Before his untimely death, he also completed Chapters Twelve and Fifteen which introduce the follow-up study and report some of the results. This book is dedicated to Robert Smith, who continued to work toward its completion even with the knowledge of his imminent death.

We are indebted to many people for contributing their ideas, energies, and encouragement. Our thanks go to Dr. Eugene L. Sielke, former superintendent of the Philadelphia State Hospital, who had the courage to ask us to undertake this enterprise and faith in our ability to complete it successfully. Without the cooperation of Dr. Emanuel Chat, assistant superintendent, the daily administrative problems encountered in an innovative project of this magnitude would have been insurmountable. To Miss Helen Edgar, director of nursing, goes our deepest gratitude for her endless support and encouragement throughout this project. Our thanks also to Donald Sullivan, chief engineer, for devoting his resourcefulness to our enterprise. In addition, we are grateful to Drs. Earl W. Biddle and Samuel Levin, clinical directors, and to Drs. Charles Oller and Anthony Dunfield, psychiatrists, for contributing their psychiatric skills to this project.

More than thanks are due our colleagues who gave unstintingly of their mental and physical energies: Mrs. Florence Albertson and Mrs. Antoinette Ranck, project nurses; Mrs. Ida Manly, Sheridan Holdridge, Mrs. Madge Molz, Mrs. Olive Rheinhardt, Mrs. Betty Sabatina, Leonard H. Whitmore, Mrs. Rita Barbera, Mrs. Anna Kraus, and John Hudson, who came from various hospital disciplines to serve as social therapists; Mrs. Gertrude Analine and Miss Jean Moir, project social workers; Dr. George F. Hunter, Clifford Levitt, Miss Marijane Hamilton, and Louis Muzekari, psychologists who served as unit administrators.

Our gratitude goes also to others who participated in various stages of this project but who, for various reasons, were unable to remain on the project long enough to see it completed: Dr. Bernard J.

Fitzgerald, former project co-director; Drs. Janice Hobkirk Kenny, Aaron Smith, Donald Clark, and Robert Powell, former unit administrators.

Wayne Leese and Mrs. Elizabeth Smith helped immeasurably with the follow-up study. They assisted Robert Smith in developing the interview format, abstracting interview protocols, and rating patients' adjustment on various measures. Mr. Leese also analyzed many of the follow-up data.

The preparation of this manuscript for publication was facilitated by the stenographic, typing, and clerical abilities of Mrs. Beverly G. Smith and Miss Susan Vickers, and by the editorial and grammatical skills of Miss Judith Fine.

To Prof. Albert Pepitone, who served as consultant during the phase of data processing and analysis, goes more than our thanks. Professor Pepitone gave generously of his ideas and his time. He not only assisted in the interpretation of data, but also carefully reviewed each chapter.

A final word of thanks is owed to the National Institute of Mental Health. The funds awarded to us did more than provide means for procuring additional personnel, supplies, and equipment. The grant provided the recognition that sustained us in the face of resistance from traditionalists and motivated us in our research endeavors.

RICHARD SANDERS
BERNARD WEINMAN

October 1967
Philadelphia

Contents

�✿✿✿✿✿✿✿✿✿✿✿✿✿✿✿✿✿✿✿✿✿✿✿✿✿✿✿✿✿✿✿✿✿✿✿✿

CHRONIC
PSYCHOSES

AND
RECOVERY

PART ONE

THE BACKGROUND

Chapter I

Conceptual Bases for
Socio-Environmental Treatment

The chronic mental patient constitutes an increasing economic and therapeutic problem whose magnitude is so great that the Joint Commission on Mental Illness and Health (1961) recommended that "all existing State Hospitals of more than 1,000 beds be gradually and progressively converted into centers for long-term and combined care of chronic diseases, including mental illness." This recommendation that the chronic psychotic be placed in centers with the intractably ill —that is, those with chronic physical diseases and geriatric impairment—reflects the pessimism then prevalent regarding the treatment potential of the chronic mental patient.

3

Although the continued-care requirements of the chronic patient were emphasized in the Joint Commission's report, there was recognition that some of these patients might be returned to extramural living through extended and specialized rehabilitation efforts. Toward this end, social therapy—"techniques of socialization, relearning, group living and gradual rehabilitation"—was recommended. However, since there was little definitive knowledge available prior to 1961 regarding the utility of social treatment in general and the efficacy of specific program elements and treatment techniques in particular, the Joint Commission's recommendation that social treatment would be useful in the rehabilitation of chronic mental patients represented a hope rather than an actuality.

The group which undertook the study described in this book shared this hope in accepting the challenge of developing a treatment program which, presumably, had some potential for improving the condition of the chronically institutionalized patient. If one ignores the complex issues surrounding the etiology of schizophrenia and assumes only that the patient's present condition is subject to change, is not static or fixed, then treatment involves essentially three problems. The first is that of autism, the fundamental break with reality which is the necessary precondition for such symptoms as delusions, hallucinations, ideas of reference, bizarre mannerisms, feelings of depersonalization, and dissociated thought processes. Second, the problem of alienation or social isolation—the patient's withdrawal from any meaningful contact with other human beings—must be considered. Third, the deficits which accrue from long years of exposure to the routine of institutional living—apathy, pessimism, and extreme dependence—operate against involvement in any active therapeutic program and must be examined. The institution's role in creating and perpetuating these deficits has been ably documented by such writers as Stanton and Schwartz (1954), Greenblatt, York, and Brown (1955), Belknap (1956), Goffman (1957), and Caudill (1958).

A substantial body of psychiatric opinion maintains that the symptoms of psychosis (hallucinations, delusions, and the like) are merely secondary manifestations of a more fundamental disruption of interpersonal relationships. Harry Stack Sullivan, one of the leading proponents of this point of view, broadly outlined for the members of the American Psychiatric Association in 1930, a program for "the socio-psychiatric rehabilitation of schizophrenics" (1931). In this address, he described a nuclear rehabilitation unit: a six-bed ward, isolated administratively from the rest of the hospital to facilitate the creation of a distinctive ward culture. He spoke of the hospital as a "school for personality growth rather than a custodian of personality failure," and described treatment as a process of "assisting in the growth by experience of a body of *relatively undeveloped* tendencies to interpersonal relations." He felt that "the situation is one of education, broadly conceived, not by verbal teaching, but by communal experience," and recognized that, since the personnel who had most contact with the patient (nurses, aides, and activity therapists) played a crucial role in such an educative experience, they must be carefully selected. He spoke of "social recovery" as a step in the direction of "real recovery," by which he meant "a true reorganization of the disordered personality." Given optimal conditions, he believed that social insight could be increased "to an extent sufficient to abolish the schizophrenic situation."

Sullivan's approach, a logical starting point for a program to treat chronic psychotics in a state hospital setting, had two major foci: the development of meaningful interpersonal relations and the creation of an environment within which this can most readily occur— hence the term "socio-environmental" therapy. In essence, Sullivan dealt only with two of the three major problems of chronic psychosis. He implied that a reduction in autistic processes would follow the successful treatment of the problem of social withdrawal. However, Sullivan worked mainly with acute schizophrenics, in whom the additional complications posed by long years of institutional living are seldom encountered. Also, although Sullivan emphasized the importance of environmental factors, the concept of a therapeutic "culture" or milieu was not spelled out in any detail.

Myerson (1939) discussed one possible approach to the problem of institutionalization. As clinical director of a large state institution, he had considerable experience with chronic psychosis. He noted that prolonged hospitalization tended to produce a kind of "prison stupor" which reinforced the retreat from social contacts characteristic of the illness itself: "The psychologic retreat of the schizophrenic is

enhanced in all directions by the usual hospital care he receives."
Myerson felt that whatever initiative the patient possessed when he
entered the hospital was gradually eroded to a point of complete pas-
sivity and disinterest, until he could no longer be influenced by the
rewards and punishments which are strong motivational factors in the
lives of most men. Myerson's remedy for this condition was a rigorous
therapeutic program which he called "total push" therapy. Its central
theme was activation, achieved through exercise and games, physio-
therapy, an enriched diet, more attention to personal appearance, and
the systematic introduction of rewards and punishments into the patient's daily life. Myerson proposed that this program be followed by
structured activities consisting of occupational therapy, music, dancing, and crafts. As the program unfolded, he observed that the additional effort was having a singularly beneficial effect on the staff's
morale.

Myerson's original formulation placed relatively little emphasis on interpersonal factors. Several years later, Pauncz (1954) re-
stated the philosophy of the "total push" movement and emphasized
what Sullivan had called the educative approach to the treatment of
schizophrenia. Pauncz rejected the term "push," which by then had
acquired negative connotations, and explained that "push" simply
meant giving the patient additional attention. Myerson's original concept of "a thoroughgoing steadfast *pressure* of humane and physiologi-
cally sound background" was greatly attenuated. Pauncz did emphasize
that treatment must take as its starting point those areas of function
that are relatively intact, since it is through these areas that the patient
continues to "live," to maintain his dignity and integrity as a person.
Pauncz also recognized the vital importance of positive staff attitudes
and urged that nurses and attendants be encouraged to play a larger
role in the treatment process.

Meanwhile an entirely new development had taken place in
England, principally as a result of atypical conditions produced by
World War II. Large numbers of troops had begun to suffer from
"war neuroses." The serious shortage of personnel trained to cope
with the problem created an ideal situation for the development of
new facilities and innovative treatment procedures. The shortage of
trained staff made it necessary to use untrained personnel under pro-

fessional guidance. This condition permitted the development of in-service training programs along functional rather than traditional professional lines. The pressure of numbers guaranteed that the innovative procedures would be developed along group rather than individual lines. From this came the concept of the "therapeutic community."

Democratization, permissiveness, communal living, and confrontation with reality are guiding principles of the therapeutic community. "In a therapeutic community, the whole of a patient's time spent in hospital is thought of as treatment" (Jones, 1953). The group becomes the principal therapeutic vehicle, and the patient is required to participate in a number of group activities. Such participation demonstrates to the patient his social disabilities and provides an opportunity for corrective emotional experience.

The immediate antecedents of the therapeutic community may be seen in the work of Bierer (1942), an analyst trained in Vienna who became somewhat dissatisfied with the limitations of the analytic method. He felt that psychoanalysis tended to reinforce dependence and reduce the range of normal activity, and that the time necessary to effect a "cure" was excessive. He saw as a further limitation the fact that classical psychoanalysis was inaccessible to inarticulate or unintelligent patients, as well as those who were simply unable to master the technique of free association. Bierer developed "situational treatment" in an effort to reach a larger number of patients. This type of treatment involved individually directed but impersonal measures undertaken by the therapist and his assistants in order to change the patient's basic expectancies concerning people and events. If, for example, a patient had a strong need to identify with a masculine authority figure, Bierer created a special situation to make this possible. Identification of the patient's needs was based on a thorough knowledge of Freudian psychodynamics. But Bierer recognized that people can solve problems through interaction with others as well as by talking about them on a couch; this assumption, of course, is basic to the therapeutic community.

Sullivan's notion of a distinctive ward culture or milieu is developed to the fullest possible extent in the therapeutic community. The traditional relationships and roles of doctor, nurse, and patient are modified to facilitate more adequate communication. Authoritarian procedures are replaced by more permissive, democratic forms of organization. The patient is given an increasingly larger share in running the ward or unit. Group processes are mobilized, and norms and sanctions emerging from the group replace those previously associated with the institution itself. Continuity and reality testing are guaranteed by the staff, the "most stable, united, and permanent group" (Jones, 1953). Staff members are expected to participate in the life of the community rather than to "treat" patients from a distance.

The therapeutic community developed at Belmont Hospital in England under the guidance of Maxwell Jones was concerned primarily with treating severe character disorders. The ultimate goal was gainful employment. Although the basic concepts of this type of therapeutic community were unquestionably applicable to a variety of treatment problems (Main, 1946; Bettelheim and Sylvester, 1948; Shatin, 1958; Wilmer, 1958), the utility of these concepts in treating chronic psychosis remained to be demonstrated. As of 1957, when our study began, there was little in the literature reporting the use of the philosophy and methodology of the therapeutic community, and certainly nothing major. Most of the available work on chronic psychosis was in the "total push" tradition. The principal studies which provided source material during the development of the rehabilitation program at the Philadelphia State Hospital are reviewed below.

Miller and Clancy (1952) were among the earliest investigators to focus on the social rehabilitation of the chronic psychotic. They divided their patients into small groups based on current social performance and assigned an attendant to work with each group. Each of these groups was made up so that the prevailing general level of social behavior was potentially accessible even to the most regressed member of the group. The treatment program was designed specifically to improve social performance, and no attempt was made to deal directly with psychotic symptomatology. Emphasis was placed on greater freedom, more responsibility, and avoidance of situations that might evoke anxiety or hostility. The activity program consisted mainly of recreation and occupational therapy. Patients initially worked on individual projects but were encouraged to cooperate with one another as the program progressed. Evaluation of the project was entirely subjective. Miller and Clancy reported need for less sedation and seclusion among these patients, a reduction in property destruction, and a marked improvement in social performance—but no change in the incidence of psychotic behavior. The discharge (release) rate was 25 per cent ($N = 100$). A similar study based on 38 female patients reported a discharge rate of 37 per cent (Miller, 1954).

Galioni, Adams, and Tallman (1953) conducted a "total push" type of study in which chronic patients responded favorably to an increased patient-staff ratio. Although the authors claimed that no new treatment procedures were introduced, the attention paid to the experimental group clearly differed quantitatively and qualitatively from that given to the control group. In addition to more time being spent in occupational, recreational, and music therapy, great emphasis was placed on formal and informal group discussion. Patients were systematically encouraged to interact with one another in regularly scheduled discussion groups and in small informal discussion sessions with personnel on the ward. Written material was often used as the basis for these discussions. The authors reported a release rate of 18.5 per cent for the experimental group ($N = 200$). The Malamud-Sands Rating Scale was completed at intervals for patients in both groups, but these data are so presented that meaningful conclusions cannot be drawn. The study generally implied that more experimental patients than control patients showed "improvement," the nature of which was not specified. Considering the enthusiasm with which they described their program, and the generally positive trends in their data, Galioni and his associates were surprisingly cautious in interpreting their results. "These data must be regarded as trends. . . . Eighteen months of treatment, no matter how intensive, with a group of schizophrenic patients cannot be expected to give definite results." Although "definite results" is not defined, we cannot avoid the impression that the authors were not altogether pleased with the improvement shown by their patients. This result is unfortunate, since the per capita cost of the experimental treatment program was more than twice that for the control group.

Kamman *et al.* (1954) described a "total push" program for regressed patients that considerably reduced such problems in the management of patients as incontinence and inability to feed or dress themselves. There was an increase in the number of working patients and of those able to qualify for ground parole, or freedom to walk about the hospital grounds unsupervised. The number of mute patients decreased sharply. The therapy program consisted primarily of toilet training, instruction in basic hygiene, care of clothing, table manners, good grooming, ward housekeeping, "homemaking" (improving the physical appearance of the ward), organized recreation, sports, crafts, and hobbies. There were also a number of "special events" such as dances, parties, Bible reading, community singing, movies, and trips to the hospital store. In addition, all patients received a course of 20 electroconvulsive treatments beginning in the second week of their stay in the experimental ward. Kamman's study provides a rich source of ideas for program material. It also is one of the few studies in which patients were followed for any length of time after termination of treatment. The authors reported that over a 12-month period male patients maintained the gains made during treatment, whereas female patients regressed to their pretreatment behavioral level. The authors recognized that "total push" therapy was relatively expensive, and they attempted to develop prognostic indicators for a more judicious selection of patients. However, none of the demographic or behavioral variables so employed could be successfully cross-validated.

Kraus (1954) felt that the problems of social isolation, motivational paralysis, and extreme dependency could best be handled by giving the hospitalized patient more responsibility for the conduct of his daily life. He argued for tolerance of deviant behavior in the interest of preserving the patient's self-esteem, for greater flexibility in hospital rules, and for procedures which would permit each case to be considered on its merits. His program for closed-ward patients included group therapy conducted by social workers and discussion groups led by nurses and attendants. Group leaders were allowed to select their own patients, a maneuver designed to insure their sympathetic attitude toward all members of the group. Kraus warned that the effort to return patients to the community might create problems where none previously existed, that is, the disruption of a "good" hospital adjustment might bring about a temporary exacerbation of symptoms. But, he pointed out, if the hospital was being run for the benefit of the patients rather than that of the staff, the goal of return to the community must take precedence over such difficulties.

The use of group activity is for the most part incidental to the "total push" approach. Except for group therapy, activities are organized on a group basis more as a matter of convenience than of therapeutic intent. In the therapeutic community, however, the group becomes the principal therapeutic vehicle. Rees and Glatt (1955) pointed out that one of the major functions of the mental hospital is to combat the loneliness and isolation characteristic of chronic mental illness. Organizing the patient's entire hospital experience on a group basis, they felt, could help in this endeavor. Their concept of the therapeutic community went far beyond mere attendance at group meetings: every patient should be encouraged to identify with a primary living group, the members of which would eat together, share the same sleeping quarters, and participate as a unit in all routine activities.

This concept is supported by Cameron, Laing, and McGhie (1955). They describe in detail the changes which occurred over a 12-month period in a group of 11 "deteriorated" patients. These patients were removed from a rather barren ward environment for six hours each day and placed in a small room well equipped for various kinds of activities. They were accompanied by two nurses who were instructed only to remain with the patients. Not knowing what to expect, the nurses were understandably very anxious at the outset. The patients were routinely sedated and the door to their room was kept locked, but these restrictions were gradually relaxed when nothing untoward occurred. Although the patients began to respond to one another within the confines of the small room, that is, to observe social amenities and cooperate in serving tea, disturbances of speech persisted, and communication remained essentially at a nonverbal level for some time. Further progress became possible as the nurses gained more understanding of the patients and of their own anxieties. The patients began to help one another with personal tasks. Trips to town were organized, and a genuine group life emerged. The study indicates that close physical proximity, in conjunction with positive staff attitudes, can lead to the emergence of meaningful interaction.

Additional support for this proposition is provided by Hyde (1953), who found that the proportion of friendly patient-patient interactions occurring in a smoking-room setting increased over a five-month period in direct relation to the proportion of friendly staff-patient interactions. After comparing the effects on patient interaction produced by members of different disciplines, Hyde concluded that "the patients themselves are the most important single group in bringing about good ward socialization." He felt that it is important to recognize the socially effective patient as an influential person in the ward, with a capacity equal to and sometimes greater than that of the staff in bringing about socialization. This statement suggests that patients themselves possess an inherent therapeutic potential which, if effectively mobilized, may contribute substantially to the total result.

The greater emphasis on interaction which characterizes most programs based on the therapeutic community concept applies to individual as well as group relationships. Patients are encouraged to learn one another's names, to shake hands, and to address one another by name (Merry, 1956). In addition to fulfilling the responsibilities of their traditional professional roles, nurses, aides, and activity therapists are expected to interact with patients on a personal level. These requirements represent an attempt to counteract the isolation and withdrawal of the chronic patient through structured interaction of a highly personalized nature.

The concept of patient self-government has appeared with increasing frequency both in "total push" and in therapeutic community programs. As early as 1941, Bierer and Haldane described the operation of a self-governed social club for patients, intended to foster the assuming of responsibility, reduce dependence, and enhance the sense of security and personal fulfillment deriving from cooperative social activity. The club was considered a social learning situation which would facilitate readjustment to the extramural community.

Hyde and Solomon (1950) regarded patient government as "a new form of group therapy." They felt that it provided an "organized," or structured, form of self-expression that resulted in the assuming of greater personal responsibility, a sense of satisfaction or worth, and increased socialization. Secondary benefits were noted in addition to the direct effects on the patient, chief among them improved communication between patients and staff, better ward management, increased staff morale, and the emergence of more organized activities on the ward. Most important, these additional benefits were realized with no increased demand on staff time. Hyde and Solomon considered patient government as more feasible than traditional group therapy, since all patients could be participants. They suggested that it might ultimately prove to be the more beneficial form of therapy.

Most of the published material on "total push" or therapeutic community programs is purely descriptive. The few investigators who have attempted anything beyond a subjective assessment of results have faced the almost insurmountable problem of establishing criteria. In most instances inappropriate criteria have been utilized. Although the most frequently specified treatment goals of socio-environmental therapy are resocialization, remotivation, reduction of dependence, and improvement in staff attitudes, the criteria of improvement most commonly employed are such ward indices as frequency of sedation, seclusion, assaultiveness, and incontinence. These indices are sometimes supplemented by statistics on ground parole, work assignments, visits to relatives, and release from the hospital. There is probably some truth to the general proposition that socio-environmental therapy tends to reduce management problems. However, the above criteria are as sensitive to changes in management policy as they are to changes in the patient. Even frequency of incontinence, a seemingly objective measure which relates directly to the patient's condition, is not a completely valid criterion (Baker and Thorpe, 1956).

Clark and Hoy (1957) were keenly aware of the criterion problem. They discovered during their investigation that most of the measures they intended to use as criteria were either inappropriate, unreliable, or unobtainable. A significant decrease in the use of sedation was rendered meaningless by a simultaneous increase in the use of chlorpromazine. A significant decrease in incontinence on one ward was attributable to the transfer of incontinent patients to another ward. The number of patients on ground parole increased automatically when certain wards were changed from a closed to an open status. In some instances, ground parole status was granted to bed patients. The use of seclusion was actually discontinued by common consent several months before the period of their study, so that the expected "decrease" could not be demonstrated. This in itself is sufficient proof that changes in restrictive measures need not be due to specialized treatment programs. An increase in the release rate for the hospital as a whole was the result of an increase in the number of short-stay patients passing through the admissions ward. There was no significant increase in the number of releases among patients hospitalized for more than one year. Assaultiveness, noisiness, damage to property, accidents, and similar behavior were too inconsistently recorded by ward personnel to be used as criteria. Other behavioral measures, such as the number of patients using the canteen, reading, and playing indoor or outdoor games, were abandoned because "the criteria were not defined carefully enough when charge nurses were interviewed."

A review of the Clark and Hoy investigation highlights an additional problem frequently encountered in reports of "total push" or therapeutic community programs, namely, the confounding effects of uncontrolled therapeutic influences. Although Clark and Hoy were attempting to evaluate the effects of "a programme of activity, occupation and freedom," that is, a thorough-going "reform" of a traditionally structured county hospital, they made no attempt to control for the marked increase in the use of electroshock and chlorpromazine with patients in the experimental group. Thus, even if their criterion measures had worked out satisfactorily, the question would remain whether the results were attributable to the social treatment or to the somatic and chemical therapies.

The use of electroshock is not uncommon in "total push" or therapeutic community treatment programs (Galioni, Adams, and Tallman, 1953; Jones, 1953; Kamman et al., 1954; Kraus, 1954; Baker and Thorpe, 1956; Merry, 1956). In most instances, this therapy is administered on an individual basis in such manner that no two patients receive the same treatment program. The *systematic* use of a course of 20 electroconvulsive treatments by Kamman and his associates is the exception rather than the rule. Specialized psychological therapies are used even less frequently, but they also contribute to the complexity of the problem. For example, 25 per cent of the patients in Maxwell Jones' sample received individual psychotherapy while in the treatment unit, and an additional 10 per cent received some form of group therapy. When interviewed approximately six months after leaving the unit, these patients, considered together, showed by far the best criterion scores. The question remains whether these patients had better criterion scores because they received this additional treatment, or whether they were singled out for group and individual psychotherapy because they were initially less impaired. It is clearly impossible to draw general conclusions about effects of an altered milieu when so many other uncontrolled therapeutic influences are concomitantly operative.

Thus, despite numerous descriptions in the literature, little was known concerning the actual effectiveness of "total push" and therapeutic community programs. Much has been written about sedation, seclusion, incontinence, and the like, but there have been few systematic attempts to evelute the effect of environmental manipulations on spontaneous social behavior or psychotic symptomatology. The only experimental study noted to have any bearing on these questions is that by Pace (1957).

Pace employed a baseline design to test this hypothesis: "A change in the situation as experienced by the chronic schizophrenic will be accompanied by a change in his behavior." Measurements were obtained over a 4-month period on 33 "deteriorated and regressed" male schizophrenics. The experimental program was then introduced and additional measurements were obtained at intervals over a 10-month period. These measurements included a "Mobility Index" that indicated movement and position of individuals in the dayroom; the Kandler-Hyde Socialization Activity Index that reflected the amount of social and motor activity in the dayroom (Kandler and Hyde, 1951); an "Interaction Protocol" that provided a record of quantitative and qualitative aspects of verbal interaction; and the Lorr Multidimensional Scale for assessing individual and group psychopathology (Lorr, Jenkins, and Holsopple, 1953). The treatment program consisted largely of mobilization of group processes among the patients in the ward and modification of the traditional roles of nurse and aide. Pace demonstrated an increase in over-all activity and a substantial increase in interaction between patients. The incidence of psychopathology was essentially unaffected, although there was some tendency toward an increase in belligerence and a decrease in paranoid projection.

Pace concluded that "by clinical judgment, 26 of the 33 patients had improved sufficiently to be assigned to an open ward following the experiment. Altercations, incontinence, feeding problems, elopements, and other management problems had all but disappeared. However, prognosis in general remained poor. Similar to traditional approaches, the situational method does not 'cure' the patient. Its greatest advantage appears to lie in resocialization, and not the correction of psychopathology per se."

The failure of this relatively well-controlled study to effect an improvement in psychopathology necessitates a re-examination of the basic assumptions underlying the socio-environmental approach to the treatment of chronic psychosis. Myerson (1939) definitely asserted that "total push" therapy was not a cure for schizophrenia, but simply a method for arresting the deterioration patients seem to undergo when hospitalized over long periods. Sullivan (1931), however, clearly expected the interpersonal approach to "abolish the schizophrenic situation." Why did the patients in Pace's study fail to show any improvement in psychiatric symptomatology? It is possible that Pace's treatment program, although designed to facilitate group interaction and the emergence of group processes, did not provide the kind of close interpersonal contact, or communal experience, that Sullivan regarded as essential to rehabilitation. A second possibility involves the question of time. At what point in the recovery process is it reasonable to expect a decrease in psychiatric symptomatology? Should there be a decrease at once, or must time elapse before the patient feels comfortable enough with his new mode of adjustment to consider relinquishing his symptoms? The entire question of the sequence in which behaviors tend to change in response to therapeutic intervention deserves more attention than it has received. We may have been looking for behavioral changes after six months or a year that cannot reasonably be expected to occur before two years. Only an extended follow-up study can provide an answer to this question.

The work done in program development before 1957 was of considerable help. The ideology underlying the application of social principles to large custodial institutions was reasonably well developed (Stanton and Schwartz, 1954; Greenblatt, York, and Brown, 1955). Consequently, there was substantial agreement among investigators about what might prove effective in the treatment of chronic psychosis.

The principal ideas and methods mentioned in the literature are summarized:

1. Increased environmental pressure toward greater activity, both physical and mental.

2. Increased environmental pressure toward greater interaction with staff and other patients.

3. Increased patient responsibility for taking care of himself and his surroundings, and giving him a voice in the management of ward affairs.

4. "Habit training," ranging from toilet training for regressed patients to training for the less deteriorated patient in good grooming, physical hygiene, table manners, and etiquette.

5. Introduction of procedures calculated to enhance individual identity and self-esteem—possession of clothing and personal effects, greater privacy, etc.

6. Systematic introduction of reward and punishment as motivating devices—payment for work done, creation of high status roles, etc.

7. Mobilization of group processes and forces—group goals, norms, sanctions, identification, etc.

8. Interaction with staff at a more personal, spontaneous level than that prescribed by traditional role relationships.

9. Inculcation of humanistic rather than custodial attitudes and values among staff.

10. Staff selection based on sensitivity to the problems of the schizophrenic patient.

11. Mobilization of the therapeutic potential inherent in the patient himself.

Research, however, had hardly advanced. Treatment goals were frequently not specified in sufficient detail to permit the development of adequate criteria. The variables involved in treatment were themselves poorly defined, and the measurement techniques necessary to monitor changes in these variables were either nonexistent or still in their infancy. For example, see the work on measurement of attitudes toward mental illneess in Greenblatt, Levinson, and Williams, 1957.

At least four basic questions remained unanswered:

1. Can sustained improvement in social adjustment be effected through manipulation of the physical and interpersonal environment?

2. What kinds of environmental manipulations are most effective?

3. Which patients are most likely to respond?

4. Is improved social adjustment accompanied or followed by decreased psychiatric symptomatology?

This book reflects an attempt to resolve these four primary issues.

Chapter II

The Setting
for the Experiment

The Philadelphia State Hospital is the largest of 19 state-operated hospitals in the Commonwealth of Pennsylvania. It comprises approximately 60 buildings situated on 1,100 acres; it accommodates 6,500 patients and employs 1,600 persons. The hospital is located on the periphery of metropolitan Philadelphia but, though it is surrounded by newly developed suburban housing areas, it remains geographically separated and isolated from the population center. This institution has traditionally had the unique function of providing care almost exclusively for chronic psychiatric patients. At the inception of the experimental socio-environmental treatment program in 1957, 92

19

per cent of the patients in residence had been treated at other hospitals and sent to the Philadelphia State Hospital for continued care and treatment.

❊ A BRIEF HISTORY ❊

The Philadelphia State Hospital was originally a city-owned custodial institution known as the Philadelphia Hospital for Mental Diseases. It was placed under the jurisdiction of the Commonwealth of Pennsylvania in October, 1938. Relatively little is known about the hospital when it was under the jurisdiction of the City of Philadelphia, from 1906 to 1938. Some people familiar with the institution during this period recall meager medical and psychiatric care, maltreatment and abuse of patients, and generally deplorable conditions. Its reputation as a bedlam, a "dumping ground," and a place of final incarceration for the deranged developed during these years. Staff members were often viewed as brutal dregs of humanity who were themselves deranged. During this period the hospital's popular name, "Byberry," based on the name of the section of Philadelphia in which it was located, took on the derogatory connotation which still prevails.

Despite the changes that have been made since 1938, the hospital is still thought of as a dumping ground for the hopelessly insane. The newspapers highlight any elopement from the institution as the escape of a dangerous lunatic, and eagerly seek out hospital occurrences which can be dramatized as evidence of staff malconduct and brutality. When the newspapers do publicize the positive aspects of the hospital, they refer to the institution as the Philadelphia State Hospital. The negative impact of the name "Byberry" is so profound, however, that most Philadelphians do not associate "Byberry" with "Philadelphia State Hospital."

Assumption of state control in 1938 did little to change the deplorable conditions prevalent in the hospital. Patients went barefoot, many were completely naked, and restraints were used indiscriminately. There was marked overcrowding in filthy, dilapidated wards reeking from the stench of incontinent patients and echoing with the screams of the abused. In an effort to shock an apathetic public and a lax legislature into action, the superintendent asked *Life* magazine to run a pictorial exposé of these conditions.

Publication of the exposé in May, 1946, spurred the Commonwealth to make improvements. In the decade following the *Life* article, eight buildings were constructed to increase the capacity of the physical plant for patient housing and treatment services; two large kitchens and a central dining room, as well as a 500-acre dairy and vegetable farm, were added to improve the dietary services to patients; automated equipment, improved roads, and a remodeled sewage disposal plant further modernized the over-all facility. In addition, increased expenditure for staff personnel and supplies for patient care permitted humanization of treatment in the hospital.

❀ HOSPITAL STRUCTURE AND STAFF ❀ ORGANIZATION

At the beginning of the rehabilitation project in 1957, the hospital was divided administratively into three general services: the Admissions Service, the Chronic Male Service, and the Chronic Female Service. The Admissions Service was located in the intensive treatment building, which had a capacity of 200 patients. Here, somatic and chemical therapies, as well as group psychotherapy, were available for selected patients. From this service patients were either returned to the community or transferred to the chronic services. The hospital also maintained two clinics in the active treatment building: a Community Clinic, which provided casework and psychotherapy for community residents, and an Out-Patient Clinic, which kept the hospital apprised of the psychiatric status and adjustment of its outpatients and provided some aftercare services to these patients.

The Chronic Female Service (more than 50 per cent of the patients were females) was housed in 12 older two-story buildings, set close together and interconnected by passageways, and 3 new large buildings located nearby. Two of these new buildings, the Tuberculosis and Geriatric buildings, also housed male patients.

In addition to the male sections of the Tuberculosis and Geriatric buildings, the Chronic Male Service included seven older buildings located in an area some distance from the Female Service, and three new buildings in the vicinity of the Female Service. Approximately half of the male patients resided in the newer buildings.

The professional staff was headed by the superintendent and the assistant superintendent. Administratively responsible to them were the clinical directors of the Admissions Service, the Chronic Male Service, the Chronic Female Service, and the directors of the Chaplaincy, Industrial Therapy, Nursing, Occupational Therapy, Psychology, Recreation, and Social Service Departments. The heads of departments not directly involved in patient treatment—Accounting, Dietary, Farming, Maintenance, Personnel, and Steward—were also responsible to the superintendent. Of the 1,500 employees of the hospital in 1957, over 900 were directly involved in psychiatric care of patients: these included 30 physicians, 184 nurses (90 of whom were registered), 7 psychologists, 15 social workers, and 689 attendants.

❀ TREATMENT EFFORTS AND CUSTODIAL ❀ SERVICES

There has been a growing interest in developing specialized programs that would have some utility for the rehabilitation of the chronic psychotic. In spite of the extreme shortage of professional staff, the Philadelphia State Hospital has also attempted to develop programs in this area. For example, before 1957 the Nursing Department introduced Remotivation Therapy in an attempt to involve groups of patients in reality-oriented experiences. Group sessions were conducted by specially selected and trained attendants. Another program, involving concentrated nursing and habit care, was designed to retrain regressed patients in personal hygiene. A special department of Industrial Therapy was created in an attempt to make the patients' hospital work experience more therapeutic. The Occupational Therapy, Recreation, Social Service, and other departments also planned to initiate specialized treatment programs.

Such special treatment as somatic, physical, psychological, and activity therapies were also available to selected patients. These patients were sent daily to centralized treatment areas, or were transferred to these areas until treatment was completed. Despite such efforts to provide therapeutic services, the Philadelphia State Hospital was in the late 1950's still primarily a custodial institution. Treatment and hospital life were viewed as separate entities. Even in the active treatment wards, the major portion of the patient's day was spent in custodial ward routines. Only a few hours were devoted to treatment. Professional staff effort was concentrated on the specialized treatment procedures.

Management of ward life was left to the attendant, who was responsible for such custodial functions as patient escort, ward hygiene, ward housekeeping, and ward order. The attendant typically organized his ward so that the duties could be carried out by patients. Submission to authority was rewarded and initiative discouraged. Freedom of choice and patient participation in decision-making processes were characteristically absent. As a further means of achieving custodial goals, heterogeneous ward populations were maintained. In each ward there were a few higher level patients capable of serving as ward workers, auxiliary "policemen," and "watchmen." The carrying out of ward chores required these patients to maintain some communication with attendants. The remainder of the ward population usually were left to their own resources. As long as these patients created no disturbance or made no demands, they had slight occasion for contact with the attendant. There was little in the ward routine to force them into interpersonal situations with either personnel or other patients. Since the attendant handled all difficulties and made all decisions, there was no need for patients to interact, communicate, or cooperate. The recreational or social activities periodically available were on a mass basis and required little interpersonal interaction. Thus, the maladaptive modes of behavior of chronic mental patients did not interfere with, nor were they challenged by, the custodial routines of the ward. The over-all effect of this type of hospital organization and procedure was that the major portion of hospital life was nontherapeutic; the ward environment was devoid of the social and interpersonal situations necessary for training in extramural living.

❁ CUSTODIALISM ENTRENCHED ❁

The organization and structure described served to maximize custodial care, minimize the potential for therapeutic intervention, and perpetuate chronicity. Before the therapeutic potential of the hospital could be fully realized, the factors underlying this custodialism had to be determined and modified. At least four factors may be seen as responsible for the entrenchment of custodialism at the Philadelphia State Hospital: limited budget, multiple subordination, vested interests, and custodial ethics and practices.

❊ Limited Budget

The existing programs at Philadelphia State Hospital are a beginning in the treatment of the chronic patient, but they were initiated under tremendous handicaps. Both the general public and those in official capacities tended to see the hospital's goal as custodial care. This orientation led to austere budget restrictions which resulted in marked staff shortages and severe overcrowding of patients. Under these conditions, even providing of adequate custodial care required considerable effort.

In 1957, the per diem cost allotted by the Commonwealth of Pennsylvania to the Philadelphia State Hospital was $3.25, below the prevailing per diem costs ($3.64) at other public psychiatric hospitals throughout the country, and well below the $4.10 allowed by the Commonwealth of Pennsylvania to state hospitals where treatment needs were perceived as having greater import. Even the $4.10 allotment was small compared to the $10–$20 per diem cost in the VA hospitals or the $25–$50 per diem cost in private psychiatric hospitals.

Despite the building program initiated in the decade prior to 1957, the hospital housed 30 per cent more patients than its official capacity in that year. The staff shortage was reflected in the exceedingly low staff-patient ratio—only 23.1 staff per hundred patients. Forty-two states had higher average ratios. This staff-patient ratio was below the average of 29.4 for all state hospital systems in the country in 1957 (Joint Information Service of the American Psychiatric Association and National Association for Mental Health, 1958), and the Pennsylvania state average of 31.3.

❊ Multiple Subordination

In his discussion of the organizational structure of a psychiatric unit, Henry (1954) pointed out that an organization's failure to achieve its goals can often be traced to the stresses created by its formal structure. The so-called "line" organization is the paradigm of "good" organizational structure, both in industry and public administration: a single direct line of command runs from the chief of the organization through his immediate subordinates to the lowest level of the hierarchy.

The so-called "oak-tree" or "functional" type of organizational structure, also quite common, especially in institutional settings, is characterized by several lines of authority running from more than one chief to a single subordinate. As Henry noted, such systems of multiple subordination create powerful stresses in task-performing organizations. Unfortunately, the multiplicity of tasks associated with the operation of a mental hospital creates a situation highly conducive to the formation of systems of multiple subordination. When essentially unrelated tasks must be performed by the same individual, multiple supervision becomes necessary. Thus, the organizational structure of most psychiatric hospitals, including the Philadelphia State Hospital, tends to be a mixture of line and functional patterns of authority. A single line of authority runs from the superintendent and the assistant superintendent to the various department heads. Below this level systems of multiple subordination appear, their complexity depending upon the organization of the separate departments.

Robert Jack Smith, a social anthropologist who studied the hospital system as part of the rehabilitation project, reported (1961):

> there is a built-in strangulation caused by the multiple subordination which has become entrenched in the Hospital structure. It will be noted that the clinical director . . . has jurisdiction over the physicians in his division. But there are, in each division, residents, many nursing personnel . . . social workers, psychologists, adjunctive therapists of various professional hues, housekeepers, dietary personnel, and many others who are administratively responsible for the administration of all buildings in his division, but his control over most of the personnel operating therein is minimal or at least mediated to a considerable extent by extra-division authorities.

> Multiple subordination is the norm in the Philadelphia State Hospital. In fact, the "felony" of "too many cooks" is compounded by the proliferation of numerous autonomous departments within

the institution. Within a division, or even within a single building, policy and practice may be fragmented by the varying interpretations of the units involved, with inter-departmental misunderstandings and decrease in "team" efficiency resulting. For example, the physician desirous of discharging a patient may make efforts in this direction, but in so doing may make a request for social service activity in a way or at a time which conflicts with established social service procedures. Such procedures may or may not have been understood and accepted by the physician. It is not the role of this report to pass judgment on the justification for particular methods of hospital departments, though they may lead quite regularly to conflicts and inefficiency. But it is a duty of this report to indicate that such conflicts and inefficiency do derive from inordinate departmental autonomy and from the rampant multiple subordination so characteristic of the oak tree-type organization, which branches out from the departmental centers and extends its roots into every segment of the hospital.

The structure of a single medical division will be examined [cf. Figure 2.1], as a means toward more complete understanding of the problem.[1] The clinical director of such a division would be in charge of perhaps 3,000 patients, housed in as many as fifteen buildings. In charge of buildings are senior staff physicians or residents. The former often remain in assignments through many years, while the residents normally rotate from service to service every six months. The amount of medical authority invested in the individual physician depends upon the policies and inclinations of the particular clinical director. Basically, the physician, staff or resident, is medically and legally responsible for the conduct of his building or buildings. This may mean that he is responsible for more than 500 patients. One is struck by the enormity of the task confronting a physician.

His medico-legal status notwithstanding, the physician is in a

---

[1] Of the four medical divisions in the hospital, three—male, female, and admissions–active therapy—are independent units, each with a clinical director and internal policies of its own. The fourth division, under the clinical director of research and training (residents), trains medical personnel who are actually assigned to the other divisions on a rotating basis. There is little formal communication among clinical directors. Meetings of the clinical directors are called very irregularly by the assistant superintendent. Most inter-division contacts are made on an individual, personal basis, if at all.

somewhat untenable position. The paper work required of him occupies much of his time. Most of the attention extended to patients by him is necessarily of a purely medical type. It is difficult to think in terms of psychotherapy or other individual psychiatric treatment when hundreds of patients are involved. If he is a resident, his problems are intensified by his lack of experience and the many hours each week spent away from the wards in training seminars and clinics. The physician generally remains aloof from the patients for whom he is responsible.

FIG. 2.1 A TYPICAL MEDICAL DIVISION*

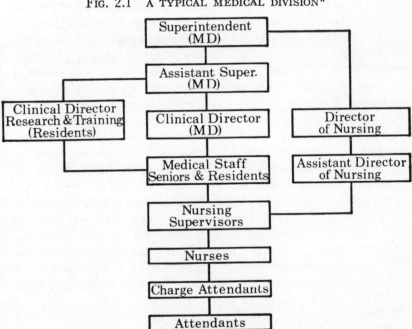

* A simplified diagram. Personnel policy, nursing training and procedures, work schedules, promotions, building censuses, and supplies, and all other administrative matters pertaining to nurses and attendants and to nursing areas, are the responsibility of the nursing department. Psychiatric-medical responsibility alone remains with physicians.

The dual role of ward physician and psychiatric resident makes the resident a pawn in the system of multiple subordination. Understandably, the clinical director of a service division must have medical manpower for all buildings in his division. But ideally, the resident should move throughout the hospital as part of his three-year training program. Service in any division should be a momentary learning experience. In reality, however, the resident must fill the role of full-fledged ward physician. This produces conflict between the goals of the clinical director of the resident training program and the needs of the clinical director of a service division. The resident receives orders from his training chief, but his service duty on a building may interfere with his training assignments. Usually, the training program bends before the pressing needs of ward service. Both the lack of much-needed medical personnel and the lack of coordination between the training clinical director and service clinical directors create great stress in the Philadelphia State Hospital's fledgling resident-training program.

Patient care is, therefore, in the hands of nursing personnel. Since nurses are so few in number, it is the attendant—hierarchical low man on the clinical totem pole—who is really in charge of patients. Theoretically, she is responsible to her charge attendant, as Figure [2.1] indicates. She is, in fact, responsible to her charge attendant, to the nursing supervisor and other nursing personnel, to the building physician and other medical personnel. And as noted, all nursing personnel are administratively responsible to the Nursing Department through an assistant director of nursing. This can lead to a bombardment of directives in a classic example of multiple subordination. Ironically, attendants, who are with the patients more, and know the individual patients better than any other persons, do not offer suggestions to the physician, who sees individual patients rarely. The general consensus of attendants was that in the presence of the physician, they should listen, say little, and appear to be busy.

Other departments also impinge on the ward personnel's day. These "intruders" may not be able to issue outright orders, but authoritative requests must nonetheless be heeded by nursing personnel. The Recreation Department, for example, may request that thirty females from a given building be made ready for an exercise walk on the grounds. Attendants will have to see that these patients are dressed for the prevailing weather. A social worker or psychologist may request escort for a patient to be interviewed or tested. Hospital volunteers may bring entertainment to a ward, requiring the preparation of patients by attendants. In a worker building, ward personnel must have patients ready to be checked out for escort to work areas by representatives of the Ergo (industrial) therapy Department. The same is true for patients who work in the various dietary areas. Such requests have somewhat the same effect as orders, inasmuch as they must be followed. And normally, it is the attendant who must do the following.

From the examples cited, it may be seen that the Medical Department is the medico-legal guardian of patient buildings, the Nursing Department provides for the daily care of patients, and various other departments interject themselves into the ward culture for a variety of patient-oriented reasons. In addition, nonclinical departments (e.g., Maintenance and Engineering) make their presence felt in patient buildings for corrective measures in the physical plant—usually at the request of nursing personnel.

❀ Vested Interests and Autonomous Functions

Historically, the primary concerns of the hospital administration were medical-legal, namely, protecting the community from the deranged person and assuming responsibility for the medical welfare of the incarcerated patient. This responsibility was borne by physicians, assisted by nursing personnel. The various hospital "auxiliary services" owed their existence primarily to their own disciplinary efforts to demonstrate a special and useful service to patients, and also to medical sanction of their presence in the hospital. The services provided by these auxiliary disciplines, although specialized, originally fell partly within the province of the medical and nursing personnel. After achieving departmental status by delimiting a service along disciplinary lines, these departments zealously guarded their hard-won domain against encroachment. Autonomous function was perpetuated by an administrative organization rife with multiple subordination and by the inability of the medical personnel to coordinate the efforts of the various departments. The vested interests deriving from this situation were cogently described by Smith (1961):

Outwardly, there is some semblance of inter-departmental cooperation. Each department honestly espouses a deep interest in patient care and treatment. And each department also pays lip service to the extensive cooperation such care and treatment demand . . . but it should be noted here that coordination and meaningful inter-departmental cooperation do not exist. The size of the Hospital is, itself, a contributing factor, if not a leading cause. But more important, the various departments historically have developed independently—with philosophies and methods of operation deriving not from the needs of the Hospital, but from the unique histories of the individual disciplines.

This had led, through the years, to a rigid system, in which change is generally thwarted, even if outwardly supported. This is more than a clash between so-called conservative traditionalism and what is called progressive, rehabilitative therapy. It is, rather, a self-protective mechanism utilized by autonomous units within the Hospital structure, which is designed to preserve the vested interests of said units from any and all encroachments—no matter what may be the source of, and reasons for, these encroachments. The observer soon realizes that the staggering problem of several autonomous but interrelated departments is woven into the fabric of the Hospital structure and culture. These are separate interest groups. One protects the territory of one's group and resists usurpation of geographical space, manpower, rights, privileges, and materials. It is often extremely difficult for such units to change habits and attitudes. There remains the underlying fear that such change may in some way affect their vested interests. It is an emotional quality, most often not consciously felt or expressed, but which can impede desired change.

❀ Custodial Ethics and Practices

Limited budget, multiple subordination, and autonomous function are aspects of the hospital organizational structure that have led to the entrenchment of custodialism. Personnel working within such a system tend to develop a philosophy and an ethic compatible with their custodial practices and resist conflicting innovative approaches. The custodial ethic postulates that most patients can attain no more than a sheltered, dependent existence within the institution; thus the efforts of both staff and patients become directed toward this end. Staff are deployed throughout the hospital so that all patients have an opportunity to receive equal services. Similarly, attendance at special activities developed by staff personnel, such as dances, movies, parties, is governed by a quota system which supposedly provides patients in all the hospital wards with equal opportunity to attend.

Consonant with these efforts to improve the care given all patients is the use of patients themselves on work assignments designed to maintain the hospital services. However, the need for patients to work toward the improvement of care available to all patients led to the view that patients who worked were more deserving of rewards than patients who did not. So the working patients began to receive special consideration and preference. Despite the prevailing ethic that affirmed equal care for all, the debilitated patient was seen as "less equal," and as a result he received fewer available services.

Any therapeutic program designed to return patients to the extramural community is antithetical to, and often conflicts with, prevailing custodial ethics and practices. Therapeutic programming requires a perception of the patient's potential for independent community existence, the selection of patients suitable for a specific treatment regimen, and the concentration of staff effort on these patients. Attempts to initiate such programs at the Philadelphia State Hospital before 1957 were met with the assumptions that patients were unfit for extramural living, that labor by patients was vital to hospital service, and that patients could not be spared to participate in treatment programs. In addition, department heads were unwilling to concentrate staff in treatment areas at the expense of further curtailing the limited services available in the rest of the hospital.

Such conditions and factors within the traditional large state hospital markedly handicapped its progress from a custodial institution to a treatment center. Clearly, before the therapeutic potential of such a hospital could be actualized, fundamental changes in the structure and organization of the hospital and in the attitudes of its personnel had to be effected.

Chapter III

Initiating an Innovative
Treatment Program

The treatment program introduced at the Philadelphia State Hospital
in 1957 was based on the assumption that social alienation is the
major obstacle to the psychotic patient's recovery. In addressing itself
to overcoming the patient's isolation from his fellow man, socio-environmental treatment progressively introduces increments in interaction in a matrix within which patients experience the social realities
of day-to-day living and learn adaptive social responses.

❀ REQUIREMENTS OF SOCIO-ENVIRONMENTAL ❀ TREATMENT

By virtue of its custodial organization, structure, and ethic, the large state hospital cannot readily provide socio-environmental treatment. It offers such mass treatment as chemotherapy to many patients, and such individualized treatment as somatic and psychological therapies to a few. It does *not* offer the patient any means to reduce his alienation through meaningful social experience. Providing the opportunity for such social experience would necessitate considerable modification of the custodial hospital.

The following requirements are basic to developing a socio-environmental treatment program (Jones, 1953; Cumming and Cumming, 1957; Wilmer, 1958):

1. A physical plant is required, geographically and psychologically separated from the custodial environment so that it can readily be structured to approximate the extramural community; for example, to permit individual privacy and access to belongings, allow freedom for modification of the living area, provide opportunity for making some decisions regarding daily life experiences.

2. Administrative authority is necessary to modify the traditional role of the patient from that of a ward of the hospital to that of a more responsible and independent member of the hospital and, eventually, of the community.

3. The program must be staffed by personnel willing to develop roles consonant with the philosophy and goals of socio-environmental therapy—reversal of the debilitating symptoms of mental illness through humanistic, socializing processes directed toward restoring to patients the responsibilities for independent daily living.

❀ BARRIERS TO CHANGE ❀

The literature reports resistances and barriers met in attempts to convert existing custodial institutions into therapeutic social settings. The established administrative organization is structured to achieve and perpetuate custodial, rather than therapeutic, goals. In addition,

the traditionalistic orientation of administrative personnel sets the tone
for devaluation of attempts at innovative programs (Cumming and
Cumming, 1957; 1962). A further problem is the orthodox adherence
by each professional discipline to its own practices. Departmental in-
dividuality leads to departmental jealousies and rivalries which preclude collaborative efforts (York, 1955). Departmental rivalry often
becomes so intense that competition results for space, budget, and
patients (Key, 1959).

❀ OVERCOMING RESISTANCE ❀

The reported efforts at surmounting these barriers to change
fall into three general categories, differing in the degree of administrative support for the innovator. Attempts to initiate therapeutic programs are apparently most successful when the administration dele-
gates whatever authority and power are necessary to develop the type
of organization required for the program. Cumming and Cumming
(1957) initiated a successful socialization program in an institution
where two previous attempts had failed, only after they were granted
the power to reorganize the nursing and business hierarchies. According to Sarwer-Foner, Ogle, and Dancey (1960) and Wilmer (1958),
discord and administrative difficulty can be avoided only when the
complete authority of the man in charge is clearly established and
supported by the administration.

When delegation of power is tenuous, innovators frequently
resort to one of two approaches. The project leader may attempt to
gain the collaborative efforts of those administrators and heads of departments affected by the innovative program. He submerges his own
ideas on theory and practice and permits a steering committee of these
executives to carry out administrative planning and policy-making.
York (1955) reported that in Massachusetts, in the Bedford VA Hospital and in the Metropolitan Hospital experiments in patient care,
allowing greater leeway for local concepts and practices resulted in the
development of socially therapeutic procedures uniquely appropriate
to the needs of the institution. However, this procedure dilutes the
ideology and effectiveness of the innovator. Cohen (1957) noted that
the most salient factor differentiating successful from unsuccessful

therapeutic communities seemed to be the presence of a dedicated leader "who sparks the whole community hierarchy with hope, expectation of improvement, a sense of knowing what to do and how to do it."

If collaborative administration is not feasible, the project director may move ahead, even with minimal support. York (1955) indicates that in such a situation the hope is that the demonstration of effective results will win the support and confidence of the administration and overcome the resistance of rival groups and departments. Pearlin (1962) noted that a favorable attitude toward change among those whom it would affect was not a necessary precursor for innovation. His evidence suggests that an important condition for overcoming resistance to change is change itself. However, according to Cumming and Cumming (1957), proceeding with innovative attempts without full administrative authority means that the innovator must persuade the old guard that the changes will not have the disastrous consequences they anticipate. Moreover, as Stotland and Kobler (1965) found, innovating without full and prior clarification of administrative responsibility can produce a crisis that may help to kill the project. An interesting account of the problems of this approach, and its ultimate failure, was reported by Kissinger (1963).

The development of socio-environmental treatment programs at the Philadelphia State Hospital was implicitly sanctioned by the administration in December, 1956, with the appointment of a new director of Psychological Services who had a strong personal investment in this type of program. Although this appointment carried with it the superintendent's approval for program development, it was not endowed with the administrative power necessary to establish and direct the type of organization required for the successful operation of a therapeutic program. The organization and structure of the Philadelphia State Hospital, described in Chapter Two, provided a barrier which at times made the basic requirements for socio-environmental treatment seem almost unattainable.

The new director of Psychological Services had as his goal the establishment of a socio-environmental program which would not only provide therapeutic service but also permit an investigation of the theory underlying such treatment. The attainment of these goals required that the administration delegate full administrative power to the director. However, the superintendent would not delegate this authority without first knowing how the staff organization for the project would affect the hospital's authority structure. In addition, since the hospital had to care for 6,500 patients, he was unwilling to make any major changes for a project which would treat relatively few patients. Consequently, the director had to find other means than direct use of authority to attain project goals.

The alternative approaches reported in the literature were not feasible in this situation. Permitting a steering committee of department heads to determine their own goals for the project would probably have resulted in a program more consonant with prevailing hospital policies, but one which was less powerful both as a demonstration of the effectiveness of socio-environmental therapy and as a test of the hypotheses underlying this treatment. An equally unacceptable alternative was to proceed with program development knowing that the compromises necessary to overcome resistances might radically alter the program and destroy the research design.

In order not to compromise the research objectives of the project, it was decided to proceed as if administrative sanction involved the delegation of power. The clinical directors were asked to relinquish to psychologists some of the administrative functions which traditionally fell to psychiatrists. Efforts were also made to convince the department heads of the desirability of the project goals and to persuade them to allocate staff who would participate in attaining these goals. The aim of this strategy was to obtain increasing commitments from the superintendent. Building on such formalized commitments, and using the right of eminent domain as a lever, the project director was gradually able to develop the organization and obtain the power necessary for the establishment and maintenance of a socio-environmental treatment program.

❀ THE PHYSICAL PLANT ❀

The procurement of the physical plant involved a variety of problems. The superintendent allocated three small cottages and a larger building to serve respectively as the Male and Female sections of the Rehabilitation Unit. These buildings formerly housed attendants, and thus none of the hospital service departments viewed these facilities as within their jurisdiction. Hence, this assignment created no difficulty.

The expansion of the physical plant during the succeeding two years was facilitated by the construction of a dining room and the renovation of a service building (S-3)—both within the geographic area of the Rehabilitation Unit. Other departments had submitted plans to the superintendent for the use of these buildings, but the project director was able to persuade him to allocate these facilities to the project. The superintendent's decision was strongly influenced by the demonstrated efficacy of the staff organization and the success of the therapeutic program, the financial support of the project by a National Institute of Mental Health grant, and national recognition deriving from the award of the grant, in addition to visits from NIMH consultants and other psychiatric authorities from all over the country. These factors only partially mitigated conflicts with the other service departments that sought to include these physical facilities in their own expansion plans.

The Dietary Service had planned to use the dining room to feed patients who worked in the adjoining central kitchen. Understandably, the Dietary Service felt that the administration had reneged on its commitment to them, and this feeling did not make them receptive to the needs of the Rehabilitation Unit. Already shorthanded, this department was not inclined to diminish services even further in order to staff the Rehabilitation Unit dining room.

Both the Occupational Therapy (OT) and Social Service departments had been involved in planning the renovation of the S-3 building, with a view toward extending their services. The OT Department planned to use the new facilities for staff offices and for the development of a rehabilitation program. Some friction developed when it became clear that the facilities would be under the Psychology Department for the purpose of providing an integrated socio-environmental treatment program. Friction mounted when the project director allocated office space in the S-3 building for project staff rather than for OT staff servicing other parts of the hospital. But despite the conflict of interests, the OT Department cooperated in carrying out program activities.

The Social Service Department had originally intended to use S-3 as a hospital-based halfway house, and the building's renovation was designed for this purpose. However, since the project director had funds to hire new personnel and the Social Service Department had insufficient manpower to staff a halfway house, the director of Social Services did not oppose the allocation of the building for a socio-environmental treatment program.

❀ PROBLEMS OF STAFF ORGANIZATION ❀

❀ Jurisdiction

The psychologist in the role of administrator of a treatment program presents a problem to both the medical hierarchy and the hospital administration. Although social treatment is not within the scope of medical training, the medical viewpoint still favors the physician as administrator of such programs. As a rule, members of this profession zealously guard both their administrative and therapeutic prerogatives. The rationale underlying this attitude tends to carry over from general medical practice. Wilmer (1958) and Sarwer-Foner, Ogle, and Dancey (1960) emphasized the physician's *prima facie* knowledge and authority. Cumming and Cumming (1962) pointed out the importance of medical training, "so that the principle of safeguarding the interests of the patient will be deeply instilled."

Parsons (1951) made the most telling point for the unequivocal recognition of the psychiatrist as the "captain" of the therapeutic team. His rationale for the primacy of the physician was based on factors other than competence, for example, "the symbolic importance of the psychiatrist's legitimating role." Parsons states that the institutionalized confidence of the general public in the physician as the custodian of the sick "leads to putting psychiatrists in positions with a large component of administrative responsibility, i.e., as heads of services. . . . This situation may well have something to do with the sensitivity of the psychiatric component of the staff to the prerogatives of their position of authority, the well-known insistence that the psychiatrist be recognized unequivocally as 'captain' of the therapeutic team. The simple fact is that a level of responsibility is often imputed to them which they are not in a position to implement successfully, and in this situation, protection against being challenged from below or outside serves to mitigate the strain." Consequently, the psychiatrist tends to be unwilling to recognize the overlap and special skills of his coprofessions and to share with them his unique status and role.

According to Jones (1965), despite the physician's indoctrination for assuming leadership and the public's reinforcement of the physician's "omnipotent fantasies," there is "a growing awareness that the psychiatric social worker or the social psychologist may, as things are at present, have had a better training in the social science dimension and often be a more appropriate leader than the psychiatrist." Although the psychologist's leadership skills have been effectively demonstrated in such nonmedical settings as industries, universities, and therapeutic-educational situations, psychologists in the medically dominated hospital systems find themselves in roles ancillary to the physician's. Psychologists who attempt to assume leadership in providing treatment services too often become embroiled in conflicts with a psychiatric administration which is unwilling to entrust such functions to them.

The state mental hospitals have traditionally been under the jurisdiction of the medical-psychiatric profession; therefore, it was not surprising that the superintendent, despite his sanctioning of the development of a socio-environmental program, wanted the program conducted under medical supervision. Since the program was initially to involve male patients, the superintendent selected a psychiatrist, the clinical director for the Male Service, to supervise program development and patient welfare. However, the motivation, ideas, and clinical background for the socio-environmental treatment program would derive from the director of the Psychology Department and his associates. On this basis, the director of the Psychology Department contended that he must have administrative responsibility for program development and evaluation. This meant that psychiatry would have to relinquish a portion of its traditional responsibilities, namely, the administration and direction of psychological treatment programs. It was particularly difficult to demarcate clear lines of authority, however, since these administrative functions are interrelated with medical-legal responsibilities.

The resistance of psychiatry to modifying its traditional functions became particularly apparent at the first meeting of the clinical director, the project director, and the heads of the various departments. The clinical director was not sure that the division in responsibility was feasible, but, reassured by the knowledge that ultimate authority for patients would still reside with him, he was willing to proceed on a trial basis. Pressured by the need to utilize the vacant physical plant, he consented to the screening of patients for the project. Together with the project director, he selected the first patients for transfer to the program. The clinical director assigned a staff psychiatrist on a part-time basis to provide medical and psychiatric services to the patients and to represent psychiatry in the program. At this point, clarifying the boundaries of authority of psychiatry and psychology ceased to be an obstacle to the initiation of the project. However, this question continued to be an issue between the psychiatry and psychology staff on the unit during the developmental phase of the program.

When the female unit of the project opened during the following year, the clinical director of the Female Service also allocated one of his psychiatrists to the project for part-time service. By this time the lines of authority maintained by each of the two disciplines had been partly clarified: psychiatry retained responsibility for the medical-psychiatric welfare of patients and for making ultimate decisions about patient disposition; psychology obtained the responsibility for program development and direction and for the therapeutic management of the patient's daily life. During the interval preceding the opening of the female unit, the psychologist's new role of program developer and administrator had become sufficiently established and crystallized to be accepted fully by the clinical director of the Female Division.

❀ Assignment

The various departments initially showed resistance to the request for assignment of staff to the project. Although a reality-based rationale was offered for this reluctance, a major underlying objection derived from the introduction of Psychology into the authority hierarchy and from the feeling that this new discipline was "taking over."

The Nursing Department was uncertain about its ability to work with psychologists as program administrators, but was willing to support an experimental program which might demonstrate the therapeutic potential of the psychiatric nurse. The director of Nursing assigned a nurse and male attendant when the male unit was opened, and another nurse and a female attendant when the female unit was added. Additional attendants were added as the need for program-activity leaders increased. Personnel were also allocated to provide supervision during the evening and night hours.

Neither the Nursing nor the Dietary Department was able to allocate sufficient personnel for the opening of the new dining room. Grant funds were used to hire dining room staff. When hospital funds became available for these new staff members, they were assigned to the Nursing Department under the supervision of the charge nurse on the unit.

The Social Service Department favored innovative treatment programs but was opposed to the principle of divided administrative–medical-legal responsibility. Despite a recognition of the need for such programs, innovative roles for social workers were not accepted or developed. No social worker was assigned to the project team, either in a therapeutic capacity or in a traditional social worker role. Social casework and placement services were made available to the project on the same basis prevailing throughout the hospital. Referrals for social services were placed in a centralized pool where they awaited the availability of a worker.

The Occupational Therapy, Hospital Industry, Recreation, and Music departments all saw primary therapeutic roles for their personnel in the new program, and they were willing for Psychology to provide the necessary leadership. The Occupational Therapy Department allocated two part-time workers to the project. This number has since been increased by one full-time worker who both conducts program activities and serves as an activity expediter; she orders supplies and equipment and insures that the prescribed educational content is presented in the appropriate activity sessions within the treatment program.

The Hospital Industry Department provided considerable staff time. In addition to the chief, who functioned on a part-time basis as a project activity leader, the services of two staff members were made available to the project for the assignment of patients to hospital industries. The chief also facilitated the acquisition of supplies and special services from the rest of the hospital. In the preliminary stages of project development, before NIMH grant funds were available, he was instrumental in raising funds to finance trips by patients into the city.

The Recreation and Music departments appreciated the project's need for the services of their personnel in a concerted therapeutic effort, rather than for the purely diversionary purposes for which they were being utilized in most parts of the hospital. The opportunity to function in a more therapeutic manner prompted these department heads to allocate four of their personnel for part-time service on the project.

❀ Divided Responsibility

Subsequent to the allocation of physical plant and the assignment of personnel, the project's major problem during the developmental phase was clarifying lines of authority and defining roles and functions. Although the various hospital departments had assigned staff to the project, there was no real decentralization of these personnel. This led to a recapitulation of the major problems prevalent throughout the hospital, namely, problems which derived from multiple subordination and its counterpart, divided responsibility.

Multiple subordination clearly results in confusion of the communication process and ambiguity of roles and functions. Shartle (1956) indicates that this is antithetical to good business management and Stanton and Schwartz (1954) as well as Cumming and Cumming (1957) report on its negative effects on hospital treatment. To be effective, a member of any organization must have a knowledge of the goals and operations of that organization. Such knowledge is vital if the individual is to appraise his own and others' efforts to attain the organization's goals. When staff members are confused regarding their roles and functions, it becomes impossible to develop a therapeutic milieu with clearly defined areas of responsibility.

While personnel from various units were assigned to the project, their former lines of report to their base unit remained. Every member of the project had at least two supervisors, one on the project staff and one in his own departmental organization. Perhaps the most difficult problems involving multiple supervisors were those faced by the nurse. In most psychiatric units the supervising nurse is the hub of a system of multiple subordination, with lines of authority emanating from Administration, Nursing Department, and Psychiatry. In the Rehabilitation Project this pattern was complicated by the introduction of psychologists as program coordinator and unit administrator, and by the presence of two psychiatrists, themselves each responsible to a different clinical director. "Which problem do I take to which doctor?" became a major question for the nurse to resolve.

The problems of multiple subordination and lines of authority affected not only the nurses but patients as well. Two "doctors" on the same unit made it difficult for the patient to differentiate the role of the unit administrator psychologist from that of the unit psychiatrist. Since nursing personnel usually were apprised of problems before other staff members and directed the patient to the appropriate authority, this problem could not be resolved until the nurse herself was fully aware of the division of function between the psychiatrist and psychologist.

It was clear that a course of action had to be taken to clarify the lines of authority. The psychologists, by virtue of their responsibility for the psychosocial activity program, established regular in-service training sessions for the staff. These formal meetings, as well as the informal meetings concerned with patients' progress, permitted them to promulgate their philosophy of treatment and to assume a central role in defining and delimiting lines of authority. Considerable discussion and actual resolution of problems finally clarified the following lines of authority: the nurse was responsible to the assistant directors of the Nursing Department for administrative supervision and nursing care of patients, to the unit psychiatrists for medical-psychiatric care, and to the psychologists who served as program coordinators and unit administrators for the patients' daily psychological regimen and for matters involving program activities and milieu.

A further example of administrative disorder became evident when the in-service training sessions were begun. Early in the project's developmental phase, the psychologists planning the program foresaw the need for special training for all rehabilitation staff. Such training would help develop a uniform philosophy and techniques unique to social treatment. The Rehabilitation Program coordinator requested that social workers providing service to rehabilitation patients attend these meetings, but their departmental director insisted that social workers were already fully trained members of a professional discipline and required no additional training. Consequently, the rehabilitation coordinator felt that these workers were never really a part of the social treatment team, and there were frequent undertones of tension and estrangement between the rehabilitation coordinator and the members of the Social Service Department.

During this period the unit administrators were developing policies and innovating program elements with rehabilitation workers and did not fully realize that such unilateral action might bring workers into conflict with other unit administrators and the program coordinator. For example, the unit administrator who supervised the nurse responsible for the monthly party directed her to structure these socials with regard to activities and content. The program coordinator and other unit administrators, however, felt that the socials should be unstructured, to permit spontaneous interaction. This difference in approach within the administrative hierarchy was a source of confusion and tension to the nurse until a consistent approach was established.

❀ Vested Interests

Although jurisdictional disputes and multiple subordination are major barriers to the innovation of treatment programs in large state hospitals, the failure to develop a modus vivendi is due to vested interests and a struggle for power. The development of the rehabilitation program at the Philadelphia State Hospital was impeded by the vested interests of the administration, the various hospital departments, and subdivisions of the rehabilitation units themselves. The Psychology Department was itself attempting to develop its own power, of course, in the establishment of the program, thus adding further complexity to an already complex set of conflicting interests.

The administration of a state hospital is responsible for safeguarding the public from the potentially dangerous mental patient and the imposition of conservative release policies fulfills this responsibility with a minimum of public criticism. In 1956 a patient could be released from the Philadelphia State Hospital only after being presented at a psychiatric staff meeting and obtaining approval for release from the clinical director of the service. Even then, he was released only to the custody of his family. Since such ultraconservative procedures would prevent the project from attaining one of its goals (the return of rehabilitated patients to the community), the project director sought more liberal release policies from the administration. He convinced the clinical director to delegate the responsibility for release of patients to the psychiatrist assigned to the unit, and he persuaded the administration to permit patients to return to the community in their own custody. These policies were already in operation when the Female Unit was established, and shortly thereafter their demonstrated utility led to their adoption as general hospital policy.

A legally bestowed vested interest of the psychiatrist is the guardianship of the welfare of the institutionalized mental patient. As the psychiatrist in charge, the clinical director was responsible for the care and welfare of the patient, and he was extremely cautious in delegating such responsibility to a nonmedical person. This reservation became apparent when psychologists requested the transfer from other buildings of those patients selected for the Rehabilitation Project. Many of these requests were refused by the clinical director, either on the grounds that the patient was too sick to engage in a rehabilitation program or that he did not wish to be transferred. In this instance, the psychiatric physician was exercising his prerogative to determine what constitutes good care for the individual patient, even though the psychologists believed that many of these patients could have benefited from the rehabilitation program. Only after the utility of the program had been demonstrated were these precautions relaxed.

In some cases, medical-legal responsibility was used to obstruct the program development efforts of the psychologists in order to maintain power and leadership status for psychiatrists. Although measures were taken to insure that patients in all buildings could be screened by psychologists, there were still instances in which the vested interests and prerogatives of the physician prevented the transfer of patients to the rehabilitation program. Only the turnover of old-guard personnel eliminated resistance to psychologists' screening patients and administering treatment programs.

Problems posed by the conflict of vested interests arose not only with the administration and psychiatry, but also with most other departments. This is particularly well exemplified by the interaction between the Rehabilitation Project and the Social Service Department, previously mentioned. The insistence by the Social Service Department on separate and independent function precluded full utilization by the social worker of the extensive knowledge of the patient's assets and liabilities gathered by the therapeutic team during the patient's stay on the project. It became necessary for the Rehabilitation Project to procure its own full-time social worker. Even then there was no immediate resolution of the problem. Initial efforts had to be directed toward resolving interdisciplinary problems, particularly where duplication of function was involved. The fact that such problems could be resolved within the project structure permitted the worker to function as a highly effective team member.

The management and servicing of large numbers of patients in the face of critical staff shortages require the institution of uniform procedures and special routines quite unlike those necessary for a rehabilitation program. The advent of the Rehabilitation Project could not help but create problems for those departments which regularly came in contact with large numbers of patients, like the Nursing and Industrial Therapy Departments. One such conflict occurred with nursing personnel regarding selection of ward patients for transfer to the Rehabilitation Project. A large-scale screening procedure was necessary to insure that those patients selected for socio-environmental treatment met the criteria established for the project rather than the criteria usually followed by those departments. Potentially eligible patients were screened by teams of two psychologists who arranged appointments with ward personnel to interview approximately ten patients at each screening session. The teams felt that the ward nursing personnel showed some resistance to the screening procedures. R. J. Smith's study (1961) revealed that the nursing personnel resented the intrusion and disruption of ward routines by the psychologists. Since they were particularly concerned with carrying out the routines necessary for housekeeping, feeding, and distribution of medication to large numbers of patients, they were particularly critical when psychologists broke or were late for appointments. In addition, they saw screening as a procedure which might deprive them of patients who could provide major assistance with the ward routines.

Resistance of this kind led the psychologists to redouble their educational efforts with nursing personnel. Lectures were given on the rehabilitation potential of chronic patients, the criteria used for the selection of such patients, and the content of the program. The approach most instrumental in improving public relations within the hospital, however, was the assignment of Rehabilitation Project staff to hospital wards to serve as "public relations agents." Comprehensive information about all aspects of the rehabilitation program and feedback on the progress of former ward patients in the Rehabilitation Project lessened some of the resistance to screening and even elicited a number of referrals for the program. It thus appears that some of the resistance did not derive from vested interests but from a lack of knowledge regarding the aims of the new treatment approach and its potential for success.

Another conflict derived from the Nursing Department's need to service all hospital patients, as opposed to the rehabilitation goal of providing an intensive experience for patients preparing to leave the hospital. This conflict became apparent with respect to the special hospital-wide social events scheduled by the Nursing Department. Because of limited space and facilities, attendance at these events was determined by a quota system, which required that each building contribute a certain number of patients. However, only a few patients from each building could attend. Since so few Rehabilitation Project patients could be present at these socials, this activity obviously could not serve as a meaningful program element. Furthermore, since patients in poor psychiatric condition attended these functions, the imposition of security procedures—escorts and supervision—were necessary. Such procedures were antithetical to the program's goals of fostering responsibility, decision-making, and independence. Attainment of these goals clearly required that social facilities and events be established within the Rehabilitation Project itself.

The interests of the Hospital Industries Department also conflicted with those of the Rehabilitation Project. Such hospital activities as Laundry, Kitchens, and Farms provide services and products essential for the hospital's operation. For the most part these divisions are dependent upon patient labor. The Hospital Industry personnel must find patients for full-time assignment to these pursuits. The goal of the Rehabilitation Project personnel, however, was to provide meaningful social experiences to prepare patients for leaving the hospital. The conflict of goals became most apparent when rehabilitation patients were shifted from full- to half-day hospital industry assignments to permit their participation in the program. This reduction in working hours resulted in considerable hardship in areas where many of the rehabilitation patients were key workers. In an attempt to compensate for this reduction in patients' working hours, the rehabilitation staff assigned two patients to each job, one to work during the morning and one during the afternoon. This solution was unsatisfactory because of the difference in performance, increased transportation problems, and continued conflicts between rehabilitation program obligations and working hours.

Although the Rehabilitation Project could not fully compensate industrial areas for the loss of key workers, a plan was developed to alleviate the general shortage. All Rehabilitation Project patients, including many with no previous hospital industry assignment, were required to engage in half-time work assignments. This requirement resulted in the establishment of a large force of worker patients. These patients were then assigned to housekeeping and dining room duties within the Rehabilitation Project area. This procedure freed nonproject worker patients for work assignments in areas other than the rehabilitation units. These patients were available for full-day work assignments and were better able to meet the work-time requirements of industrial areas in the rest of the hospital. This solution was also compatible with the aims of the Rehabilitation Project, since it permitted unit administrators to maintain much closer liaison with the industrial supervisors. These personnel could now be included in project training meetings and in communication conferences with the unit administrators.

Conflicting interests were manifested not only between the Rehabilitation Project and various departments, but also between subdivisions of the project itself. During the developmental phase of the program, a major conflict arose between the research and clinical services personnel. Despite various compromises, the basic conflict of interest between research and program needs persisted. This conflict was further intensified by the pressure on the unit administrators to accept patients from other hospital units, irrespective of the criteria maintained in the Rehabilitation Project. The rejection of referred patients because they failed to meet research criteria aroused resentment among the referral agents, particularly among the psychiatrists, who saw this both as a reflection on their treatment decisions and an infringement of their right to utilize treatment services throughout the hospital. Nevertheless, it was recognized that research interests had to prevail if the utility of socio-environmental treatment was to be demonstrated. To reduce the pressure on the unit administrators to accept "special" cases, it was decided to admit a limited number of such cases to the rehabilitation programs for clinical treatment but not to include these cases in the research sample. This partial solution did not resolve the conflict between the clinical and research sections of the department, primarily because it did not deal with the basic problem—the struggle for power.

✳ Power and Decision-Making Strategy

The Rehabilitation Project had as its goal the development of a demonstration treatment program to test the utility of socio-environmental treatment and, simultaneously, to clarify some of its theoretical underpinnings. The establishment of such an experimental treatment program required certain decisions about the exercise of leadership and the allocation of power for policy formulation. These aspects of power and decision-making strategy pose problems for most organizations, particularly during the developmental phase when the authority, power, and control aspects of the organization undergo continual modification.

There is much in the literature regarding the most effective strategy for leadership and decision-making in attaining the goals of an organization. The failure of a strict hierarchical structure to make full use of the conative and cognitive resources of its most capable members led to the currently prevalent practice of utilizing equalitarian groups for decision-making. A number of studies on group problem-solving (Kelley and Thibaut, 1954) have demonstrated that under certain conditions group solutions are superior to solutions reached by individuals. Riecken and Homans (1954) report that this is particularly evident under conditions of permissive leadership, where group participation and free expression of opinion are maximized and the leader's role is minimized. Kelley and Thibaut have attributed the superiority of group problem solving to at least four factors:

1. Greater sharpening and refinement of concepts occur when ideas are formulated for group presentation.

2. Within a group problem-solving context, the accuracy, speed, and quality of work improve, and changes in motivation and thought processes occur more in accord with group goals; that is, there is social facilitation.

3. The individual's awareness of a variety of judgments permits him to reach a more accurate solution.

4. Exchange and integration of the suggestions of group members lead to a new idea which is more tenable and satisfactory than any of the individual ideas.

The use of equalitarian groups in the decision-making process, however, is not necessarily the most effective organizational policy. The small group process can be subverted by personalized factors which impair identification with group membership and prevent participation in the attainment of group goals. Fouriezos, Hutt, and Guetzkow (1950) showed that the prevalence of a high degree of self-oriented needs was related to a decline in group effectiveness. Deutch (1949) demonstrated that competitiveness among group members was associated with the pursuit of egocentric rather than group goals. The finding by Mulder (1959) that the achievement of power led to greater satisfaction than working toward a common goal helps to explain the preference for egocentric goals. It has also been noted that the judgment of individual members is influenced by such subjective interpersonal factors as personal attachments (Kelley and Thibaut, 1954), avoidance of conflict involving potential for punishment (Festinger, 1953), and compliance with the evaluations of those members perceived as experts or as having high status (Torrance, 1954).

Bennis (1961) and Straus (1963) have raised some serious

questions about the utility of adapting the equalitarian group model for determining organizational policy. They indicate that this type of model is inappropriate for large organizations where structural factors are necessary for the control and fulfillment of ongoing, routinized work processes and activities.

The Rehabilitation Project utilized the equalitarian group model for policy- and decision-making operations. To insure the development of a creative and effective Rehabilitation Project, the director of Psychological Services recruited highly competent psychologists to participate in the planning and implementation of the program. Impressed with the caliber of these psychologists and wishing to create an atmosphere of maximum productivity, the director established a committee to serve as an equalitarian program-planning group. New psychologists recruited for the project were added to this planning group, regardless of differences in departmental rank. The planning group for the experimental program included four psychologist unit administrators, the coordinator of the Rehabilitation Program, and the director of Psychological Services.

The members of this planning committee had high ambitions both for developing social treatment programs and for fulfilling the therapeutic potential of the state hospital. Their dedication to improving conditions was matched by their willingness to volunteer considerable amounts of their own time to the development of innovative programs. However, dissension began to appear among the committee members after the developmental phase of the experimental program was completed. This dissension was manifested by committee members exceeding their authority in their dealings with other Rehabilitation Center staff. Participation in an equalitarian decision-making committee became confused with the notion that each member of this body was completely free to execute his own plans. Furthermore, the ambiguity in roles and functions that had prevailed during the developmental phase, and the ongoing reorganization of the administrative hierarchy in accord with the areas of responsibility delimited by the new and expanding project, resulted in a situation which was conducive to unilateral action by individual committee members. A consequence of this tendency to ignore or overlook the existing chain of command and to assume responsibility for a variety of independent innovations without official delegation or coordination was increased dissension among the committee members.

The dissension and struggle for power among the psychologists on the project led to duplication of functions. For example, at one point the coordinator of the Rehabilitation Project was spending a major portion of his time on independent research on social treatment, the psychologist assigned the major responsibility for project research was working out some areas of program content with an activity worker, and one of the unit administrators was innovating a new evening activity for the females. This activity, the Bible Discussion Club, was instituted without any clearance from the chaplaincy services, without the coordinator's knowledge, and without any evaluation of how it might affect the therapeutic milieu of the entire Rehabilitation Project.

Coincident with this competition for control of new areas of responsibility were efforts to undermine the competence of other members of the planning committee. Individual members used their positions on the equalitarian committee as a basis for ignoring official supervisory channels and for presenting grievances at committee meetings or directly to the project director. These complaints, including charges of dereliction of responsibilities or incompetence in the performance of duty, often had as their goal personal aggrandizement and subversion of the power of the immediate supervisor. In fact, supervisory authority could not be exercised over subordinates who had equal status in policy decision-making and program planning. It became apparent in the course of time that it was unrealistic to expect members who participated in making major decisions to act in subsidiary roles in implementing them. Superimposing an equalitarian planning structure upon hierarchic implementation proved to be impracticable.

A natural extension of this subversion of the hierarchic structure was the attempt to divest the director of his leadership authority. Freud (1918) explained the usurpation of power by ambitious subordinates as deriving from the primordial wishes of sons to destroy and replace the father. Straus (1963) noted the presence of the same phenomenon when equalitarian groups are established in industry. In such situations, the ambitions of the group members may turn them against management. The planning group's dissatisfaction with the leadership of the project director was manifested after the completion of the developmental phase. The dissatisfaction was verbalized on the basis that the director gave insufficient recognition to the psychologists who were actually doing the job, was far too conservative to head such a pioneer effort, and relied too heavily on expediency and political compromise to serve as spokesman for this humanitarian movement.

In June, 1960, the committee acted on its desire to depose the project director. It met with the director and demanded that he delegate to them full responsibility for the direction of the program. The project director had respect for the competence of the committee members. In order not to lose any of these key personnel, whom he perceived as essential to the ultimate success of the project, he consented to consider their demands. The agreement actually worked out with the committee did not change the method by which the group had been operating. The major policy issues of the project continued to be discussed and planned at the committee meetings. The director maintained veto power, since it was he who worked with the hospital administration to put into operation the plans developed at committee meetings.

The marked differences among committee members in opinions and personal ambitions would have made committee rule impossible. There was no member of the committee other than the project director whom the group could accept as a leader. Thus, this conflict resulted in "business as usual," with the project director maintaining and ultimately enlarging his position. The power struggle was essentially over. Members began to accept their designated areas of responsibility. Those who could not accept this outcome began to seek positions elsewhere.

The psychologists also applied the equalitarian group philosophy to their interrelationships with the group activity leaders. The course of events with the group leaders recapitulated the problems which arose among the psychologists. Because of their desire to work within a democratic framework and thereby obtain maximum effort and creativity from the group activity leaders, the psychologists did not prevent leaders from effecting major program modifications independently. A proliferation of uncoordinated program innovations was the consequence of this decision. Moreover, group leaders began to compete with one another for recognition as program innovators and for freedom to operate independent of unit coordination. This competition was intense enough to be manifested in open rivalry and clashes between some of the leaders. The psychologists frequently utilized this dissension as evidence that the coordinator or a particular unit administrator was unable to correct the situation. Only after the power struggle among the psychologists was resolved were they able to deal effectively with rivalries among the group leaders.

Some of the problems in decision-making processes during the implementational phase of an innovative program have been reviewed to emphasize the importance of developing administrative and leadership structures appropriate for the type and function of a particular organization. Small groups of well-meaning professionals in the mental health field have too often fallen victim to the notion that an informal leadership group for directing the course of a special project could easily be established. Such naïveté about organizational structure frequently results either in dissolution of the group and failure of the project, or in a period of disruption after which one individual assumes control and all dissenters leave. Modern organizational theory can contribute much to facilitate operational efficiency and durability of existence of such groups.

The experiences of the project group at the Philadelphia State Hospital highlight the necessity for clearly delineating the organizational structure and leadership in accordance with the general purpose and function of the organization. Bennis (1961) differentiated the structure and leadership of organizations according to their function. Two types of organization mentioned by Bennis are relevant to the Philadelphia State Hospital project: the Problem-Solving (Figure 3.1) and the Habit Organization (Figure 3.2). The former specializes in creating and implementing new ideas; the leader works toward promoting conditions favoring the congruence of individual and organizational goals. The success of this type of group depends on the self-control of its members. The Habit Organization specializes in replicating standard activities and products. Compliance with performance criteria is insured by the authority of the leader. Policy is decided by

FIG. 3.1

EQUALITARIAN
PROBLEM-SOLVING GROUP

FIG. 3.2

HABIT ORGANIZATION

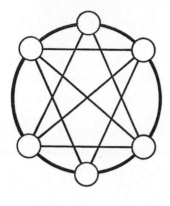

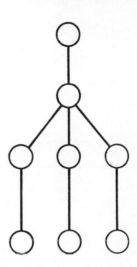

members of the upper echelons and promulgated to supervisors and subordinates; lower echelon members simply implement and have no opportunity to participate in the decision-making process.

These two types of structure were present simultaneously in the Philadelphia State Hospital Project. The equalitarian members of the Problem-Solving organization determining Rehabilitation Project policies were expected also to operate at different levels of responsibility in a Habit Organization where routine service functions were performed under supervision. It is not surprising that involvement of the same personnel simultaneously in policy-making and implementation units of the same organization led to incompatibility of roles. An individual cannot be expected to share equally in the powers of management and also to assume various hierarchic power positions in executing established policies. Such an effort can lead only to confusion and dissonance on the part of the participants, and attempts by those in subordinate positions to undermine and subvert the hierarchic structure in order to maximize their own power. It is disastrous to assign personnel to units in which they experience role incompatibility, and it is also unrealistic to conduct service and research on an informal, equalitarian basis. Although the leader must assume responsibility for setting policy and making decisions, he can augment the decision making by involving the personnel immediately subordinate to him.

Likert (1959) has suggested that such a decision-making body must approach problems from the point of view of the welfare of the total organization. Personnel in various subdivisions of the organization should have opportunities to meet with the supervisor of their work group in order to deal with problems related to their work task. This "linking-pin" organizational model for group functioning entails subordinates involved in single work groups which are linked together by supervisors who are members of more than one work group. Such a system insures that decisions will be made by personnel who are homogeneous in power and, most likely, in ability. It also permits subordinates to participate in decision-making and at the same time confines competitiveness to peer groups within the "pin" system. This type of structure thus restricts competitiveness from reverberating as a destructive force throughout the organization, but it does not eliminate competitiveness as a stimulus to productivity. Additional resource personnel can be provided at each work level through the use of consultants. The effectiveness of the "linking-pin" model is maximized for a small organization engaged in program development and research. "Pin" units can be sufficiently small and cohesive to attain the high degree of interaction and morale necessary for an effective work group (Likert, 1959); at the same time this system can eliminate the vulnerability to "noise" and loss of information in transmission that are inherent in a large system with many links. (Dubin, 1959).

Figure 3.3 illustrates the "linking-pin" system which was found to be the ideal organizational structure for what is now the Department of Psychological Services, Training, Research and Development. This system allows for the addition of new sections[1] without disrupting

---

[1] In 1963 a training section to prepare college graduates to serve as mental health workers in state hospitals and schools of the Commonwealth of Pennsylvania was established in the Psychology Department. NIMH Training Grant MH-8210 provided the funds for the salaries of the training faculty and stipends for trainees.

FIG. 3.3 LINKING-PIN ORGANIZATION

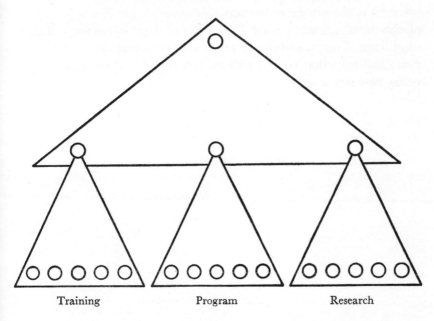

Training   Program   Research

the existing organization. It provides a single organizational structure for the operation of both the problem-solving and habit functions, and concomitantly minimizes problems of role conflict deriving from membership in dual structures.

This chapter has described the problems deriving from efforts to initiate socio-environmental treatment programs in an essentially custodial institution. Some of the problems encountered are inherent in the failure of such an organization to develop an adequate structure for the attainment of its dual goals: custody and treatment. This inadequacy in organizational structure can lead to dysfunction and abuse in the application of control. Social scientists have brought the inseparable relationship between treatment and administration to the attention of hospital administrators. In his review of the implications of the Joint Commission Report, Smith (1964) noted the need for "organizational study that is within the operational purview of hospital administration. Treatment, research, and administration are no longer separate. The ideology of the milieu and its effects have fused them. If the hospital setting and the patterns of staff organization and communication have therapeutic relevance, then administrators are involved in the process of therapy. Although we are increasingly aware of this involvement, we are less aware of how it operates. This we must learn if our hospitals are to respond constructively to the important challenges that confront them. Organizational research is a necessary new response."

Chapter IV

The Treatment Programs
and the Research Design

Socio-environmental treatment of the chronic psychotic in an institutional setting requires that the patient change from a passive recipient of custodial care to an active collaborator in the rehabilitation process. This type of treatment attempts to restore patients to responsible independent functioning by helping them develop meaningful and realistic interpersonal relationships within the institutional setting itself. Toward this end, socio-environmental therapy provides an environment and activities designed to foster, sustain, and broaden social interaction networks. Through variations in program structure, at-

59

tempts are made to control interaction by modulating the degree of social pressure and stimulation brought to bear on the patient.

❀ SOCIO-ENVIRONMENTAL TREATMENT ❀ PROGRAMS

The major components of the socio-environmental treatment programs developed at the Philadelphia State Hospital were the social living situation, the interaction activity program, and intensified group experiences.

❀ The Social Living Situation

The social living situation was established by modifying the physical environment of the state hospital, developing basic changes in staff attitude, introducing social organizations among patients, and setting up specific treatment goals and time limits for patients to achieve these goals. The physical environment was changed to approximate more closely that of the extramural community. Patients were moved from large dormitory-type buildings to smaller buildings with private rooms. Men were housed in three small cottages, each of which contained 24 private rooms. One of these rooms served as a den or game room, and in each cottage there was a large, comfortable and warm living room furnished with a television set and reading materials. Each patient was given a key to his room and had complete responsibility for its daily care. Women were housed in a larger, three-story building, the ground floor of which was devoted to office space for project personnel. The size of the sleeping rooms on the second and third floors varied, so that some patients had private rooms and others slept two to a room. The maximum capacity was 36 beds. There was a comfortable lounge on the second floor and another on the ground floor, both of which were shared by all patients residing in the building. In most respects the accommodations were similar to those provided for men. All patients were served meals "family style" in a dining hall operated and maintained in part by the patients themselves.

A second modification was the promotion in both staff and patients of attitudes conducive to the establishment of a therapeutic community. To foster the attitude that chronic mental patients could be rehabilitated through social interaction, regular staff meetings were held with the nursing personnel immediately involved in patient care. At these meetings staff members were oriented toward helping patients assume responsibility for their social community. Among the patients, a feeling for such responsibility was generated through individual conferences and regular group meetings conducted by staff members. In this manner free communication among patients and between patients and staff—a major prerequisite of a therapeutic community—was attained.

Third was the establishment of a variety of social organizations. Since these organizations were intended to provide nondidactic social groups within which spontaneous social behavior could occur, attendance was voluntary and participation informal. Monthly social gatherings and social clubs that met regularly, for example, a Model Railroad Club and a Personal Grooming Club, were available to all patients. Another organization, the Alumni Club, was open to patients who either were preparing to leave or had already left the hospital. This club provided patients with a familiar and supportive group during their initial period of adjustment to the extramural community, and it offered encouragement to patients who were ready to leave the hospital.

Fourth was the establishment of a treatment goal for all patients. The ultimate objective was extramural placement; a graduated series of responsibilities were assumed by the patient during the designated and delimited time periods. All patients understood that 12 months was the maximum period of residence in the therapeutic community and that all activities were preparatory to extramural living. From the start, the patient's adjustment to unit life was stressed, through care of his private room, improved personal grooming, participation in assigned activities, and fulfillment of a regular work assignment. If he demonstrated satisfactory progress in assuming these responsibilities, he was considered for regular city pass privileges. With the granting of a city pass, the patient assumed additional responsibilities: he was expected to become accustomed to traveling in the city and to become familiar with community resources. Most important, he was encouraged to go to such community agencies as Horizon

House and Hopetown and to establish relationships which could be maintained after leaving the hospital.

❋ The Interaction Activity Program

The interaction activity program was established by training group leaders who served as social therapists and conducted small, relatively closed activity groups. Activities were selected and developed which fostered interaction and tended to provide training in specific social behaviors. To develop a core of trained social therapists, staff members were recruited from the various services represented in the hospital. Though these people already possessed a variety of professional skills invaluable in a social interaction treatment program, they had to be trained as social therapists. They learned to use such psychological techniques as group and individual support and pressure, utilized to provide immediate corrective experiences when interpersonal problems arose, to teach individual patients more adaptive ways of relating to one another, and to insure movement of patients toward extramural placement.

The professional skills and psychosocial training of these therapists were not applied in an unsystematized manner, but were utilized within a uniform and integrated treatment effort. At regularly scheduled in-service meetings, the social therapists discussed the psychodynamics of individual patients and participated in the development and implementation of a common plan for dealing with interpersonal problems posed by these patients.

The opportunity for social interaction was maximized by dividing patients into small, relatively permanent activity groups. This type of grouping fostered the formation of enduring and mutually rewarding relationships necessary to overcome the characteristic withdrawal patterns of the chronic psychotic. Male patients were divided into four groups of approximately ten members each. Six female patients were added to each group to broaden the range of interpersonal contacts and to make the groups comparable to those found in the extramural community. Each patient in these groups was required to attend a regularly scheduled series of daily activities which occupied half his day; the rest of the day was spent carrying out some hospital industry assignment. Besides providing relaxed interpersonal situations, the program trained patients in social behavior, taught basic skills for community living, and was a source of practical experience in a community. To increase the effectiveness of such experience, staff members continuously evaluated and modified the program activities. Ten hours of each patient's week was allotted to the social training program. An outline of the current program activities is presented in the Appendix.

Some of the activities made minimal social demands; others necessitated interaction in complex, community-centered situations. The least demanding activities were music and recreation, which permitted patients to interrelate in a relatively relaxed atmosphere. In general, these activities were intended to demonstrate that social experience could be enjoyable. Since the chronic psychotic's deficit in social learning is frequently a factor in his social withdrawal, a special didactic activity, Social Skills, was developed to provide the patient with a repertoire of basic techniques for meeting and interacting with people informally, and the essentials of etiquette and social dancing. Unit socials, cooperative living, and family-style dining furnished him with opportunities for the practice and reinforcement of these social skills.

Actual preparation for extramural living was provided by such group activities as discussions and trips into the community. Patients were instructed in personal grooming, meal preparation, clothing repair, budgeting, and the use of transportation, community facilities, and community resources. Preparation for a vital aspect of independent existence—securing employment—was accomplished by teaching patients how to use want ads and employment agency resources, how to complete a job application, how to write a business letter, how to behave at job interviews, what salary deductions there would be, and the meaning of Social Security benefits.

❀ The Intensified Group Experiences

Two special group experiences, group therapy and government by the patients, requiring four hours of each patient's week, were used to broaden and intensify the resocialization process. The former augmented the interaction program and the latter the social living situation. In group therapy, patients had a special opportunity to discuss their feelings, attitudes, and current social and interpersonal experiences. Particular efforts were made to encourage adaptive behavior, to understand the reasons for maladaptive behavior, and to bring about the behavioral changes necessary for more appropriate social interaction. The resocialization process was complemented by giving patients responsibility for cottage management, and by establishing the modes of interaction for fulfilling this responsibility. The patients elected executive officers and a council. The executive officers conducted meetings at which problems could be raised for discussion and action. The patients assumed responsibility for the more routine aspects of cottage management, like the organization of housekeeping details, the scheduling of wake-up teams, and the regulation of such cottage facilities as showers and television. Elections were held frequently, so almost all patients were able to become involved in leadership functions.

❀ THE RESEARCH DESIGN ❀

The socio-environmental therapy approach to the treatment of chronic psychosis assumes that social isolation is an integral part of the primary illness—more specifically, that the psychotic patient avoids interaction with others mainly because such contacts have become progressively unrewarding and threatening. By the time the patient reaches the back wards of the typical state hospital, it may be that he is not unwilling to enter into meaningful relationships but that he has become unable to do so. In theory, if the effectiveness of his relationships with others can be enhanced, he may have less need to retreat from reality through delusion or hallucination. Thus, it was hoped that a direct attack on the social symptomatology of chronic mental illness would result in generalized improvement in the patient's social performance and psychiatric condition.

❀ The Independent Variable: Treatment Structure

The major variable in this project was social interaction. Differences in the demand for interaction were attained by systematically varying the structure of the patient's interpersonal environment, and by instituting certain requirements for interpersonal behavior. These attempts to stimulate social behavior and to shape the interaction process derived mainly from the establishment of formalized groups with assigned tasks and specified roles and duties. Such assigned group tasks and specified role functions are inherent components of both the social living situation and the therapeutic activity program; however, group tasks were found to be more amenable to manipulation in the activity program, and individual roles in the social living situation.

The interaction pattern prescribed by structuring the environment was further maintained by uniform behavior of the unit personnel toward the patients. These personnel, particularly the unit administrator, provided the sustained pressure necessary to shape and modify social behavior. Simultaneously they were the main support in helping the patient endure the stresses of the interaction program. The concept of "structure"[1] refers to experimental manipulation of the demand for interaction. It was assumed that such control of the interpersonal environment and modulation of the amount of pressure applied to the patient would augment and broaden his interaction networks.

Assuming the validity of this orientation of treatment, the degree of interaction necessary to effect the greatest therapeutic outcome remains to be determined. Is it sufficient simply to remove the physical and interpersonal support of isolation, and to substitute an environment which is more conducive to interaction? Or must additional pressures be applied to encourage the patient in the direction of greater socialization? If such pressures are necessary, what form should they take and what constitutes the optimum amount? The numerous descriptions of "therapeutic communities" and "total push" programs that appear in the literature do not provide answers to these questions. The project described here attempted to direct itself to these issues by examining the effects of three socio-environmental treatment programs on the social and psychiatric adjustment of chronically institutionalized psychotic patients. By varying the extent to which the social living situation and the therapeutic program were

[1] The authors are indebted to Albert Pepitone, who helped to clarify this concept through discussions of the papers presented in a symposium on Social Therapy, Resocialization, and Psychiatric Adjustment at the American Psychological Association Convention, Philadelphia, August 30, 1963.

structured to promote interaction, three treatment programs were designed. (See Table 4.1.)

In the Minimally Structured treatment condition, neither the social living situation nor the therapeutic program was structured for interaction. The program involved an assigned job in the hospital industry system, a weekly cottage meeting held largely for administra-

TABLE 4.1

TREATMENT UNITS, LIVING SITUATION, AND CONTENT OF THERAPY
PROGRAM ASSOCIATED WITH EACH TREATMENT CONDITION

Treatment Condition	Male Units	Female Units	Living Situation	Content of Therapy Program
Maximally Structured	A	E	Therapeutic Community with Patient Government	Group Therapy Interaction Program Indiv. Work Assign. Cottage Meeting Conf. with Unit Admin.
Partially Structured	B	F	Therapeutic Community	Interaction Program Indiv. Work Assign. Cottage Meeting Conf. with Unit Admin.
Minimally Structured	C	G	Therapeutic Community	Indiv. Work Assign. Cottage Meeting Conf. with Unit Admin.
Control	(D)	(H)	Regular Ward Environment	Regular Ward Program[1]

[1] May include work assignment, occupational therapy, group recreation, etc.

tive purposes, and individual conferences with the unit administrator (psychologist). Although there was ample opportunity for the development of interaction within the cottage living unit, no direct pressure was applied through group tasks or role assignment to insure interaction.

The Partially Structured treatment condition made some demand for interaction, since it organized the living situation to require group participation and introduced the interaction activity program described earlier. Although the living situation involved no prescribed roles, minimal demands for interaction resulted from assigning patients to teams responsible for all the housekeeping and some management aspects of their living situation. The group activity tasks were designed to make interaction among the participants the primary requirement. Activity groups were organized so that one quarter of the patients from treatment units *A*, *B*, *E*, and *F*, that is, units of both sexes, were included in each activity group. A given patient attended all seven activities with the group to which he had been originally assigned. In this way each patient was systematically exposed to repeated contact with one fourth of the patients from three other treatment units and received approximately ten hours of programmed group activity weekly. The hospital industry assignment of patients in the Partially and Maximally Structured treatment conditions was reduced to half a day in order to make time available for these group activities.

In the Maximally Structured treatment condition, the living situation and the therapeutic program were further structured. The demand for interaction in the social situation was augmented by introducing government by the patients. The responsibilities associated with each office were defined so as to make contact with other patients a necessity; the election rules were manipulated to guarantee maximum rotation of patients through the several offices. The unit administrator helped the elected patient to understand and fulfill his responsibilities effectively. The interaction activity program in the Maximally Structured treatment condition was augmented by an additional element, group therapy, intended to intensify the demand for interaction and to provide support at a deeper, more meaningful level than that offered by the group activity leaders. Two group therapy sessions a week were included in the Maximally Structured condition. At these sessions the therapist (psychologist) focused on the patients' contemporary experiences rather than on repressed conflicts. However, many patients utilized the sessions to talk about sexual difficulties or other personal problems not ordinarily discussed in the group activity program.

The research design was carried out with male and female patients, but the differences in living conditions precluded imposing identical research controls for both sexes. The availability of three separate cottages for the male patients permitted segregation according to treatment conditions; thus both the treatment program and the living situation could be manipulated independently. Since all female experimental units were housed in one building, it was difficult to establish discrete treatment groups comparable to those in the male cottages. An attempt at such segregation was made by assigning the female patients in each experimental unit to a different area of the building. This effort was only partially successful: the sharing of common lounge, lavatory, and utility rooms meant that female patients would have a greater opportunity for spontaneous interaction *across* treatment conditions throughout the period of the experiment.

The basic experimental design also included a control condition, in which no experimental structure was imposed; patients meeting the criteria for acceptance in the program remained on their respective wards for the same period of time as that spent by the experimental groups in the treatment programs. In the hospital ward for chronic patients the demand for interaction and a conducive social milieu are generally nonexistent.

Although the six experimental units were administered by different psychologists, they were the psychiatric responsibility of two phychiatrists, one of whom was assigned to the male and the other to the female unit. The patients in the Control condition, in wards throughout the hospital, were under the administrative and psychiatric supervision of their respective ward psychiatrists. The psychiatrist on an experimental unit fulfilled his medical functions in the same manner as psychiatrists throughout the hospital; his was the final decision about which experimental patients would be separated from the hospital, and he prescribed drugs solely on the basis of clinical judgment. At the completion of the research phase, it was found that ataractic drug therapy had been administered to approximately 33 per cent of the male and 86 per cent of the female patients in the experimental conditions. The corresponding percentages for males and females in the Control condition were 55 and 74, respectively. Considering males and females separately, no significant differences were found among the four treatment conditions in the amount of ataractic drugs administered. Somatic therapies were not utilized in any of the four conditions.

❀ The Patient Population

Individuals for this program were selected from the entire chronic patient population at the Philadelphia State Hospital. Screening teams of two clinical psychologists reviewed with the appropriate nursing personnel the roster of patients in each building, eliminating severely regressed and physically incapacitated patients from consideration for social treatment. The teams then interviewed, and reviewed the records of the remaining patients; several thousand patients were interviewed. Selection was based on clinical evaluation of the patient's ability to leave the hospital within 12 months as a result of the treatment program. For the most part, the better-adjusted chronic patients were selected. These were patients whose debilitating motivational, psychiatric, or social withdrawal symptoms had necessitated their continued hospitalization. Patients who appeared to be in good remission or who were in the process of separation from the hospital were not selected for the program. Alcoholics, patients who manifested extreme acting-out problems, and patients unable to modify their behavior because of rather severe organic limitations were also excluded from consideration.

The patient population showed the following characteristics: males ranged from 19 to 72 years of age, with a median age of 45. A diagnosis of schizophrenia was made for 82 per cent. Length of hospitalization ranged from one to 36 years, with a median duration of 8.6 years. Only 39 per cent had completed high school; 71 per cent had never been married. For the most part, occupations fell into the unskilled category: dishwasher, hospital orderly, domestic, laborer, factory worker. Female patients resembled male patients in all these characteristics, except marital status and length of hospitalization. Only 36 per cent of the females had never been married, and the median length of hospitalization was seven years. These descriptions indicate that the patients were low on the socio-economic scale, and most of them had been ill for many years.

Patients selected for the project were assigned to the four treatment conditions so that all groups were comparable in age, diagnosis, and length of hospitalization. To control for bias in assignment, pa-

Table 4.2

DEMOGRAPHIC CHARACTERISTICS OF THE PATIENT POPULATION
ASSIGNED TO THE VARIOUS TREATMENT PROGRAMS

Variable		Males (N = 143)					Females (N = 144)					F (ABCD · EFGH)
		A	B	C	D	ABCD	E	F	G	H	EFGH	
1. Age on Admission to Treatment	M	43.22	45.06	41.96	47.75	44.27	45.33	44.26	44.72	48.88	45.03	< .05
	σ	10.98	12.01	12.07	11.64	11.79	9.05	10.50	11.06	10.50	10.24	
2. Age on First Hospitalization	M	30.09	31.68	29.27	34.30	31.09	33.91	32.94	32.87	34.59	33.55	n.s.
	σ	10.96	12.44	9.19	10.10	11.19	9.52	11.77	10.51	10.70	10.65	
3. Chronicity (1–2)	M	13.13	13.38	12.69	13.45	13.18	11.42	11.42	11.84	11.28	11.48	n.s.
	σ	8.22	9.37	10.05	11.20	9.44	8.48	7.51	9.03	8.39	8.32	
4. Length of Present Hospitalization (mos.)	M	110.82	120.21	118.07	126.30	117.63	92.93	89.66	95.81	88.69	91.77	< .01
	σ	95.22	105.98	118.96	108.46	105.74	67.01	60.20	72.95	76.04	68.84	
5. Percentage with Previous Hospitalization		67	70	54	70	66	79	79	75	59	74	—
6. Percentage Married		26	24	31	45	29[1]	74	50	72	59	64[1]	—
7. Race												
Percentage white		77	86	92	70	82	81	79	75	72	77	—
Percentage other		23	14	8	30	18	19	21	25	28	23	—
8. Highest Grade Level	M	8.44	8.49	8.81	7.95	8.46	8.10	8.38	9.22	9.68	8.77	n.s.
	σ	2.84	2.49	2.96	2.30	2.69	2.17	2.16	2.62	2.36	2.40	
9. IQ (est.)	M	96.84	95.20	95.73	95.14	95.83	82.83	87.21	89.52	85.41	86.19	< .01
	σ	18.22	17.27	18.41	19.25	18.07	13.89	12.06	12.28	15.21	13.51	

[1] χ^2 ABCD · EFGH = 34.4, df = 1, $p < .001$.

70

tients were allocated to treatment groups by a research psychologist who had no information about patients other than these three demographic items. All treatment groups were open-ended, and new patients were moved in whenever a vacancy occurred.

Some of the pertinent demographic characteristics of the patient population, categorized according to type of treatment condition, are summarized in Table 4.2. The means and standard deviations of all variables were equivalent across treatment conditions for males and females separately. Several significant differences between the male and female populations are indicated. Significantly more females than males were married. The mean intelligence level was "dull normal" for females and "average" for males. Although the mean difference was not significant, the male patients showed greater variability than the females in IQ scores. They also were more variable than females in age on admission to treatment and length of current hospitalization.

❀ Hypotheses

This investigation was designed to test the following hypotheses:

1. Socio-environmental therapy increases the social interaction of the chronic mental patient according to the degree of structure in the program.

2. Favorable clinical outcome is related to the degree of structure in the socio-environmental program.

3. Improvement in social interaction is related to good psychiatric status.

❀ The Dependent Variable: The Criterion Problem

Long-term criteria. The ultimate measure of the utility of a treatment program such as this one is the mental health of the patients treated. However, "mental health" has so many dimensions that any program designed to improve mental functioning must utilize multiple criteria.

The usual criteria for evaluating treatment programs have major shortcomings. For example, improved functioning within the hospital tends to be unrelated to subsequent adjustment in the community (Forsythe and Fairweather, 1961). Separation from the hospital is an imperfect measure of adjustment because it may be influenced by such extraneous factors as hospital administrative policy, availability of placement resources, the placebo effect on the patient, and the halo effect on the therapist. The inadequacy of this measure is reflected in the high incidence of returns within the first month of separation from the hospital (Dinitz et al., 1961; Zolik, Lantz, and Busiel, 1965).

The best measure of mental health seems to be the ability to remain out of the hospital. This criterion is also imperfect, since it is largely dependent on such uncontrolled factors as community tolerance (Freeman and Simmons, 1958), availability of supportive community resources (for example, halfway houses, social clubs, boarding homes), the patient's financial status, and the variety of stresses produced by the vicissitudes of daily living.

The utility of this criterion would be greatly enhanced by determining the patient's adjustment during his stay in the community. The ability to stay out of the hospital and the type of adjustment made in the community are long-term, multiple criteria for evaluating the broad utility of treatment programs. In this study, the quality, range, and durability of social behavior, psychiatric symptomatology, and general adjustment constituted the long-term criteria for the follow-up study.

Short-term criteria. Measures taken at the termination of treatment served as short-term criteria for evaluating the effectiveness of the program. These estimates were made before uncontrolled events which might confound and dilute the effects of the treatment could intervene. Their major utility, however, was in determining whether, and with what success, specified treatment aims had been achieved.

The goals of this study necessitated two types of short-term criteria: measures of social behavior and of psychiatric adjustment. Improvement in social behavior was germane to the goal underlying this study, that is, that social treatment would effect improvement in social behavior, and that the degree of improvement would be related to the degree of structure of the treatment program. Measures of global social participation (Social Interaction Rating Scale), awareness of others (Photo Naming Test), verbal interaction in a structured activity setting (Verbal Interaction Scale), and spontaneous social behavior (Spontaneous Social Behavior Scale) were taken as criteria of changes in different areas of social functioning.

Additional goals of this project were to produce good psychiatric adjustment and to determine whether such adjustment was a concomitant of improved social behavior. Evaluation necessitated measures that would reflect psychiatric adjustment at completion of treatment. In this study, separation rates and degree of symptomatology served as the short-term criterion measures of psychiatric adjustment.

The short- and long-term effects of any therapeutic procedure may differ completely. If the patient learns to modify ways of coping with his problems, his personality may conceivably undergo changes in the long run. The entire question of the sequence in which behaviors tend to change in response to therapeutic intervention deserves much more attention than it has received up to this time. Whether good psychiatric condition is an immediate or a delayed result of improved social interaction can only be resolved by applying both short- and long-range criteria.

❀ The Moderator Variable: Reactivity Level

A factor apart from the principal research variables can often be uncovered which clarifies the relationship between the predictors and the criterion (i.e., the dependent and independent variables). This "third variable," "a cause or factor lying unnoticed in the off-quadrant area," has been termed the "moderator variable" by Marks (1964). Finding it usually requires hindsight, since this quest is undertaken as a means of improving the predictive efficiency or the relationship between the major research variables. Frequently, the uncovering of moderator variables leads to new hypotheses.

The patients in this study ranged from 19 to 72 years of age, with a median age of 45. Half had therefore reached or passed the middle stage of life and were experiencing psychological and physiological consequences very different from those of younger persons. From 30 to 60 years of age the individual turns from an active, manipulative engagement of his outer environment to a more passive, withdrawn orientation (Schaw and Henry, 1956; Neugarten and Gutmann, 1958; Rosen and Neugarten, 1960). He experiences a decline in emotional intensity and assertive energy (Neugarten and Gutmann, 1958; Rosen and Neugarten, 1960; Dean, 1962; Bortner, 1963) and frequently shows an increase in ego defects (Neugarten and Gutmann, 1958).

Cumming and Henry (1961) integrated their research findings with those reported in the literature on aging, and developed a Theory of Disengagement. According to this theory,

> Aging is an inevitable mutual withdrawal or disengagement, resulting in decreased interaction between the aging person and others in the social systems he belongs to. The process may be initiated by the individual or by others in the situation. The aging person may withdraw more markedly from some classes of people while remaining relatively close to others. His withdrawal may be accompanied from the outset by an increased preoccupation with himself; certain institutions in society may make this withdrawal easy for him. When the aging process is complete, the equilibrium which existed in middle life between the individual and his society has given way to a new equilibrium characterized by a greater distance and an altered type of relationship.

This disengagement, a natural concomitant of aging, can be accelerated by withdrawal from meaningful interpersonal contact. In chronic schizophrenia, such withdrawal is a consequence of the schizophrenic process which alienates the patient from others, of the institutionalization which isolates him from meaningful interpersonal experiences, or of a combination of both factors. Cumming and Cumming (1962) noted that the chronic, compared to the acute, schizophrenic shows increasing impairment in ego functioning "caused by his withdrawal and by the impoverishment of the environment." This impairment is manifested as a decline in reactivity which parallels the physical, emotional, and social disengagement that occurs with aging.

The decline in motor performance of the chronic psychotic has been amply documented in the research literature (King, 1954; Harris and Metcalfe, 1959; Rafi, 1960). In a review of the literature, Mednick (1958) noted that the flat affect syndrome or reduced emotional reactivity was manifested particularly by the chronic schizophrenic; high reactivity and extreme anxiety characterized the acute schizophrenic. Long (1961) demonstrated that this difference in reactivity also applied to socially motivating stimuli; chronic schizophrenics showed little behavioral change in response to praise or censure.

The decline in social responsiveness of the chronic schizophrenic is further evidenced by a progressive loss of verbal ability (Rabin, King, and Ehrmann, 1955). According to Wynne (1963), length of hospitalization, rather than mental or physical disorder per se, showed the strongest relationship to decline in verbal abilities. Eliseo (1963) suggested that misinterpretation of words, usually attributed to schizophrenia, was characteristic of chronic illness in general. Wing (1962) noted that further evidence of the social disengagement of the chronically ill, institutionalized individual could be seen in the gradual development of an attitude of indifference toward events outside of the hospital.

In the context of this study, reactivity level has critical relevance as a moderating variable. Treatment outcome may be determined by an interaction between the degree of structure of the treatment program and the patient's reactivity level. Age and length of illness[2] have been used as indices of reactivity in this study. Although these two variables are interrelated, they are not identical. The correlation between them for the total study population ($N = 283$)[3] was .41. Wherever possible, the experimental population was dichotomized on age and length of illness, utilizing the respective medians as cut-off points. (The median age was 45 years; the median length of illness was 12 years for males and 10 years for females.)

---

[2] The sources cited in the review of literature regarding decline in reactivity of the chronic schizophrenic defined chronicity in terms of length of illness or years of hospitalization. It is recognized that the length of illness and years of current hospitalization may be independent determinants of decline in reactivity. However, because of the high degree of relationship in this study between these two variables ($n = 283$, $r = .71$), only length of illness was used as an index of reactivity.

[3] It should be noted that of the 287 patients in the total sample the data on 4 cases were incomplete.

PART TWO

SOCIO-ENVIRONMENTAL TREATMENT: EFFECTS ON SOCIAL BEHAVIOR AND PSYCHIATRIC ADJUSTMENT

Chapter V

The Modification
of Social Behavior

The goal of socio-environmental therapy is to improve the psychiatric adjustment of the psychotic patient through the activation of interpersonal behavior. Proponents of this type of therapy consider the psychotic process directly related to deficits in social functioning. Some of the more debilitating social deficits of the psychotic are an impaired ability to adapt to group situations (Cumming, 1959) or to situations which entail interpersonal censure (Garmezy, 1952; Dunn, 1954; Webb, 1955), diminished capacity to deal with social concepts (Whiteman, 1954; Davis and Harrington, 1957), and a limitation in range of social skills (Cumming, 1959).

There is an increasing tendency to view such social deficits as prominent factors in the psychotic's inability to adjust to community living. This point of view holds that the psychotic's incapacity to perform socially appropriate instrumental acts limits his ability to maintain himself outside of the mental hospital (Freeman and Simmons, 1963) and, further, that the mental hospital must modify this socially deviant instrumental performance in the direction of greater conformity to the demands of the extramural society.

The present study set out to establish within hospital walls a program to facilitate the patient's transition from hospital to community. This program emphasized establishing social roles and structures which demand socially appropriate interaction. Such a high degree of social control was expected to result in generalized improvement in the chronic psychotic's social behavior. This chapter will present findings on improvement in social behavior effected by programs differentially structured with respect to demand for interaction. Since reactivity level has been viewed as a crucial determinant of social participation, the impact of this variable on the socializing effects of socio-environmental treatment will also be examined.

Global social behavior and changes in interaction in three specific areas of social functioning were examined. The latter may be considered to constitute a hierarchy of social initiative, the preliminary social response being awareness of others, followed by verbal interaction under pressure, and culminating in spontaneous social behavior.

❁ Global Social Behavior

The term "global social behavior" refers to the degree of social interaction or withdrawal manifested by patients in a wide spectrum of social situations. The social behavior of patients participating in this project was observed in the living situation, the work areas, the special social activities, and in individual contacts with hospital personnel. Patients engaged in the Maximally and Partially Structured programs were also observed in the various structured activities.

Description of measure: the Social Interaction Rating Scale (SIRS). The measure of global social behavior used in this study, the SIRS, was a set of five descriptions which differentiated levels of social functioning (see Figure 5.1). The descriptions were unequally spaced on a vertical scale to correct for an anticipated negative skewness in the distribution of ratings; the actual midpoint of the scale fell between the third and fourth descriptions. Scores on the SIRS were derived by dividing the scale into 15 equal intervals and then assigning the number of the interval to whatever rating marks appeared within that interval.

Procedure. A rating of social interaction was made for each patient within the first two weeks of the treatment program, and at the completion of treatment six to twelve months later. The unit administrators, who were clinical psychologists, made these ratings on the basis of personal observation and controlled interviews with patients, and from regularly scheduled meetings with personnel who came into close contact with patients in their daily activities. Patients who were returned to their original wards within the first six weeks, so-called "screening errors," did not receive post-treatment SIRS ratings.

Since the SIRS measure was not developed until after the initiation of the experimental programs, baseline data could not be obtained for all experimental patients. Posttreatment ratings on the SIRS[1] were available for all, but they could not be adjusted for initial status. For those cases where initial scores were available, the means across conditions are comparable. The posttreatment ratings for males and females were studied separately through analysis of variance. In order to examine the effects of reactivity level, ratings were dichotomized according to length of illness and age. In this way, differences in final SIRS ratings which were attributable to the degree of structure in the treatment programs or the reactivity level of the patients, or an interaction of these two variables, could be analyzed.

[1] A minimum estimate of the reliability of the SIRS was derived by having 6 psychologists rate each of 13 patients during a 45-minute screening interview. Despite the fact that these ratings were based on far less information about patients than that regularly available to the unit administrators, the findings were encouraging. The coefficient of concordance (W) was .74, and the associated *chi* square was significant beyond the .001 level. A similar study was conducted by having 6 follow-up interviewers rate 12 patients, 6 hospital and 6 community patients. In this case, the coefficient of concordance was .64 with a probability beyond the .001 level.

FIG. 5.1   THE SOCIAL INTERACTION RATING SCALE (SIRS)

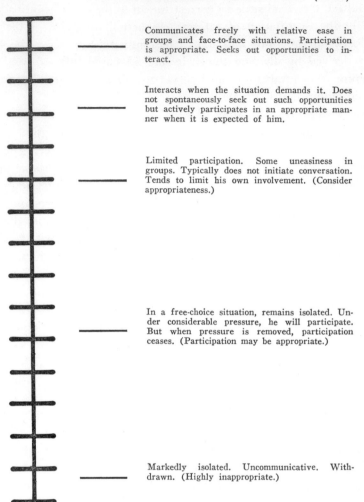

Communicates freely with relative ease in groups and face-to-face situations. Participation is appropriate. Seeks out opportunities to interact.

Interacts when the situation demands it. Does not spontaneously seek out such opportunities but actively participates in an appropriate manner when it is expected of him.

Limited participation. Some uneasiness in groups. Typically does not initiate conversation. Tends to limit his own involvement. (Consider appropriateness.)

In a free-choice situation, remains isolated. Under considerable pressure, he will participate. But when pressure is removed, participation ceases. (Participation may be appropriate.)

Markedly isolated. Uncommunicative. Withdrawn. (Highly inappropriate.)

Results.   Analysis of variance reveals significant differences in post-program SIRS ratings. The highest level of global social interaction occurs in the Maximally Structured program, the next highest in the Partially Structured program, and the lowest in the Minimally Structured program. The mean scores of the more highly structured programs (*A* and *B:* see Table 5.1) indicate significantly greater so-

TABLE 5.1

SOCIAL INTERACTION RATING SCALE MEANS AND T-TEST VALUES
FOR THE THREE EXPERIMENTAL CONDITIONS

	Means[1]	N	Sigma	Conditions Compared	Differences	t	p
Males							
Maximally Structured (A)	6.57	37	4.11	A and C	3.10	2.48	.02
Partially Structured (B)	7.19	36	3.96	A and B	.62		n.s.
Minimally Structured (C)	9.67	21	4.71	B and C	2.48	2.00	.05
F (programs) = 4.04, $p < .05$							
Females							
Maximally Structured (E)	5.73	33	3.88	E and G	1.52		n.s.
Partially Structured (F)	6.71	35	5.10	E and F	.98		n.s.
Minimally Structured (G)	7.25	28	4.58	F and G	.54		n.s.
F (programs) = .82, p = n.s.							

[1] The lower the mean score, the greater the social participation.

cial participation than does the mean score of the Minimally Structured program.

To determine whether differences between the three treatment conditions existed early in treatment and whether the final scores represent improvement or decline in social interaction, the SIRS ratings made early in treatment were examined. These early SIRS ratings, which are available for 82 per cent of the male cases (a subsample presumed to be representative of the entire male experimental population), indicate that the three experimental groups were comparable during the initial phase of treatment. When the mean scores of the restricted samples in each of the three treatment conditions are used as baselines for evaluating posttreatment global social behavior, it is apparent that the patients in both the Maximally and Partially Structured conditions show improvement, while those in the Minimally Structured condition show decline.

Length of illness has a significant bearing on posttreatment social behavior of male patients (see Table 5.2). At completion of treatment, male patients with the greater length of illness showed more social participation than those whose illness was of shorter duration. This relationship was evident in all three social-environmental treatment programs. That this finding is a result of exposure to treatment is evident when comparisons are made with the scores made early in treatment on the restricted sample. Such comparisons indicate that

TABLE 5.2

EARLY AND POSTTREATMENT SOCIAL INTERACTION RATINGS FOR MALE PATIENTS IN THE THREE EXPERIMENTAL PROGRAMS, DICHOTOMIZED ACCORDING TO LENGTH OF ILLNESS

PROGRAMS

		Maximally Structured (A)	Partially Structured (B)	Minimally Structured (C)
11 Years or Less	Early Mean	6.69 ($N = 16$)	8.85 ($N = 13$)	7.00 ($N = 11$)
	Post Mean	7.56 ($N = 18$)	8.30 ($N = 16$)	10.41 ($N = 11$)
12 Years or More	Early Mean	7.38 ($N = 13$)	7.80 ($N = 15$)	8.50 ($N = 10$)
	Post Mean	5.65 ($N = 19$)	6.19 ($N = 20$)	9.04 ($N = 10$)

Posttreatment Scores F (programs) $(P) = 4.04$, $p < .05$

Posttreatment Scores F (length of illness) $(L) = 4.59$, $p < .05$

Posttreatment Scores F (interaction) $(P \times L) = .06$, $p =$ n.s.

early in treatment there was no difference in the global social behavior of patients differentiated by the longer length of illness. Furthermore, when the early scores are used as baselines, it is apparent that at completion of treatment the patients with the longer duration of illness in the Maximally and Partially Structured conditions improve, while those in the Minimally Structured condition tend to remain unchanged. The patients with the shorter duration of illness tend to remain unchanged in the Maximally and Partially Structured conditions, while those in the Minimally Structured condition show decline.

Although the magnitude of the mean SIRS scores reported in Table 5.1 for females in the three experimental groups show a rank order congruent with the hypotheses of this study, the means do not differ significantly. The analysis of variance further indicates that reactivity level has no influence on the posttreatment social interaction of female patients. Thus, neither differences in degree of program structure nor reactivity level are determinants of the posttreatment global social behavior of female patients.

The problem of measurement. In order to arrive at a single rating of global social behavior, the unit administrator considered information on a wide array of social behaviors, such as verbal and nonverbal interaction, as well as the degree of external pressure necessary to stimulate such interaction. Relevant information was gathered by personnel who observed the patient in different situations, which tended to obscure differences among patients and hence between groups. Despite this problem in measurement, differences emerge in posttreatment global social behavior of male patients. The Maximally and Partially Structured programs are associated with greater social participation than the Minimally Structured program. Although the differences between the two more structured programs are in the expected direction, they do not reach significance, probably because of the "static" inherent in the measurement situation.

With respect to reactivity level, there is a direct relationship between length of illness and high scores in posttreatment global social behavior. However, interaction effects may also have been obscured by inexactness in measurement. More precise information regarding the differential effects of program structure and reactivity level should emerge from the investigation of specific social behaviors.

Among female patients there are no significant differences in posttreatment scores which can be attributed to program structure. This can be understood both in terms of the measurement problem noted above and the "leakage" between programs due to the common living situation. Since the latter was conducive to interaction across treatment conditions, it served to attenuate the impact of differences in program structure on social behavior, as well as on all other behaviors measured in this project. Reactivity level of the females also had no effect on posttreatment social behavior.

Summary

1. Global social behavior of male patients at completion of treatment is related to the degree of structure of the socio-environmental treatment condition. Posttreatment global social behavior in the two more structured programs is superior to that in the Minimally Structured program.

2. The longer the illness for male patients, the better the scores attained in posttreatment global social behavior. This relationship holds regardless of degree of structure of treatment condition.

3. Neither degree of program structure nor reactivity level, that is, age and length of illness, is a significant determinant of posttreatment global social behavior in female patients.

❀ Awareness of Others

Socialization has its roots in the differentiation between self and others. Before meaningful interaction with another is possible, one must first become aware of the other's identity as a person—as a human being distinguishable from all other human beings. The psychotic's degree of awareness of others can be taken as an inverse measure of his social withdrawal. It seems reasonable to expect progress toward resocialization to be accompanied by increased awareness of others.

Description of measure: the Photo Naming Test (PNT). The PNT was developed to measure awareness of others through the identification of fellow patients from recent photographs. Each patient was asked to identify by name 33 photographs of patients currently in the various treatment units. He was credited with one point for each photograph correctly identified, either by first or last name, or by nickname. The photographs were of one third of the patients in each of the six treatment units involved in the project, seven patients from each male unit and four from each female unit. Photographs of patients no longer in the project were removed and those of new arrivals were added; each patient was photographed shortly after he arrived on the project. The test sample was randomly redrawn at intervals to insure that it was current and representative.

Procedure. The PNT was administered two to four weeks[2] after the patient was transferred to the Rehabilitation Center and again at completion of the treatment program.

Three types of comparison are possible with PNT data. The first involves the patient's ability to identify fellow patients within his own treatment unit; the second is concerned with identification of males in other groups, and the third with females in all the experimental groups. The findings will be reported only for male patients.[3]

Results

1. *Identification of patients in same treatment unit.* The patient's awareness of individuals in his own treatment unit was studied because it was hypothesized that a basic effect of differences in program structure would be differential awareness of members of his own unit. Analysis of variance of scores obtained early in treatment was made to ascertain the influence of program structure during the initial phase of treatment.

Table 5.3 shows the mean number of photographs correctly identified by patients in the three experimental groups at the initial testing. There were seven photographs in the test sample. The overall *F* ratio for these data is significant beyond the .01 level. This indicates that differential effects on awareness of others are manifested

[2] Scheduling problems made it impossible to test all patients after a standard interval in the project. This fact introduced the possibility that different lengths of time in residence prior to the first testing might influence the means of the initial group. Accordingly, the correlation between number of days in residence and number of patients correctly identified was computed. This correlation was —.01 for 67 subjects, indicating that exposure time is not a factor in determining initial awareness. A zero-order correlation was also obtained between time in treatment and number of photographs identified at completion of the treatment program.

[3] Since the male patients in the three experimental conditions were assigned to three physically separate cottages, both the treatment program and the character of the living situation could be manipulated independently. As indicated above, female patients all resided in the same building and shared the same lounge and lavatory facilities. Since opportunities for spontaneous interaction both within and between treatment units were greater for female patients throughout the experimental period, partial contamination of the treatment conditions was unavoidable.

TABLE 5.3

COMPARISONS BETWEEN TREATMENT GROUPS AT INITIAL TESTING:
NAMING PATIENTS WITHIN ONE'S OWN UNIT

Treatment Conditions	N	Mean Number of Photos Identified	Comparisons	t	p (two-tailed test)
Maximally Structured (A)	24	4.33	A vs. B	2.30	.025
Partially Structured (B)	24	3.00	A vs. C	3.49	.01
Minimally Structured (C)	19	2.42	B vs. C	.94	n.s.

F (programs) $= 5.66$, $df = 2/63$, $p < .01$

within the first two weeks of treatment, and that these differences tend to correspond to the degree of program structure.

The largest differences in mean number of photographs correctly identified are obtained when the Maximally Structured program is compared to each of the other programs. These results suggest that the social organization in the Maximally Structured program is a potent factor, at least during the first few weeks of residence. Government by patients, the primary element differentiating the Maximally Structured from the two other programs, undoubtedly produces a high degree of awareness in members of this group. Theoretically, this influence should continue throughout the patient's stay in the unit and also affect the postprogram means. However, the postprogram means are distorted by a "ceiling effect." At the completion of treatment, some patients would have been able to identify more than the seven photographs in the test sample, had they been given the opportunity. This effect is most pronounced in Group A, which has the largest number of "perfect" scores.

Table 5.4 presents the mean number of photographs identified at the postprogram testing. The overall F ratio for these data is significant beyond the .025 level. Despite the presence of the "ceiling effect," the comparisons between individual pairs of treatment units which were significant at the initial testing continue to be significant.

2. *Identification of patients in experimental treatment units other than the patient's own unit.* Since the problem of re-establishing

TABLE 5.4

COMPARISONS BETWEEN TREATMENT GROUPS AT POSTPROGRAM
TESTINGS: NAMING PATIENTS WITHIN ONE'S OWN UNIT

Treatment Conditions	N	Mean Photos Identified	Comparisons	t	p (one-tailed test)
Maximally Structured (A)	24	6.38	A vs. B	1.73	.05
Partially Structured (B)	24	5.67	A vs. C	2.80	.01
Minimally Structured (C)	19	5.16	B vs. C	1.17	n.s.

F (programs) $= 4.00$, $df = 2/63$, $p < .025$

normal channels of social intercourse between male and female patients is of particular interest in a state hospital setting, data on generalization of awareness were analyzed separately for like-sex and opposite-sex criterion groups. It has already been shown that both early in and at completion of treatment, the awareness of others within one's own group tends to correspond to the degree of structure of the program. Does this awareness generalize to individuals outside one's own treatment group?

Certain differences can be expected simply on the basis of unequal contact between treatment units, as specified by the requirements of the three experimental conditions. If these differences do not emerge, increased contact with others may be assumed to be ineffectual in reducing social isolation. Such findings would thus be damaging to the case for socio-environmental therapy. Comparisons of the Maximally and Partially Structured programs with the Minimally Structured program were expected to be significant purely on the basis of differing amounts of contact between treatment units. These comparisons are enclosed by parentheses in the tables which follow.

The identification of female patients in Group G, with whom all patients had equal programmed contact, provides the main test of the differential effectiveness of the three programs in improving awareness of others. All comparisons between the Maximally and Partially Structured programs are based on equal amounts of programmed exposure to the criterion groups. It was hypothesized that awareness of patients in other treatment units would increase in direct relationship to the extent of structured interaction in the treatment, that is, the social living situation and the activity program.

Analysis of covariance was employed to control for differential contact between experimental patients before transfer to the Rehabilitation Project. This analysis insured that any postprogram differences actually derived from exposure to the treatment conditions. In the absence of a genuine preprogram baseline measure, scores obtained during the first month on the unit were used as the control variable. This procedure resulted in a more conservative test, since it cancelled out any advantage gained during the first two to four weeks of residence.

Table 5.5 shows the mean number of photographs identified by patients in each experimental condition at the conclusion of treat-

TABLE 5.5

COMPARISONS BETWEEN TREATMENT GROUPS AT POSTPROGRAM
TESTING: NAMING OF PATIENTS IN OTHER MALE UNITS

Treatment Conditions	N	Mean Number Named: Initial Testing	Adjusted Post-program Mean	Comparisons	t	p (one-tailed test)
Maximally Structured (A)	24	2.42	6.29	A vs. B	.30	n.s.
Partially Structured (B)	24	2.96	6.06	(A vs. C)	(2.49)	(.01)
Minimally Structured (C)	19	1.89	4.29	(B vs. C)	(2.18)	(.025)

F (programs) $= 3.60$, $df = 2/63$, $p < .05$

ment. The test series contained 14 photographs of like-sex patients from other treatment units. No difference emerges between the two more highly structured programs. The differences between these conditions (A and B) and the Minimally Structured condition (C) are significant, but these differences are attributable to different amounts of exposure to the test sample.

Table 5.6 summarizes the results of the analysis of covariance of posttreatment PNT scores, categorized according to age and type of program. Adjusted mean differences in scores at termination of treatment are significantly related both to age and program structure. Younger patients in the Maximally Structured program manifest significantly greater awareness of others at completion of treatment. Age significantly determines the number of patients identified only in this treatment program. A comparable analysis of covariance reveals no significant differences in adjusted posttreatment PNT scores attributable to length of illness. The significant effect of degree of program structure is also apparent in this analysis.

TABLE 5.6

COMPARISONS OF HIGH AND LOW AGE GROUPS AT POSTPROGRAM
TESTING: NAMING OF PATIENTS IN OTHER MALE UNITS

Treatment Conditions	Adjusted Means	Comparisons	t	p (one-tailed test)
Maximally Structured (*A*)				
45 years and older	4.32	Older vs.		
44 years and younger	7.56	Younger	3.10	< .01
Partially Structured (*B*)				
45 years and older	6.15	Older vs.		
44 years and younger	5.93	Younger	.21	n.s.
Minimally Structured (*C*)				
45 years and older	2.93	Older vs.		
44 years and younger	3.14	Younger	.17	n.s.

F (programs) $(P) = 3.60$, $p < .05$
F (age) $(A) = 5.29$, $p < .05$
F (interaction) $(P \times A) = 2.20$, $p = $ n.s.

Analyses of covariance for number of opposite-sex photographs identified at postprogram testing reveal significant differences attributable to program structure (see Table 5.7). There were eight photographs in the test series. All predictions involving the relationship between improvement in awareness of others and degree of program structure are confirmed. Significant differences related to age or length of illness do not emerge.

TABLE 5.7

COMPARISONS BETWEEN TREATMENT GROUPS AT POSTPROGRAM
TESTING: NAMING OF PATIENTS IN FEMALE UNITS

Treatment Condition	N	Mean Number Named: Initial Testing	Adjusted Postprogram Mean	Comparisons	t	p (one-tailed test)
Maximally Structured (A)	24	.62	3.14	A vs. B	1.75	.05
Partially Structured (B)	24	.62	2.30	(A vs. C)	(3.82)	(.01)
Minimally Structured (C)	19	.47	1.19	(B vs. C)	(2.18)	(.025)

F (programs) $(P) = 7.78$, $p < .01$
F (age) $(A) = .08$, $p =$ n.s.
F (interaction) $(P \times A) = .23$, $p =$ n.s.

Experimental groups A, B, and C could be simultaneously compared on one test sample with which all had equal, programmed contact, Group G, the female Minimally Structured treatment condition. Group G was represented in the test sample by four photographs. The initial testing revealed little awareness of members of group G; only 12 of the 67 patients could identify photographs from group G, and 10 of these 12 could correctly name only one photograph. These 12 patients were equally distributed among groups A, B, and C, a circumstance which made it possible to examine postprogram scores without reference to an initial baseline measure.

Postprogram PNT results for the Group G subsample were dichotomized into scores of 0-or-1 and 2-or-more. This division insured that patients who identified one photograph at the initial testing were not automatically counted as "successes" in the postprogram scoring without having learned at least one additional name. The *chi* square test was applied to the data.[4]

[4] The small number of responses necessitated a nonparametric analysis

TABLE 5.8

COMPARISONS BETWEEN TREATMENT GROUPS AT POSTPROGRAM
TESTING: NAMING OF PATIENTS IN GROUP G

Treatment Condition	Number Named 0–1	2–4	Comparisons	χ^2	df	P (one-tailed test)
Maximally Structured (A)	14	10	A vs. B	3.80	1	.05
Partially Structured (B)	21	3	A vs. C	3.40	1	.05
Minimally Structured (C)	16	3	B vs. C	.02	1	n.s.

Over-all $\chi^2 = 6.57$, $df = 2$, $p < .05$

The results of these analyses are reported in Table 5.8. The over-all *chi* square value reaches the .05 level of significance. Patients in the Maximally Structured treatment condition identify significantly more Group G photographs than do patients in the Partially Structured or Minimally Structured programs. The difference between the latter two is not significant.

Program structure and awareness of others. Patients in all three treatment conditions manifest increased awareness of others over a period of time (see Tables 5.3, 5.4, 5.5, and 5.7). However, the Maximally Structured treatment condition is clearly more effective than the Partially Structured condition in increasing this awareness, except for identifying males in other units. Differences in PNT scores are obtained in all comparisons involving the two more highly structured programs with the Minimally Structured program. The greater the programmed contact with the test sample, the larger the differences. In the one comparison where all three groups had equal programmed contact with the criterion group, patients in the Maximally

---

of the data. Moreover, the small number of subjects did not allow the subdivisions necessary to analyze the effects of reactivity level (i.e., age and length of illness).

Structured program surpass those in the other two programs. Scores for individuals in the Partially and Minimally Structured programs do not differ.

The superiority of those in the Maximally Structured program condition (A) in naming patients of the opposite sex is probably attributable to the effects of group therapy. This additional programmed experience with female patients, occurring in a very personal, problem-oriented setting, may have enabled Group A patients to initiate more contacts with female patients outside the therapy situation. The socializing effects of government by the patients appear to be most pronounced within the patient's own living group. Neither group therapy nor patient government was effective enough to make group A superior in identifying patients of the same sex.

The failure of the Partially Structured program (B) to surpass the Minimally Structured program group (C) in naming patients of the opposite sex is surprising. The difference in amount of programmed contact between the sexes was clearly greater between Groups B and C than between Groups A and B. However, Group B's extensive experience with female patients in the group activity program apparently promoted no generalization of awareness. The implication is that the quality of structured interaction is much more important than sheer quantity in influencing patients' awareness of others.

Reactivity level and perceptual defense. Reactivity level apparently has some influence on awareness of patients of the same sex. This is most pronounced for younger patients in the Maximally Structured program. The greater mental alertness of these younger patients may explain their increased awareness. However, the absence of comparable findings for awareness of patients of the opposite sex, as well as for global social behavior (reported above), raises questions about the validity of this inference. Heightened awareness of other male patients may in fact be a defensive reaction, reflecting hypervigilance against the potential threat posed by male patients. Anxiety-associated stimuli have been shown to produce increased perceptual awareness. In a review of the literature, Jensen (1958) notes that "threat-induced . . . anxiety enhanced perceptual constancy; it increased frequency of closure, perceptual rigidity, and speed of establishing a stable configuration." Schafer (1948) suggests that Picture Completion scores which are excessively high in comparison to the other Wechsler-Bellevue subtest scores are associated with a high degree of awareness of the environment and indicate watchfulness and paranoid overcautiousness.

The high PNT scores of the younger males could have been due either to increased social responsiveness or to defensive hypervigilance. The PNT and the global social behavior scores were correlated in order to clarify this issue. Rank-order correlations between post-treatment[5] PNT scores for identifying males in other units and post-treatment global social behavior scores for the older and younger patients in the Maximally Structured program are .64 ($N = 13$, $p < .02$) and $-.05$ ($N = 11$, $p = $ n.s.), respectively. The absence of a significant relationship for younger males indicates that their heightened awareness is not related to increased social behavior. The fairly high correlation in the older patient group and the zero-order correlation in the younger group suggests that among this latter group some factor disrupts the relationship between awareness of others and general social responsiveness, and hypervigilance is postulated as this disruptive factor.

Summary

1. All three socio-environmental treatment conditions result in increased awareness of others.

2. The Maximally Structured condition generally surpasses the other two conditions in effecting increased awareness of others. The Partially Structured condition does not consistently surpass the Minimally Structured condition.

3. Younger males in the Maximally Structured condition show greater awareness of other male patients than do older patients. This is viewed as a function of hypervigilance rather than as a reflection of increased social responsiveness.

❀ Verbal Interaction

The rationale underlying this project predicts that the structured social experiences provided by the different treatment programs

---

[5] Similar results are obtained when the difference between posttreatment and initial PNT scores is taken as the measure of improvement in awareness.

will lessen the isolation of the chronic psychotic. One manifestation of this reduction in isolation was expected to be an increase in interaction within the group activity program common to both the Maximally and Partially Structured treatment groups. It was further anticipated that the augmented interpersonal experience and the highly defined social framework of patient government and group therapy within the Maximally Structured program would produce even a greater gain in interaction. Verbal interaction was selected as the measure of social behavior, since this type of interaction is easily quantified and can be reliably measured.

Description of measure: the Verbal Interaction Scale (VIS). The VIS consisted of three items selected from an earlier nine-item scale.[6] Item 1 involved amount of interaction; the group leader was asked how much a particular patient talked in comparison with the other patients in the group. Items 2 and 3 were focused on the direction of interaction. Item 2 asked how much of a patient's conversation was directed toward the group leader, and how much toward other patients in the group, and item 3 was concerned with the number of other patients the patient spoke with during the group session. For each item group leaders designated on a four-point frequency scale the amount of interaction that occurred during an activity session. A verbal interaction score was obtained by totaling the individual scores on the three items.

Procedure. It was felt that these ratings would be most accurate if a group leader was required to rate only a small number of patients per session. This number was limited to four. The research staff devised a rating schedule[7] to insure that each patient was rated

---

[6] The larger scale had been designed to evaluate both the quality and quantity of verbal and nonverbal interaction. Items dealing with nonverbal interaction, such as "amount of interest" or "constructiveness" of a patient's contribution, were either not sufficiently reliable or failed to discriminate adequately. Ratings of the quality of verbal interactions also had to be discarded because the subjective nature of these judgments contributed to their unreliability. Since the purpose of the ratings was to record changes in group functioning, it was essential that rater bias be minimized. This was achieved by retaining only those items which referred to easily quantifiable dimensions of verbal interaction.

[7] An estimate of interrater reliability was obtained on six separate occasions during the three and a half years the scale was used. The coefficients of

in each of the seven activities at least once a month. Before the activity session, each group leader was given an envelope containing the names of the patients to be rated in that session and was instructed not to open the envelope until after the meeting. Leaders were thus prevented from focusing their attention on the patients to be rated and selectively influencing the interaction of those patients. A monthly VIS score was computed for each patient by averaging the VIS scores obtained in each of the seven programmed activities during that month. Since time in treatment was clinically determined for each patient and varied from patient to patient, monthly group means could not be taken as a basis for group comparisons. Improvement scores based on the monthly VIS scores obtained by each patient during his full course of treatment were utilized for this purpose. These individual gain scores[8] (*betas*) were derived by calculating the regression between monthly total VIS scores and number of months in treatment. These gain scores were used to compare the effects of the treatment programs in enhancing verbal interaction during the total time a given patient spent in treatment.

Analysis of variance was used to determine the effects of degree of program structure, reactivity level, and the interaction between these two variables on the verbal interaction *betas*. This analysis was carried out separately for males and females. Within each sex sub-

---

concordance (corrected for continuity and ties) are .88, .85, .71, .82, .74, and .85—all are significant at $p < .01$. These values reflect a reasonably high degree of interrater reliability in making judgments about patients' verbal interaction in group activities.

All items in the VIS were considered to have face validity because of their essentially quantitative nature. Since the procedure required group leaders to make the ratings after the end of a group session, however, the validity of these ratings was checked. On three separate occasions ratings of group leaders were compared with actual frequency counts of behavior appropriate to each item. The recall aspect of the rating procedure in no way detracted from the validity of the ratings.

[8] For a variety of reasons unrelated to treatment effects, during a given month a number of cell values might either be missing or based on proportionately too few observations to be considered. When this occurred, an estimate of the cell score was derived by calculating the regression of verbal interaction on time, based on the total length of time the patient remained in treatment. Cases with more than two missing cells were dropped from the analyses.

group the *betas* were dichotomized according to length of illness and age in order to study the effects of reactivity level.

Results. Improvement in verbal interaction in either male or female patients throughout treatment does not relate either to type of program or to level of reactivity when length of illness or age is used as an index of reactivity. However, the interaction of these two factors does have a significant effect on improvement of verbal behavior (see Table 5.9).

Among males, the older patients show greater improvement in verbal interaction in the Maximally Structured program than in the Partially Structured program (see Table 5.10). In fact, scores for older patients decline markedly in the Partially Structured program.

TABLE 5.9

VERBAL INTERACTION SCALE BETAS OF MALES IN THE TWO
EXPERIMENTAL PROGRAMS, DICHOTOMIZED ACCORDING TO AGE

		Maximally Structured Program (A)	Partially Structured Program (B)
45 Years or Older	Mean	50.69	42.82
	N	15	13
44 Years or Younger	Mean	48.30	52.04
	N	11	13

F (programs) $(P) = .82$, $p = $ n.s.
F (age) $(A) = 1.98$, $p = $ n.s.
F (interaction) $(P \times A) = 6.11$, $p < .05$

Although the scores of younger patients in these two treatment programs do not differ significantly, younger patients in the Partially Structured program show significantly greater gain scores than do older patients in this program.

The influence of early failure. For male patients, the interplay between age and degree of structure in the socio-environmental treatment program clearly affects social outcome. The older patients in the Maximally Structured condition show significantly greater improvement scores in verbal interaction than their counterparts in the Partially Structured condition. This is the first instance in which low reactivity level patients are found to have been differentially affected by degree of program structure. The difference between the scores of the older patients in the two structured programs appears to be a valid reflection of their response to treatment. However, the significantly greater improvement scores of younger as compared with older patients in the Partially Structured condition appears to be due to a treatment artifact: the high number of early treatment failures among the younger patients.

It must be emphasized that the analysis included data derived from only those patients who had been in the program for at least six months. The requirement that the verbal interaction improvement scores be based on scores gathered over a six-month period reduced the sample of experimental cases. An examination of the full sample

TABLE 5.10

t-TEST COMPARISONS OF VERBAL INTERACTION IMPROVEMENT SCORES, DICHOTOMIZED BY PROGRAM AND AGE

Comparison	t	p
Younger vs. Older Patients: Maximally Structured Program (A)	.67	n.s.
Younger vs. Older Patients: Partially Structured Program (B)	2.86	$< .01$
Program A vs. B: Younger Patients	1.02	n.s.
Program A vs. B: Older Patients	2.47	$< .02$

of experimental cases (excluding screening errors) for whom verbal interaction scores were available for any time period reveals that a large number of younger patients were dropped from the Partially Structured program[9] before completing six months of treatment. These

[9] In the Partially Structured condition, 33 per cent of the younger patients were returned to their wards before completing six months of treatment. The comparable figure for the Maximally Structured program is 13 per cent. This should not be construed to mean that the attrition rate for younger patients is greater in the Partially Structured than in the Maximally Structured program. Most of the early dropouts from the Maximally Structured program were screening errors. When the screening errors and early program failures are combined, the attrition rate for younger patients is comparable for the two struc-

"dropouts" had significantly poorer final verbal interaction scores than the young patients who remained in the program more than six months (Mann-Whitney $U = 10.05$, $p < .01$, one-tailed test). Apparently, the discrepant findings on the verbal interaction measure are a function of the fact that the younger patients constitute a select group from which those who did poorly were excluded during the early phase of treatment.

In order to compensate for this sampling bias in the Partially Structured program, the last two verbal interaction scores of dropouts, regardless of length of time in the program, were averaged and included in the sample. The use of final verbal interaction scores instead of derived improvement scores (*betas*), made it possible to compare the outcome of treatment for older and younger patients. Analysis of this enlarged sample shows a tendency for older patients to manifest somewhat higher verbal interaction scores than younger patients.

Summary

1. For male patients, degree of program structure and level of reactivity are not independent determinants of improvement in verbal interaction during treatment. The interaction of these two variables, however, is a significant determinant of improvement. This finding is obtained when age rather than length of illness is used as the measure of reactivity level.

2. Older male patients in the Maximally Structured program show greater improvement in verbal interaction than do older male patients in the Partially Structured program.

3. Younger male patients in the Partially Structured program show more improvement in verbal interaction than do older males in this program. This treatment condition appears to have greater success with younger males because the younger patients who do poorly are eliminated from this program early in treatment.

4. Improvement in verbal interaction among female patients is not a function of degree of program structure, level of reactivity, or the interaction of these two variables.

---

tured programs (41 per cent for the Maximally Structured and 35 per cent for the Partially Structured program).

❀ Spontaneous Social Behavior

Any investigation of the influence of socio-environmental therapy on the interaction of the chronic psychotic must also consider spontaneous social behavior. Interaction of patients under direct pressure from staff members may not be comparable to interaction when the patient is left to his own devices. Spontaneous social behavior may also have import for the patient's subsequent adjustment to the community, in that the community does not provide selective pressure to prevent the chronic psychotic's regression to his characteristic pattern of apathy and withdrawal. Apparently, then, one of the tasks of socio-environmental therapy is to provide the patient with the resources and initiative that will enable him to establish interpersonal contacts under conditions of minimal social pressure. In the study described here, the monthly social offered the best opportunity for comparing spontaneous social behavior of patients in the three treatment conditions.

Description of measure: the Spontaneous Social Behavior Scale (SSBS). The instrument developed to measure spontaneous social behavior, the SSBS, utilizes direct observations by trained observers of specific behavior at monthly socials.

The monthly social was planned and executed by the patients themselves, under the general supervision of a member of the nursing staff. The content of these parties became fairly well standardized during the nine-month developmental phase which preceded the inception of this research. Typically, there were a number of structured activities, such as group games, dancing, and singing, in which patients were actively encouraged to participate by members of the planning committee or by project personnel. In the intervals between such activities, patients were free to engage in conversation, partake of refreshments, perform host functions, or dance to music provided by a small orchestra. These intervals provided the occasion for measurement of spontaneous social behavior. Selected for observation, on the basis of generality and accessibility, were behaviors considered to be representative of the range of available behaviors and sufficiently overt to be reliably[10] observed.

[10] The reliability of the SSBS was estimated by interrater agreement.

The weighted scoring system of the SSBS is based on three assumptions: that interaction with the opposite sex is (for chronic mental patients) a higher order of social behavior than interaction with the same sex; that more personal forms of interaction take precedence over relatively impersonal (task-oriented) interactions; and that participation without genuine interaction is nevertheless more desirable than no participation at all. The behaviors included in the final version of the scale and their associated scoring weights are given in Figure 5.2.

FIG. 5.2   THE SPONTANEOUS SOCIAL BEHAVIOR SCALE

WEIGHT

Dancing with opposite sex	4
Engaging in game with opposite sex	4
Talking with opposite sex	4
Eating with opposite sex (nonverbal interaction such as male patient serving a specific female patient)	4
Dancing with same sex (female patients only)	3
Engaging in game with same sex	3
Talking with same sex	3
Performing voluntary host function (serving, emptying ash trays, collecting dishes, etc.)	2
Eating alone	1
Not actively participating	1
Could not locate	0

Procedure. Data obtained on spontaneous social behavior are based on four 5-minute observation periods. The minimum interval between observation periods was 15 minutes. Scorers were instructed to record the single behavior which represented the "highest" form of interaction noted for each patient during each 5-minute observation period, no order of preference being specified among behaviors of equal scoring rank. During the observation period the code number of the observed behavior was noted on a previously prepared data

---

Four observers working independently recorded the spontaneous social behavior of 18 patients selected from the 3 male treatment programs. The coefficient of concordance (W) computed for these data is .655, uncorrected for ties. The associated *chi* square is 44.54 (significant at $p < .001$).

sheet. One of the observers acted as timekeeper, signaling the beginning and end of each observation period, choosing the periods to coincide with the intervals between structured activities.

The social nature of the occasion permitted the observers to circulate freely among the patients, thus facilitating accurate, though seemingly casual, observation. However, there were too few observers available over an extended period of time to permit continuous observation of all six treatment units. Therefore, to obtain a complete record on male patients, observation of female patients was discontinued shortly after the project began.

Scores from the four observation periods were summed to yield a total score for each patient at each social.[11] These scores ranged from 0 to 16. A score of 0 identified the extreme isolate who either did not attend at all, or who came but did not stay long enough to be observed. Although patients were required to attend, they could leave at any time after their arrival. In the relatively few instances when the unit administrator excused a patient from attending, no score was entered for that month.

[11] Fifty-three of the 120 patients originally assigned to the 3 treatment groups are not included in the present analysis. Seven of these were lost because of medical or administrative problems which necessitated their transfer out of the project. Six patients were dropped from the analysis because they lacked the required minimum of at least 5 scores obtained during the first 7 months in the treatment program. Three additional cases were lost from the analysis because of too many missing cells in the data on these patients during their total period of treatment. (Later analysis of data obtained during the first 7 months of treatment includes these three additional cases.) There are no differences among the 3 treatment programs in the number of patients lost for these reasons.

An additional 37 patients were transferred from the various treatment programs to other wards of the hospital before completion of the minimum treatment requirement (six months). These patients were either unable or unwilling to meet the minimal requirements of residence in the Rehabilitation Center (i.e., attendance at scheduled activities, getting to meals on time, refraining from physical violence, and paying adequate attention to personal hygiene). The loss here was: Group *A*, 27 per cent; Group *B*, 40 per cent; Group *C*, 22 per cent. The disproportionate loss in Group *B* has been discussed in the section on the verbal interaction measure and will be discussed again later. The apparent sampling bias is in no way prejudicial to the present analysis.

The analysis of the SSBS data involved a study of individual gain scores based on total months in treatment.[12] A measure of the rate at which socialization increased or decreased during the total time spent in the treatment program was obtained by calculating individual regression coefficients (*betas*[13]) for the relationship between months in unit and social interaction scores. *Betas* were converted into *T* scores so that a zero gain score was represented by a *T* score of 50.

Results. Differences in variance in SSBS improvement scores in the three treatment groups precluded the simultaneous study of their mean differences by analysis of variance. Table 5.11 presents the means and variances of the individual SSBS gain scores for each of the three treatment groups, as well as comparisons between groups. For ease of computation, the regression coefficients—many of which were negative in sign—were transformed into *T* scores so that all scores became positive. A *beta* of 0 was converted to a *T* score of 50. The data presented in this table are based on male patients in the three groups; data on this measure were not collected for females.

Table 5.11 shows that Group *C* clearly differs from Groups *A* and *B* in terms of variance, and that the mean gain score for Group *B* is lower than that of Group *A* or Group *C*. An examination of these means and variances suggests a tendency for Group *A* to manifest the greatest over-all degree of improvement, with some patients declining considerably. Group *B* shows the greatest over-all decline, although

[12] Monthly group means on the SSBS could not be used as a basis for group comparisons, since time in treatment was clinically determined and varied from patient to patient. Thus, as was the case with VIS scores, individual improvement scores were determined for each patient over his full course of treatment, and these scores were used to study differences among the treatment groups.

[13] Improvement scores (*betas*) based both on the SSBS and the VIS were available for 43 patients. The correlation between the SSBS and VIS *betas* is .36 ($p < .02$). Posttreatment global social behavior as measured by SIRS ratings is not significantly related to either of the gain scores; the correlations are .11 ($N = 105$) and .16 ($N = 67$) for the verbal interaction and spontaneous social behavior *betas* respectively. Intercorrelations between awareness of others as measured by the PNT and either posttreatment global social behavior or the two gain scores were not computed because the PNT data were not comparable across treatment conditions and hence precluded intercorrelation with the other measures.

TABLE 5.11

MEANS, VARIANCES, AND COMPARISONS BETWEEN MEANS AND
VARIANCES OF INDIVIDUAL SSBS GAIN SCORES FOR
THE THREE TREATMENT GROUPS

Treatment Condition	Mean	N	Variance	Comparisons	t	p (one-tailed test)	F	p
Maximally Structured (A)	52.00	27	121.00	A vs. B	1.97	.06	1.00	n.s.
Partially Structured (B)	46.00	22	115.83	A vs. C	.17	n.s.	4.81	.01
Minimally Structured (C)	51.58	18	25.17	B vs. C	2.25	.05	4.60	.01

some patients improve considerably. In Group C there is general mild improvement with little variation among members. These relationships emerge more clearly in Table 5.12, where the distribution of gain scores are divided into upper, middle, and lower thirds.

TABLE 5.12

DISTRIBUTION OF SSBS GAIN SCORES BY TREATMENT PROGRAM

	Maximally Structured (A)	Partially Structured (B)	Minimally Structured (C)	Total
Upper Third	12	6	5	23
Middle Third	7	7	12	26
Lower Third	8	11	2	21
Total N	27	24	19	70

$$\chi^2 = 11.12, \, p < .05$$

More than half of the scores in the upper third of the distribution occur in the Maximally Structured treatment condition, whereas more than half of the scores in the lower third fall in the Partially Structured condition. In the Minimally Structured Treatment condition, gain scores tend to cluster around the mean for the entire distribution. These data clearly show that the Maximally Structured program produces the greatest improvement and the Partially Structured program the greatest decline.

Analyses of variance were performed to determine how program structure and reactivity level and the interaction of these two factors affected improvement in spontaneous social behavior. These analyses were performed only on data from Groups A and B; Group C was eliminated from this analysis because of the significant difference in variance in this group when compared to Groups A and B.

Two separate analyses of variance were performed. In one, the SSBS improvement scores were dichotomized according to length of illness, and in the other by age. Both analyses again evidenced a program difference. The Maximally Structured condition (A) is superior to the Partially Structured condition (B) in effecting improvement in spontaneous social behavior. This difference is significant at the .05 to .10 level. Reactivity level, that is, length of illness and age, is not a significant determinant of improvement, nor is there a significant interaction between reactivity level and degree of program structure.

Program structure and variability in improvement. Considerable variability in improvement in spontaneous social behavior throughout treatment is found for patients in the Maximally and Partially Structured treatment conditions. The Maximally Structured condition is clearly more effective than the Partially Structured condition in inducing improvement in spontaneous social behavior. The majority of patients in the Maximally Structured condition tend to show improvement, while most patients in the Partially Structured condition tend to decline. Although the mean gain manifested by patients in the Minimally Structured condition does not differ from that of the Maximally Structured condition, this is clearly a result of the difference in variability between the two groups. Patients in the Maximally Structured condition show greater positive and negative gain scores than patients in the Minimally Structured condition. Patients in the Minimally Structured condition show relatively little change throughout treatment.

Reactivity level is not a significant determinant of improvement in any of the three treatment conditions. The failure to find a significant relationship between improvement in spontaneous social behavior and decline in reactivity may stem from the emphasis placed on motor activity in the SSBS. For example, the scale assigns the highest weight to dancing, although older and more chronic patients engage in this activity only to a limited degree. If the SSBS systematically penalizes the less reactive patients, differences in the number of dancing responses made by the older and younger patients should be apparent over the full course of treatment. Examination of the scores obtained by the experimental patients in Groups A, B, and C reveals that the younger patients do manifest a significantly greater number of dancing responses than the older patients (Mann-Whitney $U = 462$, $Z = 1.68$, $p < .05$). No differences were found between these two groups in the other highly weighted social behaviors which were not as physically taxing. Thus, patients with declining reactivity are at a disadvantage in manifesting improvement in social behavior on the SSBS.

Summary

1. The Maximally Structured Treatment condition is clearly the most effective of the three in improving spontaneous social behavior.

2. Patients in the Partially Structured condition tend to show a decline in spontaneous social behavior, while those in the Minimally Structured condition show little improvement.

3. There are no significant findings attributable to reactivity level. This can be explained by the design of the spontaneous social behavior measure, which handicapped the older patients by placing strong emphasis on motor behavior.

Chapter VI

The Improvement Sequence

What of the impact of program structure on the interaction process? Month-by-month data on social interaction were analyzed to investigate this relationship. The Maximally and Partially Structured programs were comparable for a treatment period of about six or seven months, after which patients began to leave the treatment units at different rates. The interaction measures utilized in this study were the Verbal Interaction Scale (VIS) and the Spontaneous Social Behavior Scale (SSBS). Verbal Interaction Scale scores were studied over a six-month period and Spontaneous Social Behavior Scale scores over a seven-month period.[1]

[1] Although the minimal length of stay in treatment was six months, comparable data across all treatment conditions were available on the SSBS for

108

❀ Verbal Interaction[2]

The VIS, described in Chapter V, was used by group leaders to record the readily quantifiable dimensions of verbal interaction manifested by patients during various group activities. Patients were rated in each of seven activities at least once a month, and each session was classified in terms of its activity format, that is, whether it was predominantly task- or discussion-centered.

There is evidence that activity format may influence the degree of verbal interaction generated. According to Beard, Goertzel, and Pearce (1958), participation in a manual task facilitates the development of group processes particularly beneficial to chronic patients. The findings of this study suggest that task-centered group activities will probably elicit a greater degree of verbal interaction than discussion-centered activities. The latter may be more threatening to chronic psychotics, particularly at the outset of treatment. For this reason, this analysis will compare the relative improvement in verbal interaction in both discussion and performance types of activities. The general improvement sequence in verbal interaction, regardless of activity format, will also be considered.

One of the components of the reactivity level variable—age— was earlier shown to be a significant determinant of change in verbal interaction. A significant interaction between age and degree of program structure was reported: the older patients in the Maximally Structured condition and the younger patients in the Partially Structured condition showed the greatest improvement in verbal interaction. Since the other index of reactivity level, length of illness, did not emerge as a significant determinant of change in verbal interaction, this analysis will be restricted to the effects of age on the improvement sequence.

Procedure. VIS scores, which were available for the Max-

---

the first seven months of treatment. Ratings on the VIS were made throughout the month, but SSBS data were collected only at socials which were held at the middle of each month. Thus, seven monthly ratings on the SSBS could be obtained before patients began leaving the treatment programs.

[2] This section derives partly from a study by Levine (1963).

imally and Partially Structured conditions, were analyzed to compare these two treatment conditions. Ratings made during the first six months of treatment were compared with respect to the improvement sequence in all activities, regardless of activity format, and in discussion and performance activities considered separately. Data were collected for males and for females; these data were dichotomized by age.

A patient's ratings for any given month in the program were averaged to obtain his monthly verbal interaction score. This score was combined with scores of other patients in the same treatment condition, and a monthly group mean[3] was calculated. The mean verbal interaction scores for each of the first six months in the program were treated as repeated measures in a multifactor analysis of variance.[4] This technique permitted simultaneous study of four variables: treatment condition, age, activity format (discussion-performance), and time in the treatment program. These analyses were performed on VIS scores of 49 male and 50 female patients.

Results for Male Patients: Determinants of Verbal Interaction, Regardless of Activity Format. Table 6.1 summarizes the analysis of variance performed on VIS scores of male patients for their first six months of treatment. When activity format is not considered, differences in program structure do not influence the quantity of verbal interaction. It is also clear that neither age itself nor the interaction between age and program structure affects verbal interaction. Time in treatment, however, is an important variable; there is a significant change in verbal interaction during the first six months in the program. This time variable is also a factor in producing a significant interaction between program structure and age.

---

[3] Missing cells were replaced by an estimate of the cell score, derived by calculating the regression of VIS scores over the six-month period of treatment. Cases with more than one missing cell were dropped from the analyses. Five per cent of the total number of cells in the matrix were replaced in this manner. These replaced values were randomly distributed over treatment conditions both for discussion and performance activities. With respect to the distribution of replaced data over months, a disproportionately high number of vacant cells occurred during the first and sixth months for the female units. However, this disproportion was of little consequence, since the monthly group means changed only slightly when calculated without the replaced values.

[4] The least squares solution was used (described by Winer, 1962).

TABLE 6.1

ANALYSIS OF VARIANCE OF VIS SCORES OF MALE PATIENTS
FOR THE FIRST SIX MONTHS OF TREATMENT

Source of Variation	df	MS	F	p
Between Subjects	48	158.79		
A (Structure)	1	34	< 1	
B (Age)	1	90	< 1	
A × B	1	152	< 1	
Error (Subj. w. Groups)	45	163.24		
Within Subjects	539			
C (Months)	5	70.40	5.55	.001
A × C	5	3.40	< 1	
B × C	5	13.00	1.02	
A × B × C	5	26.20	2.06	.07
Error (C × Subj. w. Groups)	225	12.69		
D (Discussion-Performance)	1	969	49.44	.001
A × D	1	36	1.84	
B × D	1	181	9.23	.005
A × B × D	1	48	2.45	
Error (D × Subj. w. Groups)	45	19.60		
C × D	5	14.00	1.62	
A × C × D	5	17.00	1.97	.08
B × C × D	5	19.20	2.22	.05
A × B × C × D	5	8.40	< 1	
Error (C × D × Subj. w. Groups)	225	8.65		
Total	587			

The effects of time in treatment on VIS score are presented graphically in Figure 6.1. In the Maximally Structured condition, older males show greater rate of improvement and longer duration of improvement. In the Partially Structured condition, this pattern characterizes younger rather than older males. Although younger males in the Maximally Structured condition and older males in the Partially Structured condition also manifest gain, this improvement tends to be dissipated by the end of the six-month study period.

Results for Male Patients: Determinants of Verbal Interaction in Performance and Discussion Activities. The quantity of verbal

FIG. 6.1   MEAN MONTHLY VIS SCORES OF OLDER AND YOUNGER
MALE PATIENTS IN THE TWO TREATMENT CONDITIONS

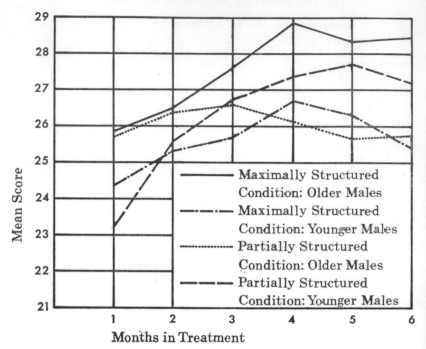

Months in Treatment

interaction clearly differs in performance and discussion activities. Table 6.1 shows a significant F for the main effects of activity format. The relationship between time in treatment and activity format is graphically presented in Figure 6.2. Manifestly, performance activities are superior in generating verbal interaction although improvement also occurs in discussion activities. This finding supports the hypothesis that performance activities in particular facilitate improvement in verbal interaction.

Activity format also interacts with age and time in treatment. Table 6.1 reports a highly significant interaction between activity format and age. Figure 6.3 clearly shows that the highest degree of verbal interaction is attained by older patients in performance activities. On the other hand, older patients show the least verbal interaction in discussion activities. The mean scores (listed at the bottom of the

FIG. 6.2 MEAN MONTHLY VIS SCORES OF MALE PATIENTS IN
PERFORMANCE AND DISCUSSION ACTIVITIES

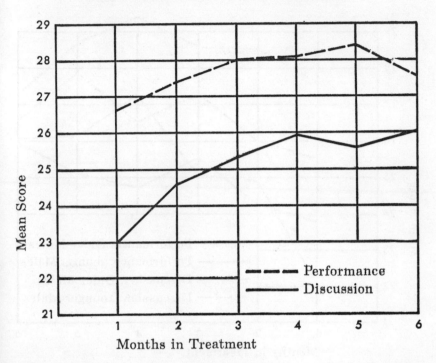

graph) indicate that younger patients in the two types of activity session interact at intermediate levels.

Table 6.1 further indicates that activity format interacts with program structure and time in treatment. This interaction approaches significance at the .08 level. In Figure 6.4, it is again evident that, regardless of type of treatment, performance activities elicit greater verbal interaction than discussion activities. The Maximally Structured condition surpasses the Partially Structured condition in verbal interaction in both types of activities. In addition, the Maximally Structured condition apparently produces continued and sustained gains in verbal interaction in performance activities, whereas improvement in performance activities for patients in the Partially Structured condition is completely lost by the end of the study period.

To determine the characteristics of the improvement curves

Fig. 6.3*   MEAN MONTHLY VIS SCORES OF OLDER AND YOUNGER
MALE PATIENTS IN PERFORMANCE AND DISCUSSION ACTIVITIES

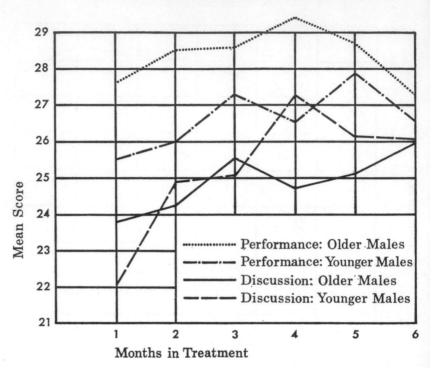

* Average Mean VIS Scores for the First Six Months in Treatment.
Performance: Discussion:
          Older Males: 28.53   Older Males: 24.92
          Younger Males: 26.63   Younger Males: 25.24

for the two treatment groups in performance and discussion activities,
trend analyses were performed on the mean monthly VIS scores. In
the Maximally Structured condition, significant linear improvement
occurs both in discussion ($F = 7.75$, $df = 1$, $p < .01$) and performance activities ($F = 7.71$, $df = 1$, $p < .01$). In the Partially Structured condition, significant linear gain occurs only in the discussion
activities ($F = 15.76$, $df = 1$, $p < .01$); the trend in the performance
activities is quadratic ($F = 3.65$, $df = 1.116$, $p < .06$). The trend
analyses indicate that the two treatment conditions show the greatest
difference in the area of performance activities. With this type of ac-

FIG. 6.4 MEAN MONTHLY VIS SCORES OF MALE PATIENTS IN
PERFORMANCE AND DISCUSSION ACTIVITIES IN
THE TWO TREATMENT CONDITIONS

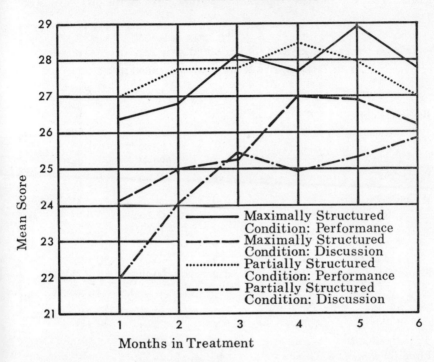

tivity, patients in the Maximally Structured condition manifest regular increments in verbal interaction, while patients in the Partially Structured condition are characterized by early gains and a subsequent decline to the initial interaction level.

Results for Female Patients: Determinants of Verbal Interaction, Regardless of Activity Format. The findings indicated in Table 6.2 show that, when activity format is not considered, age differences do not determine change in verbal behavior in female patients. However, degree of program structure does influence the quantity of verbal interaction (Figure 6.5). Although improvement in VIS ratings occurs in both treatment programs in the course of time, females in the Partially Structured condition clearly surpass those in the Maximally Structured condition in verbal interaction.

The influence of time in treatment on the quantity of verbal interaction is evidenced by the significant F reported in Table 6.2. Time in treatment also interacts with age in effecting change in VIS scores. This interaction approaches significance at the .07 level (see

TABLE 6.2

ANALYSIS OF VARIANCE OF VIS SCORES OF FEMALE PATIENTS
FOR THE FIRST SIX MONTHS OF TREATMENT

Source of Variation	df	MS	F	p
Between Subjects	49			
A (Structure)	1	814.43	5.50	$< .025$
B (Age)	1	25.00	< 1	
$A \times B$	1	280.64	1.89	
Error (Subj. w. Groups)	46	148.15		
Within Subjects	550			
C (Months)	5	66.05	6.34	$< .001$
$A \times C$	5	15.63	1.50	
$B \times C$	5	21.81	2.09	$< .07$
$A \times B \times C$	5	5.95	< 1	
Error ($C \times$ Subj. w. Groups)	230	10.42		
D (Activity)	1	1255.71	54.06	$< .001$
$A \times D$	1	44.81	1.93	
$B \times D$	1	5.92	< 1	
$A \times B \times D$	1	2.88	< 1	
Error ($D \times$ Subj. w. Groups)	46	23.23		
$C \times D$	5	8.66	< 1	
$A \times C \times D$	5	9.96	1.08	
$B \times C \times D$	5	2.18	< 1	
$A \times B \times C \times D$	5	1.50	< 1	
Error ($C \times D \times$ Subj. w. Groups)	230	9.22		
Total	599			

Table 6.2). The nature of this interaction is described graphically in Figure 6.6: the scores of the younger females are clearly more erratic than those of the older females. The greater gain shown by the younger females at the sixth month of treatment may be more related to this greater fluctuation in their scores than to actual improvement.

Results for Female Patients: Determinants of Verbal Interac-

FIG. 6.5   MEAN MONTHLY VIS SCORES OF FEMALE PATIENTS IN
THE TWO TREATMENT CONDITIONS

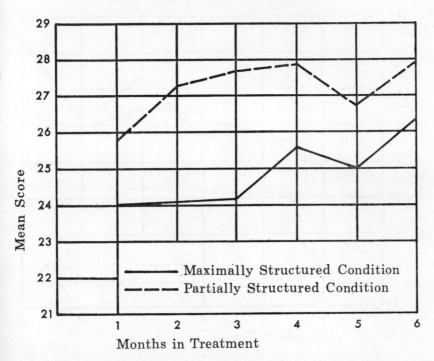

Months in Treatment

tion in Performance and Discussion Activities. Table 6.2 reports a very significant *F* for activity format. Performance activities are unquestionably more effective than discussion activities in generating verbal behavior (see Figure 6.7), and this superiority persists throughout the first six months of treatment. Thus, the major effect of activity format is the same among males and females, but for female patients no significant interactions occur between activity format and the other variables investigated.

Factors Influencing the Improvement Sequence. The finding that the Maximally Structured condition is associated with greater verbal interaction among older than younger males is consistent with previously reported results regarding improvement in social behavior over the full course of treatment (see Chapter Five). The greater gain of younger over older males in the Partially Structured condition is

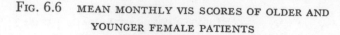

Fig. 6.6   MEAN MONTHLY VIS SCORES OF OLDER AND
YOUNGER FEMALE PATIENTS

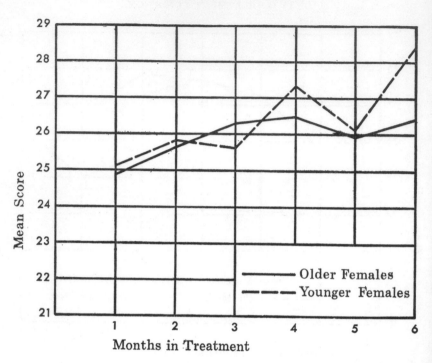

in accord with data on improvement in verbal interaction throughout the full course of treatment, but it is incongruent with findings on global social behavior at completion of treatment. This discrepancy has already been discussed in terms of differences between samples of patients studied. Data on global social behavior were gathered on the full sample of younger patients in the Partially Structured condition. However, in rating verbal interaction, younger patients who did poorly were eliminated from the sample early in treatment, before six months.

Among female patients verbal interaction is associated with degree of treatment structure, but the direction of this relationship is opposite to that predicted by the basic hypothesis of this study. Females in the Partially Structured condition manifest substantially better VIS scores than their counterparts in the Maximally Structured program.

FIG. 6.7   MEAN MONTHLY VIS SCORES OF FEMALE PATIENTS IN
PERFORMANCE AND DISCUSSION ACTIVITIES

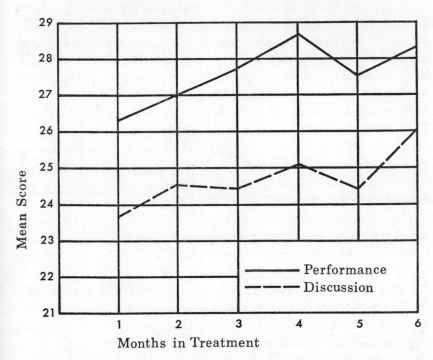

The two additional program elements of the Maximally Structured condition—patient government and group therapy—may have
inhibited verbal interaction among females. Schooler (1963) found
that females with comparatively low levels of intellectual functioning
(such as female patients in this study) were anxious for others not to
express their negative feelings. Since group therapy would encourage
the expression of such feelings, this program element may have sup-
pressed rather than facilitated improvement in social behavior.

This inhibition, however, may represent merely an initial reaction which is eventually overcome. It should be noted that inhibition
is most evident during the first three months of treatment; verbal interaction is facilitated during the second three months. Although the
magnitude of this heightened gain in interaction is equivalent to that
shown by patients in the Partially Structured condition over the entire

six-month study period, it is still insufficient to eliminate differences in interaction in the two experimental groups.

No significant differences in social behavior were reported in Chapter Five for females in these two treatment conditions at completion of treatment (the duration of which was individually determined and varied from six to twelve months). The failure of females in the Maximally Structured condition to manifest significantly greater social interaction at completion of treatment might have been due to early inhibition resulting from the heightened demand for interaction. These considerations indicate that, if females are to be exposed to a maximally structured socio-environmental program, the treatment period should be longer than that of the present study.

The format of group activity sessions is a significant determinant of quantity of verbal interaction. Chronic patients apparently feel less threatened and are more readily able to verbalize in situations where a concrete task provides the focus for group involvement. Verbal interaction during actual task performance can be spontaneous, informal, and not necessarily related to the nature of the task. In discussion sessions, on the other hand, verbal interaction is constrained by the requirement that each response be relevant to the topic being discussed. Interaction may be further inhibited by the feeling that responses are continually scrutinized and evaluated for appropriateness. Therefore, it is suggested that the early stages of a social rehabilitation program consist largely of task-centered activity groups. Such performance-oriented activities should facilitate verbal interaction and the integration of the chronic psychotic into a social matrix.

Quantity of verbal interaction in discussion and performance activities among males is influenced by age. In discussion activities, younger patients show a broader range and greater fluctuation of scores than older patients. When the improvement sequences of the two age groups are compared, younger patients show considerably lower initial scores, far surpass the scores of older patients by the fourth month, and decline to the level of the older patients by the sixth month. This erratic verbal behavior suggests that younger males are more sensitive than older patients to the threat, discussed earlier, implied in verbal activities. Although they overcome the initial stress and show gains in verbal behavior, their improvement declines at the fifth month when the threat is even more heightened because group discussions are concerned with planning to leave the hospital.

Throughout the six-month period, the level of verbal interaction in performance activities of older males remains superior to that of younger males. This consistent quantitative difference in verbal interaction level suggests differences in approach to performance situations among older and younger male patients. Clinical observations reveal that younger male patients become involved in motor rather than verbal interactive aspects of performance tasks.

Age differences in female patients do not affect the level of verbal interaction in either type of activity. This finding is consistent with the finding reported by Cumming and Henry (1961) that, unlike adult males, adult females do not shift their interests with age. Regardless of age, adult females are generally more involved with social than with motor or instrumental behavior.

The quantity of verbal interaction in performance and discussion activities for males is also related to degree of program structure. Both socio-environmental treatment programs produce linear gains in verbal interaction in discussion activities. In performance activities patients in the Partially Structured condition are clearly unable to sustain their initial gains, while patients in the Maximally Structured condition show linear gain throughout the six months. These findings suggest that male chronic psychotics require intensified group experiences such as patient government and group therapy in order to sustain regular increments in interaction.

Summary

1. Structured socio-environmental treatment (the Maximally and Partially Structured conditions) effects a significant increase in verbal interaction in male and female patients in the course of time. Among males, older patients in the Maximally Structured condition and younger patients in the Partially Structured condition show sustained improvement in verbal interaction. Among females, the interaction between degree of program structure and age does not determine the verbal behavior, although patients in the Partially Structured condition surpass those in the Maximally Structured condition in level of verbal interaction.

2. The quantity of verbal interaction for both males and fe-

males is greater in performance than in discussion activities.

3. Among older males, the greatest degree of verbal interaction is found in performance activities, and the least in discussion activities. Younger male patients show somewhat greater verbal interaction in performance than in discussion activities, but the difference is small. Age does not determine verbal interaction in either type of activity among female patients.

4. Males in the Maximally Structured condition tend to surpass males in the Partially Structured condition in verbal interaction, in both types of activities. In addition, the Maximally Structured condition produces consistent increments in verbal interaction in both performance and discussion activities. In the Partially Structured condition, consistent increments occur only in the discussion activities. Degree of program structure does not determine level of verbal interaction in either type of activity among female patients.

✿ Spontaneous Social Behavior

Spontanous social behavior has been viewed as an area of direct relevance to the patient's adjustment to community life. The Spontaneous Social Behavior Scale (SSBS) and the monthly social at which such behavior was rated have been described. Improvement in spontaneous social behavior throughout the total treatment period was considered; now, the improvement sequence during the first seven months of treatment will be discussed. A detailed study of the interaction process becomes possible when time in treatment is held constant and the degree of spontaneous social behavior occurring in the three treatment groups during the first seven months of treatment is examined.

Procedure. To compare the improvement sequence in spontaneous social behavior across the three treatment programs, each patient's monthly SSBS scores for the first seven months of treatment were arranged sequentially in seven columns; column 1 contained all scores obtained during the first month, column 2 all scores for the second month, etc. This procedure permitted the computation of monthly means[5] for each of the three treatment groups. The means

---

[5] Missing cells were replaced by an estimate of the cell score derived

and variances of these scores were then compared for program differences.[6] Trend analyses were also performed.

Results. Table 6.3 shows the means and variances of the three treatment groups for the first seven months of treatment. The between-groups variances differ significantly for three of the seven months. The variance of scores for Group *A* is consistently greater than the variance of either Group *B* or Group *C*, and the differences between Groups *A* and *B* are generally larger than those found be-

TABLE 6.3

MEANS AND VARIANCES OF THE THREE TREATMENT GROUPS

FOR THE FIRST SEVEN MONTHS OF TREATMENT

	Means					*Variances*			
	Max. Str.	Part. Str.	Min. Str.			Max. Str.	Part. Str.	Min. Str.	
Mo.	*A*	*B*	*C*	*Sig. Diff.*	*Mo.*	*A*	*B*	*C*	F_{max}
1.	6.78	7.17	5.05	none	1.	26.72	17.10	14.05	1.90
2.	7.18	8.00	5.00	*B-C*[1]	2.	28.46	17.30	8.89	3.20[1]
3.	7.00	8.58	5.63	*B-C*[1]	3.	26.54	15.30	9.13	2.91[1]
4.	7.30	8.29	6.16	none	4.	28.37	16.82	14.92	1.90
5.	8.30	8.58	5.89	*B-C*;[1] *A-C*[1]	5.	15.76	10.60	13.77	1.14
6.	7.92	8.00	5.79	none	6.	30.69	17.48	10.73	2.86[1]
7.	8.84	6.88	5.74	*A-C*[1]	7.	24.41	16.90	13.09	1.86

[1] .05 level.

tween Groups *B* and *C*. One effect of increased social pressure clearly is a correspondingly greater variation in social response.

The mean SSBS scores for Groups *A* and *B* are consistently

---

by calculating the regression of SSBS scores over the seven-month period of treatment. Cases with more than one missing cell were dropped from the analysis. The estimated value used in the subjects-by-months data matrices were randomly distributed over months ($x^2 = 9.40$; $p > .10$). Between 13 and 16 per cent of the cells in each of the three matrices were filled in this manner. The influence of the estimated values on the means was negligible.

[6] The original approach involved an analysis of variance with a two-factor repeated measurements design. However, this plan neglected to take into account the possibility of differential treatment effects on the variances, as well as the means, and the finding of a nonlinear relationship. Neither the between-groups nor within-groups variance components were homogeneous on examination. Transformations were ineffectual.

higher than those for Group *C*. Moreover, significant differences occur in two months for which the variances constitute no problem
(months 5 and 7). Although the means for Group *B* are slightly
higher than those for Group *A* during the first six months, the apparent superiority of Group *B* must be interpreted in light of the sampling bias in Group *B* (noted in Chapter Five, footnote 11). When
the SSBS scores for all patients transferred out of these two treatment
programs during the first six months are added to those included in
the present analysis, Groups *A* and *B* show virtually identical means
through the fifth month.

Although the means for the first month of treatment do not
differ significantly, they are sufficiently discrepant to raise a question
about the adequacy of the randomization of subjects. Again the differences are more apparent than real. A score for the first month could
be obtained at any time during the first four weeks in treatment.
Analysis of data on other measures has demonstrated that important
gains in social behavior can occur during the first three or four weeks
after transfer to the project (Smith *et al.*, 1963). On the assumption
that a similar effect was operating, SSBS scores obtained during the
very first week were isolated and compared. The mean scores for
Groups *A*, *B*, and *C* (5.14 [$N = 7$], 5.44 [$N = 9$], and 5.11
[$N = 9$] respectively) indicate that all three treatment groups started
at essentially the same level of interaction. It should be noted that
using the inflated first-month baseline scores for Groups *A* and *B* introduces a conservative bias into all analyses which deal with gain in
interaction as a function of time in program.

The Spontaneous Social Behavior Scale scores for male patients
in the three experimental socio-environmental programs are presented
in Figure 6.8. Inspection of the curves in this figure suggests that the
general trend of social behavior differs considerably for the three treatment conditions. The curve for Group *A* most nearly approximates
the theoretical expectancy, which is for an increase in spontaneous
social behavior during each month in the treatment program. Group *B*
shows a strong initial improvement response, reaches its apparent maximum rather rapidly, and begins to decline in the sixth month. Group
C manifests a somewhat delayed initial response and then loses its
momentum as early as the fourth month.

FIG. 6.8   MEAN SPONTANEOUS SOCIAL BEHAVIOR SCORES FOR
EACH TREATMENT CONDITION DURING THE
SEVEN MONTHS IN TREATMENT

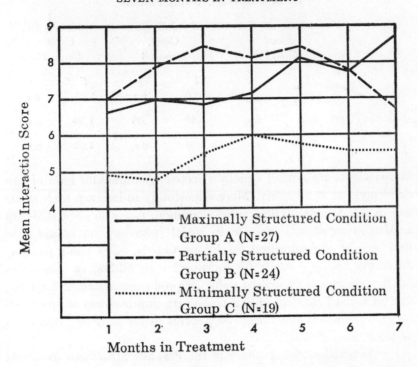

To define the nature of these trends more precisely, the data were analyzed for linear and quadratic trend components (Winer, 1962); the results are summarized in Table 6.4. The relationship between social interaction score and time on unit is linear for Group *A*, whereas the corresponding relationship for Group *B* is best represented by a quadratic function. The trend for Group *C* is basically linear, but the total gain in interaction is too small to reach significance. The difference between the mean scores for the first and seventh months is significant for Group *A*, but not for Group *C*.

Program structure and sustained improvement in spontaneous social behavior.   Spontaneous social behavior among male patients clearly can be increased through manipulation of the physical and interpersonal environment. However, it is also apparent that such

TABLE 6.4

COMPARISON OF LINEAR AND QUADRATIC TREND COMPONENTS
OVER A SEVEN-MONTH PERIOD

	Maximally Str. Cond. Group A		Partially Str. Cond. Group B		Minimally Str. Cond. Group C	
	F	p	F	p	F	p
Linear Trend	8.93	.01	1.00	n.s.	1.63	n.s.
Quadratic Trend	1.00	n.s.	6.49	.05	1.00	n.s.
Residual	1.38	n.s.	1.00	n.s.	1.00	n.s.

manipulations are not all equally effective. A minimum level of sustained pressure is necessary. Mere opportunity to interact, such as existed in the Minimally Structured condition, is not in itself sufficient to effect a significant increase in social behavior—no matter how attractive the environmental conditions. On the other hand, partially structuring the opportunity for socialization by adding an interaction activity program is of limited value in producing sustained improvement in social behavior; only a temporary improvement in spontaneous social behavior was shown by patients in the Partially Structured condition.

As noted earlier, patients in the Partially Structured treatment condition also showed temporary improvement with respect to verbal interaction in performance activities. Both verbal interaction in performance activities and spontaneous social behavior in monthly socials are determined more by patient than by leader. The fact that quadratic trends characterize the behavior changes which occur in both types of situations indicates that for male patients the Partially Structured condition may not be sufficient to maintain early gains in social behavior in situations where the patient is left to his own devices.

The Maximally Structured Program does produce sustained improvement in social behavior in activities requiring initiative on the part of the patient. Two program elements, group therapy and patient government, differentiate the Maximally Structured from the Partially Structured treatment condition. It is implied that the effects of these two program elements generalize to the behavior observed in the other program activities.

The absence of comparable sustaining influences in the Partially Structured program may account both for the higher incidence of program failures early in treatment and the subsequent tendency of patients in this treatment group to regress toward their initial interaction level. This study is by no means the first to encounter negative effects from socio-environmental programs. Both Pace (1957) and Fairweather *et al.* (1960) reported that some patients were adversely affected by group interaction therapy. This study suggests that such negative effects are related to the degree of structure in the treatment program.

Summary

1. The Maximally Structured condition is clearly the most effective of the three socio-environmental programs in improving spontaneous social behavior.

2. Although the Partially Structured condition is effective in generating early gain, it is unable to sustain this gain throughout the first seven months of treatment.

3. The Minimally Structured condition produces a slight but insignificant improvement in interaction. The effects of this condition in augmenting spontaneous social behavior are negligible.

Chapter VII

Clinical Impact of
Socio-Environmental Therapies

A review of the more carefully controlled studies of socio-environmental treatment reveals contradictory clinical findings on such posttreatment measures as psychopathology, release rates, and adjustment. Pace (1957) and Spohn (1963) found that socio-environmental treatment had little effect on the correction of psychopathology. In fact, Spohn's treatment group actually showed an increase in tension and psychopathology. On the other hand, the group-living program studied by Fairweather *et al.* (1960) effected a decline in psychopathology and an improvement in adaptive behavior among short-term psychotics. Fairweather (1964) also reported that his small, autonomous, patient-led group-treatment program resulted in better posttreatment adaptation among the acute than among the chronic psychotics. Ellsworth (1963), however, found that socio-environmental therapy was more successful with the chronic patient in producing heightened release rates and positive posttreatment adjustment. Lee (1961–1964)[1] also reported that socio-environmental therapy enhanced release rates for male patients who had experienced long hospitalization.

Such inconsistent findings suggest that the specific variables associated with successful socio-environmental therapy have not yet been defined. This investigation is predicated on the hypothesis that degree of program structure and patient reactivity level, variables which have a significant influence on social behavior (see Chapter Five), are also general determinants of clinical outcome. Hopefully, these two study variables will prove to be unifying constructs which may clarify some of the contradictory results reported in the literature.

Two major criteria of clinical outcome, commonly used as indices of the effect of treatment on psychiatric symptoms, have been utilized in this project: ratings of psychiatric status, and release from the hospital at completion of treatment.

❀ Description of Measures

The Psychiatric Status Scale (PSS). The psychiatric status of each patient was evaluated by clinical psychologists using the PSS (see Figure 7.1), a graphic rating scale containing five behavioral descriptions of symptomatology which differentiated levels of psychiatric status. The descriptions were unequally spaced on a vertical scale to correct for an anticipated negative skewness in the distribution of ratings; the actual midpoint of the scale fell between the third and fourth descriptions. Scores were derived by dividing the scale into 15 equal intervals and assigning the number of the interval to whatever rating marks appeared within that interval.

Disposition Status. Disposition status is a global measure of psychiatric condition. The decision to release a patient to the com-

[1] This is the only study of those reviewed which dealt with both male and female patients. For female patients there was no significant difference in release rates between experimental and control conditions.

munity may be determined by a multitude of factors, some not directly relevant to the psychological health of the patient, for example, number of beds or administrative policy. However, in this study a patient was required to show some control of psychotic symptomatology to obtain approval for release. The psychiatrist was the final judge of the status of the patient. For patients in the experimental units, disposition status at completion of a treatment period, which varied from patient to patient, was taken as the criterion. For patients in the control condition, disposition status within a one-year period following assignment to this condition was considered the criterion.

✿ Procedure

Ratings of psychiatric status were made within the first 2 weeks of treatment, and again 6 to 12 months later when treatment was completed. Because the PSS was still in the developmental phase during the initial stage of the project, early treatment ratings using this instrument were made only for a reduced sample of patients. PSS ratings at completion of treatment were obtained for the total experimental population. PSS ratings were made by the unit administrators,[2] who were clinical psychologists. These ratings were based on personal observations in interviews and daily ward contacts, and on information obtained from personnel in close daily contact with the patient. Patients who were returned to their original wards within the first six weeks, so-called screening errors,[3] did not receive posttreatment PSS

[2] A minimum estimate of the reliability of the PSS was derived by having 6 psychologists rate each of 13 patients during a 45-minute screening interview. The coefficient of concordance (W) for the unit administrators' ratings was .64, and the associated *chi* square was significant at the .001 level. The coefficient of concordance for the ratings made by the follow-up interviewers was .71, significant beyond the .001 level. The fact that each group was rated by its own administrator posed certain problems. Although the unit administrator was the person most familiar with each patient, his personal biases may have influenced his evaluation of the patient and hence of the treatment outcome. In order to reduce the effects of bias, training sessions were held to insure uniform standards for rating. In these sessions, definitions were reviewed and practice ratings were made and discussed.

[3] Approximately 15 per cent of all patients assigned to the experimental programs were returned to their original wards within the first six weeks because their psychiatric symptoms precluded participation in program activities.

FIG. 7.1   THE PSYCHIATRIC STATUS SCALE (PSS)

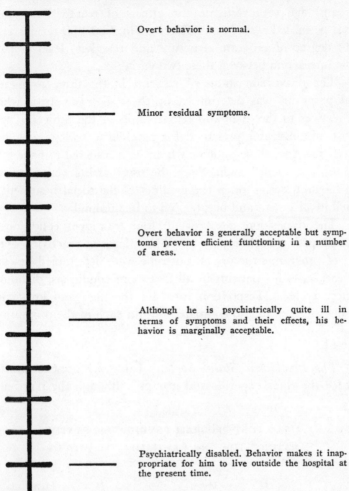

———— Overt behavior is normal.

———— Minor residual symptoms.

———— Overt behavior is generally acceptable but symptoms prevent efficient functioning in a number of areas.

———— Although he is psychiatrically quite ill in terms of symptoms and their effects, his behavior is marginally acceptable.

———— Psychiatrically disabled. Behavior makes it inappropriate for him to live outside the hospital at the present time.

ratings. Patients in the control groups were not rated because observations by staff were not available.

Posttreatment PSS ratings were averaged for each treatment condition and compared by analysis of variance[4] for males and fe-

[4] Analysis of variance rather than covariance was used to compare groups on posttreatment measures because in some cases initial scores were not available. For those cases where initial scores were available, the means across conditions were comparable.

males separately. Each sex group was also dichotomized by length of illness and age to investigate the effects of reactivity level. These analyses permitted a study of differences in final PSS ratings attributable to degree of program structure and reactivity level of patients, and the interaction between these two variables.

The disposition status of patients in the three socio-environmental programs was determined by the two psychiatrists who provided services to the male and female units of the project. Typically, the unit administrator presented for psychiatric review, at a disposition staff meeting, those patients whom he considered to have attained maximum treatment benefit. Since the psychiatrists were not involved in the research design or in the conduct of the social treatment, their personal involvement and bias tended to be minimal.

The disposition rates for all four treatment conditions were compared within each sex group. The effects of reactivity level and degree of program structure on outcome were determined by comparing release rates for patients in all treatment conditions, dichotomized by reactivity level. Disposition rates for the high and low reactivity level subgroups were also compared within each of the programs.

❀ Results

The Psychiatric Status Scale. Table 7.1 presents mean PSS scores for the three experimental groups. Although the posttreatment

TABLE 7.1

MEAN POST-PROGRAM PSYCHIATRIC STATUS
RATING* FOR THE EXPERIMENTAL GROUPS

| | Male | | | Female | | |
	N	Mean	σ	N	Mean	σ
Maximally Structured	37	7.92	3.80	33	6.03	4.44
Partially Structured	36	8.92	4.42	35	7.20	4.71
Minimally Structured	21	8.81	4.63	28	8.14	4.78

F (programs) $= .94$, $p = $ n.s. F (programs) $= 1.50$, $p = $ n.s.

* The lower the score, the better the psychiatric status.

TABLE 7.2

MEAN POSTTREATMENT PSYCHIATRIC STATUS RATINGS* FOR MALE
PATIENTS IN THE THREE EXPERIMENTAL PROGRAMS,
DICHOTOMIZED BY AGE

Age	Maximally Structured (A)		Partially Structured (B)		Minimally Structured (C)	
	Mean	N	Mean	N	Mean	N
44 Years and Younger	8.45	(15)	10.02	(21)	9.93	(11)
45 Years and Older	7.27	(22)	7.73	(15)	7.67	(10)

F (programs) $(P) = .94$, $p = $ n.s.
F (age) $(A) = 4.27$, $p < .05$
F (interaction) $(P \times A) = .23$, $p = $ n.s.

* The lower the score, the better the psychiatric status.

TABLE 7.3

MEAN POSTTREATMENT PSYCHIATRIC STATUS RATING* FOR MALE
PATIENTS IN THE THREE EXPERIMENTAL PROGRAMS,
DICHOTOMIZED BY LENGTH OF ILLNESS

	Maximally Structured (A)		Partially Structured (B)		Minimally Structured (C)	
	Mean	N	Mean	N	Mean	N
11 Years of Illness or Less (short-term)	9.52	(18)	9.43	(16)	9.16	(11)
12 Years of Illness or More (long-term)	6.48	(19)	8.42	(20)	8.59	(10)

F (programs) $(P) = .55$, $p = $ n.s.
F (length of illness) $(L) = 3.90$, $p = .05$
F (interaction) $(P \times L) = .78$, $p = $ n.s.

* The lower the score, the better the psychiatric status.

psychiatric status of patients in the Maximally Structured condition surpasses that of patients in the other two conditions, the differences between the three types of programs are not statistically significant.

Tables 7.2 and 7.3 present the analyses of variance of post-treatment psychiatric status ratings for male patients in the three experimental conditions dichotomized by age and length of illness respectively, the reactivity level variables. The older patients are consistently characterized by better psychiatric status at completion of treatment, regardless of socio-environmental treatment program. Similarly, male patients with longer duration of illness also show the better outcome in each treatment.

Interpretation of these results necessitates referral to the PSS ratings made early in treatment, to determine whether patients at high and low reactivity level were comparable at the start of treatment and whether the superior posttreatment PSS ratings of patients at low reactivity level actually reflect psychiatric improvement. The early PSS ratings, available for 82 per cent of the male experimental population (a subsample presumably representative of the entire experimental population), indicate no statistically reliable differences between the high and low reactivity level variables during the initial phases of treatment. Numerical differences noted between older and younger patients favored the latter. When the mean scores[5] for the restricted samples are used as baselines for evaluating the posttreatment psychiatric status of the total sample, the low reactivity level patients show some improvement at completion of treatment, but the high reactivity level patients manifest considerable decline. Reactivity level is clearly a significant determinant of posttreatment psychiatric status.

Reactivity level has no apparent bearing as a determinant of outcome for female patients. Analyses of variance, comparable to those performed for psychiatric status ratings of male patients, revealed no significant differences.

___

[5] Using age as the index of reactivity level, the means of the early PSS ratings for the restricted samples of older and younger patients are 8.17 and 7.38 respectively. When length of illness is the index, the means early in treatment for the patients with the longer and shorter duration of illness are 7.76 and 7.82 respectively.

TABLE 7.4

DISPOSITION OF PATIENTS* FROM THE DIFFERENT TREATMENT CONDITIONS AT TERMINATION OF PROGRAM

| | Male | | | | | Female | | | | |
| | | Failures | | Successes | | | Failures | | Successes | |
	Total N	Screening Errors	Returned to Ward	Returned to Community N	Returned to Community per cent / Total N	Total N	Screening Errors	Returned to Ward	Returned to Community N	Returned to Community per cent / Total N
Maximally Structured	44	7	17	20	45	42	8	13	21	50
Partially Structured	46	10	16	20	43	38	3	10	25	66
Minimally Structured	25	4	11	10	40	31	3	11	17	55
Control Condition	20	0	14	6	30	32	0	19	13	41

* The original sample included 287 patients. However, such factors as death and physical illness resulted in the reduction of the sample to 278.

135

TABLE 7.5

PROGRAM DISPOSITION OF MALE PATIENTS, DICHOTOMIZED BY AGE

	Age	Returned to Community	Returned to Ward
Maximally Structured (A)	45 yrs. and older	14	8
	44 yrs. and younger	6	16
Partially Structured (B)	45 yrs. and older	10	13
	44 yrs. and younger	10	13
Minimally Structured (C)	45 yrs. and older	6	4
	44 yrs. and younger	4	11
Control Condition (D)	45 yrs. and older	1	10
	44 yrs. and younger	5	4

Condition (A): Older vs. Younger, $\chi^2 = 5.99$, $df = 1$, $p < .02$
Condition (B): Older vs. Younger, $\chi^2 = 0$, $df = 1$, $p =$ n.s.
Condition (C): Older vs. Younger, $\chi^2 = 2.75$, $df = 1$, $p =$ n.s.
Condition (D): Older vs. Younger, $\chi^2 = 4.40$, $df = 1$, $p < .05$

Over-all Comparison, all conditions: $\chi^2 = 14.68$, $df = 7$, $p < .05$

TABLE 7.6

PROGRAM DISPOSITION OF MALE PATIENTS, DICHOTOMIZED
BY LENGTH OF ILLNESS

	Length of Illness	Returned to Community	Returned to Ward
Maximally Structured (A)	12 yrs. or more	13	8
	11 yrs. or less	7	16
Partially Structured (B)	12 yrs. or more	11	12
	11 yrs. or less	9	14
Minimally Structured (C)	12 yrs. or more	5	5
	11 yrs. or less	5	10
Control Condition (D)	12 yrs. or more	0	9
	11 yrs. or less	6	5

Over-all Comparison, all conditions: $\chi^2 = 12.95$, $df = 7$, $p < .08$

TABLE 7.7
PROGRAM DISPOSITION OF FEMALE PATIENTS

	Age Subgroups*			Length of Illness Subgroups*	
	Returned to Community	Returned to Ward	Length of Illness	Returned to Community	Returned to Ward
Maximally Structured (E)					
45 yrs. and older	14	9	12 yrs. or more	11	10
44 yrs. and younger	7	12	11 yrs. or less	10	11
Partially Structured (F)					
45 yrs. and older	14	5	12 yrs. or more	13	7
44 yrs. and younger	11	8	11 yrs. or less	12	6
Minimally Structured (G)					
45 yrs. and older	10	7	12 yrs. or more	9	7
44 yrs. and younger	7	7	11 yrs. or less	8	7
Control Condition (H)					
45 yrs. and older	6	11	12 yrs. or more	5	11
44 yrs. and younger	7	8	11 yrs. or less	8	8

* Over-all comparison, all conditions: χ^2 not significant.

137

Disposition Status. Data on disposition rates (see Table 7.4) reveal that the three experimental treatment groups tend to exceed the control group in percentage of patients released from the hospital. However, these differences are not significant. Although females tend to have higher release rates than males, this difference also does not reach significance.

The results indicate that when the reactivity level variable is not considered, no program differences emerge. The effect of the reactivity level variables on disposition among males in the different treatment conditions is summarized in Tables 7.5 and 7.6.

Table 7.5 shows that age has a mediating effect on disposition in the Maximally Structured and Control conditions. In the Maximally Structured condition more older patients are returned to the community, whereas in the Control condition older patients tend to remain in the hospital. These observations are corroborated when the effect of age is evaluated statistically for each of the treatment conditions. Marginal totals were used as a basis for determining the theoretical frequencies, a procedure described by Castellan (1965).

When disposition data for male patients in the four treatment conditions are dichotomized according to length of illness, the *chi* square approaches significance at the .08 level (see Table 7.6). An inspection of the contingency table reveals a trend similar to that observed when age is used as the index of reactivity level: a greater proportion of patients with longer duration of illness in the Maximally Structured condition are returned to the community, but similar patients in the Control condition tend to remain in the hospital. For male patients, then, degree of program structure and level of patient reactivity are factors of considerable importance in determining treatment outcome.

For female patients with low reactivity level, socio-environmental treatment tends to be more effective than the Control condition (see Table 7.7). Although trends similar to those found for male patients are noted, findings for female patients do not approach statistical significance.

It has been demonstrated that among the low reactivity level patients, the Control condition was generally of little benefit in effecting a return to the community. The fact that the Control condition consisted of the treatment services prevalent throughout the hospital suggests that these services are ineffectual with low reactivity level patients. Table 7.8 presents hospital-wide release rates[6] (excluding those in the Rehabilitation Center), categorized according to length of current hospitalization. These data substantiate the conclusion that the potential for release of the more chronic patient is far greater from socio-environmental treatment than from the traditional hospital program.

TABLE 7.8

RELEASE FIGURES FOR THE HOSPITAL POPULATION,* CATEGORIZED
ACCORDING TO LENGTH OF HOSPITALIZATION

Hospitalized Less than	Total Hospital Population	Number Released from Hospital	Percentage of Total Released
1 year	756	402	48
1 to 4 years	1213	266	32
5 to 9 years	1002	84	10 ⎫
10 to 19 years	1632	65	8 ⎬ 20
20 or more years	1935	18	2 ⎭
	6538	835	

* The figures are based on the population resident in the hospital as of January 1, 1960. This date was selected because it was the midpoint of this project. The release figures represent the number of patients released during the period from January 1, 1960, through December 31, 1960.

❀ Comparison of the Two Measures of Clinical Outcome

As expected, the two measures of clinical outcome utilized in this investigation—posttreatment psychiatric status and release rate—are highly related. The over-all correlation is .77 ($N = 190$) for male

[6] Hospital release rates are taken from reports to the central office which categorize these data in terms of patients' length of current hospitalization. Since data were readily available in this form, length of current hospitalization was used as the index of chronicity. Although length of current hospitalization and length of illness are not identical indices of chronicity, there is some evidence that these two variables are highly related. See footnote 3 in Chapter Four.

and female patients in the socio-environmental programs. The magnitude of this correlation suggests that the findings with both measures should be consistent. For female patients differences in age or in degree of program structure have no significant effect on either posttreatment psychiatric status or release rate.

Although both of these variables affect clinical outcome for males, there is a major discrepancy between findings on the two measures. Older males make better posttreatment psychiatric status scores than younger males, regardless of the degree of structure in the treatment program. Release rates, however, are selectively affected by both age and degree of treatment structure—older patients in the Maximally Structured condition show the higher release rates. It should be noted that no PSS ratings were obtained for patients in the Control condition, although release data were available for these patients. The absence of PSS data for the Control condition restricted the sampling for the PSS instrument and may have reduced the sensitivity of this measure to the effects of the experimental variables. Since the Control condition was the least effective of the four treatment conditions in gaining release for older patients, the PSS ratings for this treatment condition would probably also have been poorer than all other treatment conditions. Accordingly, the absence of such PSS data for the Control condition may have reduced the possibility for the emergence of a significant interaction between degree of program structure and either of the two indices of reactivity level.

When the individual programs are examined, however, a difference attributable to reactivity level does emerge: the Maximally Structured condition is more effective with patients having a long- rather than short-term illness $(t = 2.17, p < .05$; see Table 7.3). This is not the case for the other two programs. Thus, fairly consistent results are obtained with the two measures of clinical outcome, except where sampling affected the sensitivity of the PSS measure.

❀ An Attempt at Integration of Findings Reported in the Literature

The findings indicate that socio-environmental therapy apparently is of least benefit to high reactivity level male patients and most advantageous for low reactivity level males. Furthermore, the Maximally Structured program is the most effective type of socio-environmental treatment for low reactivity patients. Are these two variables, which have such an important bearing on clinical outcome in the current study, of general significance, and can they be utilized to clarify divergent findings reported in other studies? Results of other investigations of socio-environmental treatment with male patients will be summarized and compared to results from the present study to determine whether similarities and differences in findings can be explained by reactivity level and degree of program structure. Since classification by level of patient reactivity[7] and degree of program structure[8] are unique to the current study, the reader is cautioned that inferences about these two variables in other studies must be drawn from reported descriptions of patient characteristics and treatment programs.

Fairweather (1964) grouped psychotic patients three ways: those with up to two years of hospitalization, those with two to four years, and those with four or more years. His program consisted of autonomous, patient-led task groups, and it was clearly specified that patients would have a role in making decisions relevant to the daily life and future plans of all members of the task groups. Although this study reported no comparisons between experimental and control groups at termination of treatment, patients who completed the small group program tended to show significantly less recidivism and more favorable community adjustment. The positive results of this program were due primarily to the response of the acute psychotics; the small group program apparently had no appreciable effect on the community adjustment of the chronic psychotics.

The absence of concerted staff pressure and direction seems to result in failure to alter the adjustment level of the chronic patient. Chronic patients apparently require a higher degree of structure for interaction than that provided by Fairweather's program. Similar results were obtained in the current study with high and low reactivity

---

[7] In this study, male chronic patients were categorized so that low reactivity level included those who were 45 years or older, or had an illness duration of 12 or more years. High reactivity level included those who were 44 years or younger, or had an illness duration of up to 11 years.

[8] "Degree of program structure" refers to the experimental manipulation of the demand for interaction through systematic variations in assigned group tasks, specified role functions, and sustained staff demands.

level chronic patients in the Minimally Structured condition, where there was a modicum of staff direction and control.

Pace (1957) and Spohn (1963) did not divide their chronic patients into subgroups. From the description of their patient populations it can be inferred that both high and low reactive chronic patients were included in their study samples. It can also be assumed that the programs developed by these investigators are comparable to the Partially Structured condition in the current study: programmed group activity, elements of a structured social milieu, and the absence of such intensifying group experiences as patient government and group therapy. The results reported by Pace and Spohn indicate that, regardless of reactivity level, partially structured programs were no more successful than control conditions in effecting the release of chronic patients.

Regarding the effects of these programs on psychiatric condition, Pace noted that his experimental treatment was ineffective in correcting psychopathology; Spohn found that socio-environmental therapy even produced an increase in psychopathology for some patients. Their conclusions concur with those of the present investigation, which also showed that when reactivity level was not considered, the Partially Structured condition (or any type of socio-environmental therapy) had negligible value in reducing psychopathology and in increasing release rates. This study also corroborates Spohn's finding that socio-environmental therapy can produce an increase in psychopathology; however, this effect was observed only among high reactive chronic patients.

The socio-environmental treatment program in Lee's study (1961–1964) incorporated elements of a structured milieu and a group activity program but included no experiences that would intensify group interaction. This type of treatment may also be viewed as partially structured. Lee reported that more long-term chronic patients tended to be released from the experimental program than from the control condition (*chi* square approached significance at the .09 level). The impact of even a partially structured socio-environmental treatment program on low reactivity level patients becomes manifest in Lee's study. A similar trend was found in the current investigation.

Fairweather *et al.* (1960) investigated the effects of a group living program on both a short-term psychotic group (less than one year of previous hospitalization) and a long-term psychotic group (more than one year of previous hospitalization). In addition to containing elements which might be said to characterize partially structured treatment, such as patient-centered work activity and shared responsibility for group living situations, his program also included group therapy. The short-term psychotics in socio-environmental treatment manifested greater adaptive changes on behavioral and other measures of adjustment than their counterparts in the control group. However, long-term psychotics showed the greatest degree of change. Although much of this reported change was in the direction of increased psychopathology, positive effects were also noted. In fact, at completion of treatment, the long-term psychotics in the experimental program showed the highest level ward behavior.

Ellsworth (1963) described his program as "a situation in which both the patient and the aide experienced maximum structure." The aide interacted closely with the patient and tried to make him aware of behavior expected in specific situations, of others' reactions, and of the consequences of his actions. Treatment derived from the feedback framework, the attendant attempting to modify the patient's behavior progressively so that he could move from a Closed to an Open and ultimately to an Exit ward. Although the elements of Ellsworth's socio-environmental treatment differed from those of the current study, the purpose and design of both programs may be seen as an effort to provide a maximum degree of structure for the reshaping of interpersonal behavior.

Ellsworth's study population included three groups: Acutes (up to two years of hospitalization during the preceding five years), Semichronics (two to five years of hospitalization during the preceding five years), and Chronics (continuously hospitalized during the preceding five years). Among the Acute group, he found that patients in his experimental program demonstrated better posttreatment behavioral adjustment than patients in the control condition but did not show higher release rates. In both the Semichronic and Chronic patient groups, those in the experimental program surpassed their control group counterparts in posttreatment adjustment and release rates.

Ellsworth's findings for his Acute group cannot be confirmed by results from the current investigation, which included no acute patients. The findings for Ellsworth's Semichronic patients differ from those noted for high reactive patients in this study: patients in the Maximally Structured program did *not* surpass those in the Control condition in release rates. This divergence in findings cannot be reconciled from present data. However, the two studies differ essentially in the type of patients involved and the time spent in treatment. Very few patients in this study would fit into Ellsworth's Semichronic category. The great majority of high reactive patients in the current study had been hospitalized for considerably longer than five years, whereas Ellsworth's Semichronic group was characterized by only two to five years of hospitalization during the preceding five years.

As for differences in duration of treatment, Ellsworth computed release rates over a 30-month period of treatment in contrast to the 12-month treatment period of the current study. In fact, in the present investigation most of the treatment failures among the high reactive chronic patients had been designated program failures and returned to their wards before they had completed six months of treatment.

Although Ellsworth's Semichronic group was not really comparable to the high reactive group in the current study, his Chronic group, hospitalized for an average of 12.2 years, can be compared directly to the low reactive group. Ellsworth's findings for his Chronic group agree essentially with those noted for low reactivity level patients in the present study. In both studies, the maximally structured type of socio-environmental treatment was most effective with these patients.

✿ Summary

1. Comparison of the three socio-environmental treatment programs on psychiatric status of male patients reveals that differences in treatment structure produce no differences in posttreatment status.

2. When reactivity level is considered, all socio-environmental programs effect better posttreatment psychiatric status in older male patients and those with long illness duration; the Maximally Structured condition effects the highest level psychiatric status with patients who have experienced long duration of illness.

3. Although there are no differences among release rates of the experimental and control conditions, the Maximally Structured condition is most effective, and the Control condition least effective, in achieving the release of older male patients and those with longer duration of illness.

4. With respect to female patients, neither degree of structure in the socio-environmental treatment nor reactivity level influences posttreatment psychiatric status or release rate. Furthermore, in comparison with a control condition, socio-environmental therapy does not produce higher release rates, even when reactivity level is considered.

Chapter VIII

The Effect of Modified
Social Interaction on
Psychiatric Adjustment

The relationship between psychopathology and disrupted social functioning has long been recognized. Freud (1948) postulated that withdrawal of affect from persons in the environment was a primary factor in psychosis. Sullivan (1947) and Cameron (1947) formulated more explicit views of schizophrenia as a disorder of human relationships. Sullivan stressed alienation from others as the central mechanism in the schizophrenic's disordered thinking and communication. Cameron felt that loss of the social foundations of the role-taking ability was

146

fundamental to the schizophrenic process. Faris (1944) postulated a causal relationship between early social isolation and the development of schizophrenic symptoms. He considered the disorganization of social systems within a geographic area to be as deleterious as intrapsychic factors in precipitating the isolation which might end in schizophrenia.

This investigation is not founded on the premise that the etiology of schizophrenia lies in interpersonal isolation. However, its underlying rationale does relate psychopathology to disrupted social functioning. The central hypothesis of this study states that increased social interaction is associated with good psychiatric status. Socio-environmental therapy has been shown to produce progressive increments in social behavior (see Chapter Five above). Therefore, investigation should be made to determine if, at completion of socio-environmental treatment, gain in social behavior is associated with good psychiatric adjustment, and decline with poor psychiatric adjustment.

✿ Description of Measures

The Verbal Interaction Scale (VIS) and the Spontaneous Social Behavior Scale (SSBS) were used to determine variations in social behavior during the treatment period.[1] This investigation did not involve a predetermined time in treatment. Duration of treatment varied according to individual needs as clinically determined by the staff. Change scores for each patient (*beta* coefficients—see Chapter Five) on each measure were derived by computing the regression between months in treatment and monthly interaction scores for the entire treatment period.

The criterion measure of psychiatric adjustment was the psychiatric status rating made at completion of treatment. The unit administrators made these ratings, using the Psychiatric Status Scale (PSS— see Chapter Seven) to estimate the degree of symptomatology which characterized a particular patient.

[1] The correlation between the VIS and SSBS improvement scores is $+ .36$ ($n = 58$, $p < .01$) for the two male groups (experimental Groups *A* and *B*) for whom both measures were available. Although an expected communality derives from the common focus on improvement in social behavior, the correlation is low enough to suggest that the two scales do not measure the same aspects of change in social behavior.

❀ Procedure

As has been shown, degree of structure in the treatment program and reactivity level related significantly to improvement in social behavior among male patients. The greatest social improvement was reported for low reactivity male patients in the Maximally Structured program. For this reason, reactivity level will be considered as the variable mediating the relationship between change in social behavior and psychiatric adjustment. Furthermore, since this general relationship is the focal point of the present inquiry, degree of program structure will be disregarded in this context; gainers and nongainers will be studied, regardless of the degree of program structure they experienced.

The product-moment coefficient of correlation and analysis of variance[2] were utilized to investigate the relationship between improvement in social behavior and posttreatment psychiatric status for patients differing in reactivity level. Analyses of variance were performed by dichotomizing the experimental population first into improvers and nonimprovers in social behavior and then into high and low reactivity level subgroups. Psychiatric status ratings were then compared.

Since the effect of varying degrees of program structure was not the basic concern of this study, data on patients in the Maximally and Partially Structured conditions were combined.[3] For male patients, data were available on both the VIS and the SSBS; for female

[2] Since the correlation coefficient takes into account all points on both distributions, it is the most efficient measure of the extent to which change in social behavior is associated with psychiatric status. However, this type of analysis in itself is not sufficient for the purposes of this study because it does not permit an investigation of the effect of the interaction of two experimental variables on the dependent variable (i.e., the effect of improvment in social behavior and reactivity level on psychiatric status). Such an investigation is possible with an analysis of variance, but power efficiency is lost in this type of analysis because it does not utilize individual rankings on social behavior. Therefore, both types of analyses were utilized in order to make full use of the available data.

[3] Data on the patients in the Minimally Structured condition were not included because no information on either measure was available for female patients, and information on only one measure (SSBS) was available for male patients.

Table 8.1

CORRELATIONS BETWEEN CHANGE IN VERBAL INTERACTION AND PSYCHIATRIC ADJUSTMENT EARLY IN TREATMENT*

| | Over-all | | Low Reactivity Level | | | | High Reactivity Level | | | |
| | | | Longer Illness Duration | | Older | | Shorter Illness Duration | | Younger | |
	r	n	r	n	r	n	r	n	r	n
Males (Groups *A* and *B*)	.02	(43)	.13	(24)	.01	(25)	−.06	(19)	.04	(18)
Females (Groups *E* and *F*)	−.08	(50)	.11	(23)	−.18	(30)	−.32	(27)	.05	(20)

* Based on a restricted sample of cases.

Table 8.2

CORRELATIONS BETWEEN CHANGE IN VERBAL INTERACTION AND PSYCHIATRIC ADJUSTMENT AT COMPLETION OF TREATMENT

| | Over-all | | Low Reactivity Level | | | | High Reactivity Level | | | |
| | | | Longer Illness Duration | | Older | | Shorter Illness Duration | | Younger | |
	r	n	r	n	r	n	r	n	r	n
Males (Groups *A* and *B*)	.43*	(52)	.28	(29)	.18	(28)	.61*	(23)	.69*	(24)
Females (Groups *E* and *F*)	.00	(53)	.17	(25)	−.09	(32)	−.11	(28)	−.13	(21)

* $p < .01$.

149

patients, data were available only on the VIS. Improvement in verbal interaction is studied separately for males and females.

❀ Results

Verbal Interaction and Psychiatric Adjustment. It can be seen from Table 8.1 that in the restricted sample of male patients[4] there is almost no relationship between psychiatric status early in treatment and change in verbal interaction over the full course of treatment. Also, no relationship is found when the restricted sample is dichotomized on reactivity level. However, a significant relationship emerges between modification in verbal interaction and psychiatric adjustment at completion of treatment (see Table 8.2). Furthermore, when the change scores are categorized according to reactivity level, it is apparent that this relationship is characteristic of the high reactivity level patients, that is, the younger patients and those with the shorter duration of illness.

TABLE 8.3

MEAN POSTPSYCHIATRIC STATUS SCORES* OF MALE PATIENTS, DICHOTOMIZED BY CHANGE IN VERBAL INTERACTION AND REACTIVITY LEVEL

| | Age as an Index of Reactivity Level | | Length of Illness as an Index of Reactivity Level | |
	Older	Younger	Longer	Shorter
Increased Verbal Interaction	7.67	6.27	6.54	7.21
Decreased Verbal Interaction	7.62	11.67	8.19	10.67

F (age) $(A) = 1.78$, $df = 1$, $p = $ n.s.　　　F (length of illness) $(L) = 2.12$,
F (change) $(C) = 7.25$, $df = 1$, $p < .01$　　$df = 1$, $p = $ n.s.
F $(A \times C) = 7.55$, $df = 1$, $p < .01$　　　F (change) $(C) = 5.94$, $df = 1$,
　　　　　　　　　　　　　　　　　　　　　　$p < .05$
　　　　　　　　　　　　　　　　　　　　　　F $(L \times C) = .88$, $df = 1$, $p = $ n.s.

* The lower the mean score, the better the psychiatric status.

　　[4] Chapter Seven discusses why PSS data early in treatment are available only for a restricted sample of patients.

Table 8.3 presents the mean posttreatment psychiatric status scores of male patients, dichotomized by reactivity level (age and length of illness) and type of change in verbal interaction. The *F* tests indicate a significant interaction between reactivity level and change in verbal behavior when age is used as the index of reactivity level. The poorest psychiatric status is clearly found among younger patients who declined in verbal interaction. There is little difference between the posttreatment psychiatric status mean scores of older patients, regardless of improvement or decline in verbal interaction.

Although the interaction between improvement and reactivity level is not significant when length of illness is used as the measure of reactivity level, the pattern of results is similar to that observed when age is the moderator variable (see Table 8.3). In both instances the greatest mean difference in psychiatric status occurs among high reactivity level patients. The high reactivity level patients who show a decrease in verbal interaction have the poorest psychiatric status. The analysis of variance therefore confirms the findings of the correlational analysis: posttreatment psychiatric status is related to change in verbal interaction, and this relationship is most pronounced for high reactivity level patients.

A comparable analysis of variance for female patients reveals no relationship between change in verbal interaction and posttreatment psychiatric status. Reactivity level also fails to yield significant findings when used as a moderator variable. For female patients there is no significant relationship between change in verbal interaction and psychiatric status, either early in treatment or at completion of treatment (see Tables 8.1 and 8.2). Negligible correlations are found for the over-all relationship, as well as for data categorized according to reactivity level. The results of the correlational analysis agree with those obtained from the analysis of variance: no differences in mean posttreatment psychiatric status scores are attributable to reactivity level, change in verbal behavior, or to the interaction of these two variables.

Spontaneous Social Behavior and Psychiatric Adjustment. An analysis of variance on post-treatment psychiatric status ratings of male patients (Conditions *A* and *B*), dichotomized by reactivity level and change in spontaneous social behavior, reveals no significant findings. There is a tendency for low reactivity level patients with increased spontaneous social behavior to have the best posttreatment psychiatric status scores. A correlational analysis of this trend (see Tables 8.4 and 8.5) indicates no relationship between change in spontaneous social behavior and psychiatric status early in treatment. However, a relationship between change in spontaneous social behavior and posttreatment psychiatric status does emerge. It is primarily the low reactivity level patients (older patients and those with longer illness duration) whose posttreatment psychiatric status is related to degree of change in spontaneous social behavior. This relationship is not significant for high reactivity level patients.

❀ The Influence of Reactivity Level

Degree of psychopathology displayed at completion of treatment is clearly related to change in verbal interaction throughout treatment. However, this relationship is mediated by the reactivity level of patients. It is the high reactivity level patients among whom this relationship is most pronounced, especially with respect to age: younger patients who improved in verbal interaction showed good posttreatment psychiatric status while those who declined in verbal interaction received poor posttreatment ratings.

Comparable findings are not noted for low reactivity level patients. An examination of verbal interaction change scores indicates the greatest degree of both improvement and decline among the younger patients.[5] Those who improved in verbal interaction had a mean score of 57.53, and those who declined a score of 38.55. Among the older patients the comparable scores were 53.17 and 42.31 respectively. To determine whether younger patients showed significantly more extreme change scores than older patients, the two age groups were compared on the magnitude of departure of their verbal interaction change scores (regardless of direction) from a gain score of zero.[6] The mean deviations from a gain score of zero are 18.98 ($\sigma = 10.85$) for the younger patients and 10.86 ($\sigma = 6.25$) for the

---

[5] In investigating improvement scores, age was used as the primary index of reactivity level because of the more decisive findings with this variable.

[6] In this analysis, a T score of 50 represented a gain score of zero.

TABLE 8.4

CORRELATIONS BETWEEN CHANGE IN SPONTANEOUS SOCIAL BEHAVIOR AND PSYCHIATRIC ADJUSTMENT EARLY IN TREATMENT*

| | Over-all | | Low Reactivity Level | | | | High Reactivity Level | | | |
| | | | Longer Illness Duration | | Older | | Shorter Illness Duration | | Younger | |
	r	n	r	n	r	n	r	n	r	n
Males (Groups *A* and *B*)	−.01	(44)	−.09	(24)	−.09	(26)	.13	(20)	.09	(18)

* Based on a restricted sample of cases.

TABLE 8.5

CORRELATIONS BETWEEN CHANGE IN SPONTANEOUS SOCIAL BEHAVIOR AND PSYCHIATRIC ADJUSTMENT AT COMPLETION OF TREATMENT

| | Over-all | | Low Reactivity Level | | | | High Reactivity Level | | | |
| | | | Longer Illness Duration | | Older | | Shorter Illness Duration | | Younger | |
	r	n	r	n	r	n	r	n	r	n
Males (Groups *A* and *B*)	.31*	(49)	.47**	(28)	.48**	(28)	.12	(21)	.04	(21)

* $p < .05$.
** $p < .01$.

older patients. The younger patients show significantly greater variance than the older patients ($F = 2.46$, $df = 23$ and 27, $p < .05$).

The more exaggerated responses of younger patients to social treatment are assumed to derive from their greater volatility and sensitivity to interpersonal events. The restricted range of responsiveness of older patients is attributable to their more subdued reactions and might have been expected on the basis of their low reactivity level. Such restricted responsiveness tends to preclude accurate discrimination and measurement of behavior change, and to obscure any relationship between change in verbal interaction and psychiatric status.

The high degree of structure under which verbal interaction was measured also imposed more restrictions on social responsiveness among older than among younger patients. Verbal interaction was measured in scheduled activity sessions, during which the group leader directed discussions and attempted to involve the more withdrawn patients. The intensity of the response to interpersonal stimulation (approach or avoidance) among younger patients often transcended the group leader's control. The more subdued older patients tended to be more influenced by the leader's directions, making it difficult to ascertain which of them were truly improving (by becoming more socially inner-directed) and which of them were being directed entirely by the structure of the situation.

A measurement situation relying more heavily on spontaneous social behavior should result in a greater range of interaction, and more accurate discrimination of social improvement among older patients. Spontaneous social interaction could be measured at the monthly socials. Ratings on the SSBS were made during intervals when there were no structured activities and when patients could either engage in the social behavior of their choice or withdraw into isolated behavior. The type of behavior which represented the highest level of interaction during these intervals was scored (see Chapter Five). There is clearly a positive relationship between improvement in spontaneous social behavior and posttreatment psychiatric condition for low reactivity level patients.

The significant relationship between change in spontaneous social behavior and posttreatment psychiatric status noted for low reactivity level patients does not apply to high reactivity level patients. In this instance, the failure to obtain results with high reactivity patients is apparently attributable to the type of behavior measured. The SSBS focused more often on motor activity than on social behavior among high reactivity patients. Indeed, younger patients were rated significantly more frequently for dancing than older patients. It may be that the high scores for younger patients are often more related to activity level and sexual interest than to adaptive social behavior. Hyperactivity and a loosening of controls, concomitants of disturbed psychiatric condition particularly evident in high reactivity patients, can result in spuriously high scores on the SSBS. Since low reactivity level patients are generally less active, there is little possibility that hyperactivity would obscure actual improvement in spontaneous social interaction among these patients.

It is evident that reactivity level may selectively influence different types of social behavior in ways that obscure the relationship between change in social behavior and posttreatment psychiatric status. Future investigations which attempt to modify psychopathology through changes in social behavior must take into account the influence of the patient's reactivity level on his social behavior.

❄ Summary

There was a positive relationship between change in social behavior and psychiatric status at completion of treatment for male patients. This relationship was shown to be significantly influenced by reactivity level.

1. The significant relationship between change in verbal interaction and psychiatric status was primarily attributable to high reactivity level patients—the younger patients and those with the shorter duration of illness.

2. The significant relationship between change in spontaneous social behavior and psychiatric status was due mainly to the responses of low reactivity level patients—the older patients and those with the longer duration of illness.

3. These differential findings for high and low reactivity level

patients were discussed in their relation to the requirements of the measurement situation.

For female patients, there was no relationsship between change in verbal interaction (the only measure on which data were available for females) and posttreatment psychiatric status.

Chapter IX

A Preliminary Integration
of Findings

The chronic schizophrenic has been described as highly withdrawn. However, there is evidence to indicate that he is responsive to social forces. Numerous techniques have reportedly been successful in improving the chronic schizophrenic's level of social participation: reinforcement of social behavior (Peters and Jenkins, 1954; Ayllon and Haughton, 1962; Spohn and Wolk, 1963; Hingtgen and Trost, 1964), small group discussions including group therapy (Bierer, 1942; Polan and Spark, 1950; Semon and Goldsteen, 1957), group life experiences (Fairweather et al., 1960; Fairweather, 1964), ward- or hospital-wide humanistic social settings (Wilmer, 1958; Wing and Brown, 1961), structured ward procedures to maximize environmental and interpersonal interest (Miller and Clancy, 1952; Scher, 1958), and "total push" activity programs (Myerson, 1939; Galioni, Adams, and Tallman, 1953; Greenblatt, York, and Brown, 1955; Schnore, 1961).

Although the social functioning of the chronic psychotic can be enhanced by a variety of methods, it is difficult to evaluate the significance of changes. In many instances, such changes bear little or no relevance to the kinds of behavior required in the community, for example conditioning patients to use tokens cooperatively to gain entrance to the dining room (Ayllon and Haughton, 1962). Unless such conditioned behavior can be shown to generalize to other acts of cooperation, this form of response has little utility either within the hospital or in the extramural community. In other instances the magnitude of change in social behavior is not great enough to effect an appreciable difference in the social life of the individual. Appelby (1963) reported that, although ward treatment programs increased social participation, patients nevertheless continued to spend 80 per cent of their nontreatment time in nonsocial pursuits.

Another problem to be considered in this context is whether increased social behavior actually reflects socialization. Although various studies report change in social behavior as a consequence of socio-environmental treatment, these studies do not indicate whether such change is progressive throughout treatment or whether it occurs early in treatment and then levels off and declines. An initial improvement may merely reflect the patient's response to situational forces. If this interpretation is valid, there is little reason to expect the heightened level of social interaction to be maintained outside of treatment for any length of time. In fact, it is not unusual for patients to regress to a pretreatment level of social behavior after completion of treatment (Kamman et al., 1954). Such regression supports the notion that much reported improvement represents only a temporary response to situational stimuli and not a pervasive improvement in social behavior.

❊ The Meaning of Increased Social Behavior

Secord and Bachman's theory of personality stability and change (1961) is particularly relevant to the formulation of criteria of meaningful change in social behavior. According to these authors, change in behavior is a consequence of a person's striving for congruence among his self-concept, behavior he perceives to be relevant to his self-concept, and behavior of significant "others" with whom he interacts. Change in one or more of these components, it is hypothesized, creates incongruities among the components. This disharmony must be resolved through modification of the remaining component(s). A change in an individual's social behavior must be predicated upon his perception of change in the behavior of others or an alteration of his own self-concept. Modification of the psychotic's social behavior thus involves manipulation either of his self-concept or of the behavior of others—and the expectations and demands implied by this behavior. Socialization may be viewed as adaptation to a succession of varying patterns of demands and expectations by others over an extended period of time. The repeated introduction of incongruent elements requires continual resolution. In this process, the behavior of others compels a constant reorganization of previously established behavior patterns and self-conceptions. Such reorganization brings behavior into accord with social reality.

With respect to socio-environmental treatment of the psychotic, this process implies progressive change in social behavior. Each patient's response to the treatment program creates imbalances to which other patients react; these reactions produce further imbalances. Progressive change can also be expected on the basis of the increased demands made by the treatment programs and the agents who administer them. Change effected by the resolution of incongruent elements should be quite generalized. The patient in socio-environmental treatment exists in a highly interdependent field. If his social behavior is altered in one situation, an incongruity may be created with respect to another situation. Changes in social behavior also have implication for modification of the self-concept. These modifications may in turn mediate changes in a variety of social situations.

In terms of incongruity theory, meaningful change in social behavior should be progressive and trans-situational. A consequence of such meaningful behavioral change should be positive psychiatric adjustment. Conceivably, any positive change in self-concept which derives from enhanced social behavior should be accompanied by improvement in psychiatric status, to the extent that psychiatric symptoms are related to aberrations in the self-concept. Thus, the results of the present study may be evaluated not only in terms of the two criteria of meaningful change in social behavior—progressive increments in, and generalization of, social behavior—but also in terms of the psychiatric consequences of such enhanced socialization—improved psychiatric status and release from the hospital.

❀ The Course of Improvement in Social Behavior

The immediate discussion will be limited to findings for male patients; findings for female patients will be discussed in the section dealing with sex differences.

A pattern of progressive increments in social behavior has been postulated as an important criterion of meaningful change in social behavior. The three socio-environmental programs utilized in this study may be evaluated in terms of their effectiveness in generating such increments. Spontaneous social behavior is the only area of social functioning for which data are available on progressive improvement for all three experimental conditions. When time in treatment is held constant, the sequence analysis for a seven-month period indicates that only in the Maximally Structured condition do male patients evidence progressive improvement—a significant linear trend—in spontaneous social behavior. The Partially Structured condition generates early gain in spontaneous social behavior, followed by a decline after the fifth month to the initial level. The Minimally Structured condition has relatively little effect on spontaneous social behavior. The Partially Structured socio-environmental program apparently has greater initial impact than the Minimally Structured program, but only the Maximally Structured condition results in sustained improvement.

Such increments were also examined in the area of verbal interaction. However, data on this measure were available only for the Maximally and Partially Structured programs. When time in treatment is held constant, the sequence analysis for the six-month period shows no difference in verbal interaction between the two conditions. With respect to performance activities, however, the Maximally Structured program generates progressive improvement whereas gains in the Partially Structured program show a curvilinear pattern. In summary, findings indicate that only the Maximally Structured condition consistently generates progressive increments in spontaneous social behavior and verbal interaction.

✿ Generalization of Social Behavior

Generalization of social behavior, the second criterion of meaningful behavioral change, is also influenced by degree of program structure. At completion of treatment, patients in the Maximally and Partially Structured programs attain higher global social behavior ratings than do patients in the Minimally Structured condition. But because the global social behavior measure involved ratings of behavior which occurred both within and outside the programmed activities, it does not completely reflect generalization of social behavior.

A more adequate measure of generalization of social behavior among male patients in the three programs is their ability to identify photographs of females in the Minimally Structured condition. The male experimental patients had no programmed contact with females in the Minimally Structured condition. Learning their names involved initiative and social interaction outside the programmed activities. Male patients could choose to join these females for meals, visit them at their residence, socialize with them during free evening hours, or attend social events in the community with them. Consequently, if a treatment program resulted in increased ability to identify females in the Minimally Structured program, generalization of social behavior could be inferred. At completion of treatment only males in the Maximally Structured program show an increased awareness of these females. Male patients in the Partially and Minimally Structured conditions do not improve in their ability to identify the females.

Another suitable index of generalization is the degree of spontaneous social behavior shown by patients at the monthly party at which they could either interact or withdraw. It is assumed that social behavior generated within the programmed activities generalizes to the relatively unstructured situation provided by the party. Findings for patients in the Maximally Structured condition support this assumption: this program yields the greatest number of patients who show improvement in spontaneous social behavior. In addition, by the seventh month of treatment these patients manifest a higher mean level of spontaneous social behavior than patients in the other two conditions.

In brief summary, modifications of social behavior generated by the Maximally Structured condition fulfill the two criteria of enduring change in social behavior associated with personality reorganization: progressive gains and generalization. The other two conditions fail to meet these criteria.

The failure of the Partially Structured condition to surpass the Minimally Structured condition in producing meaningful social change is inconsistent with Secord and Bachman's theory. This is surprising, since there is a much greater difference in degree of structure between the Partially and Minimally Structured programs than between the Maximally and Partially Structured conditions. The Partially Structured condition incorporates many more programmed activities than the Minimally Structured condition, but only two activities (patient government and group therapy) differentiate the Maximally and Partially Structured treatment groups. Apparently quality, rather than sheer quantity, of structured interaction is the significant factor.

A high demand for interaction seems insufficient in itself to surmount patients' resistance to behavioral change. The addition of the intensified group experiences in the Maximally Structured program reduces the magnitude of resistance and provides a sustaining influence for social behavior. The functions and responsibilities established for each individual within the patient government system may help patients organize into acceptable social roles much of the behavior learned in programmed activities. It is also possible that this system of interlocking roles and responsibilities cushions the impact of these additional demands for interaction, because such behavior is congruent with the expectancies of other patients and is sanctioned by staff authority. In the socio-environmental programs which do not include patient government, social interaction directed toward ordering the milieu may be discouraged by conflict deriving from divergent expectancies among the patients.

The group therapy situation may provide patients with an additional safety valve for internal pressures generated by demands for interaction. Problems and feelings seldom discussed in other group sessions, especially problems of a sexual nature, often are discussed in group therapy. The group therapy situation stresses discussion of feelings about social experiences; it therefore permits the therapist to focus upon patients' perceptions of these experiences and to bring patients' inner experiences and self-concepts into congruence with the overt behavior demanded by the structured programmed activities.

Of the three socio-environmental treatment programs, only the Maximally Structured condition clearly fulfills the two criteria of change. Therefore, the psychiatric adjustment of these patients at completion of treatment can be expected to surpass that of patients in the two other programs. Although patients in the Maximally Structured program are characterized by somewhat better posttreatment psychiatric status mean ratings than patients in the other two programs, the differences are not significant. Moreover, no differences in the release rates for the three socio-environmental treatment conditions are noted.

❧ Reactivity Level as a Determinant of Change in Social Behavior

Modification of social behavior of male patients is a function not only of the structure of socio-environmental treatment but also of reactivity level, that is, age and duration of illness. Among low reactivity level patients—the older patients or those with long duration of illness—the Maximally Structured program seems to effect progressive increments and generalization of social behavior. Low reactivity level patients surpass the high reactivity level patients in global social behavior scores at completion of treatment, in level of verbal interaction during the first six months of treatment, and in degree of improvement in verbal interaction throughout the full course of treatment. These patients also surpass their low reactivity level counterparts in the other two socio-environmental conditions in these three areas of social behavior. However, this systematic difference does not emerge for the spontaneous social behavior measure and in the ability to identify patients in the other experimental units. The failure of low reactivity level patients to manifest higher levels of improvement in spontaneous social behavior has been attributed to the emphasis placed on motor activity in ratings of spontaneous social behavior. Such emphasis insures poor ratings for the less physically active patients of low reactivity level.

In addition to generating significant behavioral change in low reactivity level patients, the Maximally Structured condition also contributes to their psychiatric adjustment. Low reactivity level patients in this treatment program manifest significantly better psychiatric status at completion of treatment than do high reactivity level patients. This finding applies to older patients as well as to those with a long illness duration. Patients in the Maximally Structured condition with a long duration of illness also show more positive psychiatric status than their counterparts in the other two socio-environmental programs. With respect to release rates, only in the Maximally Structured condition do low reactivity level patients surpass high reactivity level patients.

The Partially Structured condition is characterized by inconsistent findings regarding reactivity level as a determinant of behavioral change. Low reactivity level patients demonstrate better global social behavior at completion of treatment than high reactivity level patients, but this trend is not evidenced in the areas of verbal interaction or identification of patients in the other experimental units. This inconsistency suggests that the mediating effects of reactivity level on behavioral change are not nearly as powerful in the Partially Structured condition as in the Maximally Structured condition. To substantiate this conclusion, although low reactivity level patients show better psychiatric status at completion of treatment, there is no difference in release rates for low and high reactivity level patients.

In the Minimally Structured condition low reactivity level patients show better scores on the global social behavior measure at completion of treatment than do high reactivity level patients. This difference is attributable to a decline in global social behavior among high reactivity level patients and an absence of marked change on this measure among low reactivity level patients. The global social behavior ratings of these low reactivity level patients are still considerably below those of their counterparts in the two more structured treatment programs. No differences attributable to reactivity level are evidenced either in spontaneous social behavior or in ability to identify patients in the other experimental units. Reactivity level does not seem to be a major determinant of change in social behavior in the Minimally Structured condition. Findings regarding psychiatric adjustment for the reactivity level subgroups are similar to those noted for the Partially Structured condition: low reactivity level patients surpass high reactivity level patients in posttreatment psychiatric status, but there are no differences between the two subgroups in release rates.

Reactivity level clearly mediates the impact of program structure in effecting changes in social behavior and psychiatric adjustment. The relationship between change in social behavior and psychiatric status at completion of treatment has already been demonstrated (Chapter Eight): improvement and decline in social behavior are accompanied by good and poor psychiatric adjustment respectively. However, the magnitude of change in social behavior far exceeds that shown in the area of psychiatric adjustment. Reactivity level mediates change in social behavior, but such change is directly influenced by degree of program structure. Change in psychiatric adjustment becomes evident only when the interaction between reactivity level and program structure is considered. Since the treatment programs are primarily directed toward the modification of social behavior, the greatest degree of change can be expected in this area. In addition, a logical concomitant of improved social behavior is decreased psychiatric symptomatology. However, although the relationship between change in social behavior and posttreatment psychiatric adjustment is noted in general for both high and low reactivity level patients, the low reactivity patients manifest improved psychiatric adjustment and the high reactivity patients show increased symptomatology in response to socio-environmental treatment.

Low reactivity level, a concomitant of aging or long-term illness and institutionalization, is usually considered indicative of poor prognosis. Patients showing physical, emotional, and social decrements have been assumed to be intractable to the interaction demands of socio-environmental therapy. In the current study, however, low reactivity level emerges as a determinant of successful socialization and positive psychiatric adjustment among patients in the Maximally Structured treatment condition, and to some degree among those in the two less structured conditions. Low reactivity level patients in general, and those in the Maximally Structured program in particular, responded more positively than high reactivity level patients to demands for social interaction.

These findings are clarified when emotional intensity or drive level is considered as a primary component of reactivity level. The inability to regulate and control emotional impulses or drives is generally conceived as one of the fundamental disturbances of the psychotic (Bellak, 1958). This impaired capacity for dealing with such drives as anxiety is considered the major antecedent of the psychotic episode. More adequate control of behavior, it has been postulated, derives from a reduction in drive level. Psychosurgery and the ataractic drugs are commonly used means to improve behavior by preventing emotional stimuli from reaching the cortex. Aging and long-term illness have been established as factors leading to reduced physiological energy and drive level. In his review of behavioral changes accompanying old age in the chronic psychotic, Ehrentheil (1964) reported that the aging process resulted in an attenuation of impulses. He cited several instances in which such drive-level reduction was associated with marked improvement in the behavior of long-term psychotics.

Aging and long duration of illness do not remove the symptoms of the psychosis; indeed, they often produce ego deficits and the entrenchment of the psychosis. Chapter Four reviewed the impairments in ego functioning associated with two indices of reactivity level. According to Lemkau and Crocetti (1958) and Zubin (1959), the prognosis is generally poor for the older, more chronic psychotic. The current study has also demonstrated that the majority of low reactivity level patients who do not experience socio-environmental treatment remain in the hospital.

It is contended that the low reactive patient undergoes a reduction in drive level, and although his capacity for control remains unchanged his drive level rarely reaches the disruptive intensity of earlier years. He thus requires a high degree of stimulation and pressure to bring about any change in his social behavior, but his reduced drive level makes him better able to withstand external stress and to regulate his behavior in accord with the demands of the social environment. In contrast, the high reactive patient may be too laden with inner affective pressure to withstand the further drive arousal produced by a marked demand for social interaction. It is particularly difficult to shape and broaden the interaction pattern of a patient who may be struggling to maintain control of his sexual or destructive impulses. A heightened demand for social interaction may only precipitate disruption of behavior in this type of patient. The high reactivity level patient may require limited demand for interaction and sheltered, supportive situations for drive reduction and control resumption to occur.

✿ Sex Differences in Social Behavior and Psychiatric Adjustment

Data for female patients on the two criteria of meaningful change in social behavior are limited. Information on verbal interaction, which is the only measure of progressive increments in treatment, is available only for females in the Maximally and Partially Structured conditions. Over the full course of treatment (which differs for each patient) the two experimental conditions show no difference in improvement scores. When time in treatment is held constant for all patients and verbal interaction scores are analyzed for the six-month period, both treatment groups manifest progressive improvement. However, patients in the Partially Structured condition are characterized by a higher level of verbal interaction than are patients in the Maximally Structured condition. A consideration of activity format uncovers no difference between the experimental programs in the quantity of verbal interaction produced in discussion and performance activities. Apparently, for female patients, both of the more structured treatment conditions fulfill the criterion of progressive gain in interaction, but the Partially Structured condition is somewhat more effective in producing improvement.

Data relevant to generalization of social behavior are available only on the global social behavior measure. Good ratings here tend to be associated with increased program structure, but there are no significant differences among the three treatment conditions. The findings also suggest that none of the programs yields significant improvement in global social behavior at completion of treatment. Thus, although the two structured conditions do effect progressive increments in social behavior among females, there is no evidence that such improvement generalizes to situations outside programmed activities.

Neither of the two measures of psychiatric adjustment at completion of treatment—psychiatric status and release from the hospital —is associated with any differences attributable to program structure.

The influence of reactivity level as a mediator of change in social behavior and psychiatric adjustment among females can be determined by analyzing the two measures of social behavior—global social behavior and verbal interaction—and the two measures of psychiatric adjustment. These data indicate that among females reactivity level is not a determinant of social or psychiatric response to socio-environmental treatment.

It is very difficult to compare findings on male and female patients. First of all, data for females are not available in all the measures utilized in this study. In addition, the findings are undoubtedly clouded by the inability to maintain the physical segregation of females required by the experimental design. As a result there was little difference in the amount of interaction among female patients within, or across, treatment programs. A third difficulty involves a disparity in the mean IQ scores of male and female patients in this study. There is a 10-point difference on an abbreviated WAIS; the mean score for males falls within the "Average" range, while the mean score for females lies in the "Dull Normal" range.

Despite such problems, it would appear clear that at completion of treatment the determinants of successful change in social behavior and psychiatric adjustment among males—program structure and reactivity level—are not significant for females. Although the social behavior of female patients tends to improve with socio-environmental treatment, these gains are not related to degree of program structure or to reactivity level. The elements of the three treatment programs which differentially structure the demand for interaction among males apparently facilitate no change in social response among females.

Data indicating sex differences in response to the two critical variables (degree of program structure and reactivity level) in this study are confirmed by other researchers. Schooler (1963) found that females of lower level intellectual functioning, such as those in this study, did not want other patients to express negative feelings. Since a major component of the Maximally Structured condition, group therapy, encouraged the expression of feelings, this program element may have inhibited rather than facilitated improvement in the social behavior of females.

Another important sex difference emerges in the response of low reactivity level males and females to hospitalization. In Schooler's study, length of hospitalization[1] (a variable closely related to duration of illness) among male patients was related to unwillingness to socialize with others. No such relationship was found for females; despite long periods of hospitalization, they showed continued willingness to socialize.

A further sex difference among low reactivity level individuals is described by Cumming and Henry (1961): men and women differ in the personality reorganization which accompanies ego energy decline associated with aging—men become more passive and introverted; women maintain their sociability but become more self-centered and give more expression to egocentric demands.

These findings suggest that the chronic psychotic female patient is generally more socially oriented than her male counterpart. The current study revealed consistent differences between males and females in social interaction early in treatment; females manifested significantly higher level social behavior. Whether low reactivity level females would benefit from a more intensive and demanding socialization experience, or whether they require a treatment program aimed more directly at their egocentrism, remains unresolved.

Secord and Bachman (1961) note that for any form of therapy it is necessary to specify and systematize ". . . the behaviors required of the change agent for successful facilitation of modes of resolution leading to the desired changes in the self-concept and behavior of the *S* . . . [and the] techniques for blocking those modes leading to maintenance of undesirable aspects of self and behavior." The sex and reactivity level of patients must be considered in developing program elements for socio-environmental therapy. The treatment programs investigated in this study have the greatest utility for low

---

[1] In the current study, length of hospitalization and duration of illness were highly correlated ($r = .75$).

reactivity level male patients. The development of more appropriate programs for female patients must take cognizance of sex differences in social ability, in emotional response to social stimulation, and in personality reorganization accompanying decline in reactivity level.

PART THREE

CLINICAL OUTCOME AND THE PROBLEM OF PREDICTION

Chapter X

Community Tenure and
Patterns of Movement of Patients

The major clinical objective of the rehabilitation project was to return the patient to the extramural community. One approach to the evaluation of long-term treatment effects is through comparison of measures of community tenure, two of which are readmission rates and total number of months in the community during the three-year follow-up period.

Figure 10.1 shows the percentage of patients in the study sample residing in the community at each six-month interval after completion of treatment. The percentages are based on the number of patients for whom information was available at each point in time.

173

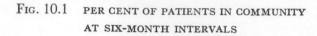

FIG. 10.1   PER CENT OF PATIENTS IN COMMUNITY
AT SIX-MONTH INTERVALS

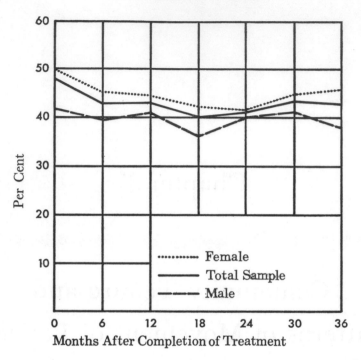

Months After Completion of Treatment

Of the 278 cases for whom disposition data were available, only 11 could not be located at one or more intervals during the 3-year follow-up period. The 13 patients who died during this period were removed from the total N at each interval after death occurred. From Figure 10.1 it is clear that the percentage of patients residing in the community is remarkably stable as time passes. The net decrease for all groups combined is only 5 per cent. Although female patients are more likely than male patients to leave the hospital on completion of treatment, there is no difference between the proportion of male and female patients in the community by the end of the first year.

Figure 10.2 shows the percentage by treatment programs of patients residing in the community. The numbers next to the legend show the sample N (successes and failures combined) at initial disposition and at 36 months. The difference represents the number of

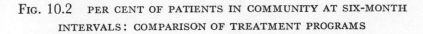

Fig. 10.2   PER CENT OF PATIENTS IN COMMUNITY AT SIX-MONTH
INTERVALS: COMPARISON OF TREATMENT PROGRAMS

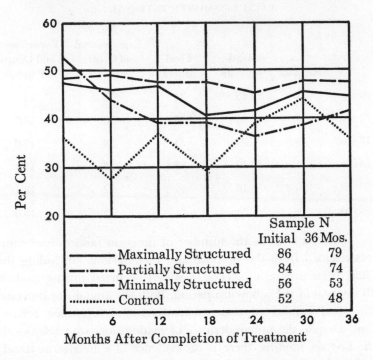

cases which could not be followed for the entire three-year period.
There are no significant differences between treatment programs in
this respect. Although the control group has proportionately fewer
people in the community at the outset, the difference between the control group and the experimental treatment groups decreases with time.
This is a result entirely of the high "latent" release rate for female
control patients. The male control group shows a net loss of 19 per
cent for the 36-month period, whereas the female control group reg-
isters a 10 per cent gain. There are no significant differences among
treatment programs at any point.[1]

[1] The baseline date for patients in the control group was set at 12
months after assignment to control status. Patients remaining in the hospital
beyond 12 months were considered equivalent to patients returned to other
wards from the Rehabilitation programs.

TABLE 10.1

NUMBER OF RELEASES AND READMISSIONS DURING
EACH SIX-MONTH INTERVAL

	Releases	Read-missions	Total Moves	No. Experimental and Control Patients	% Experimental and Control Patients
Up to 6 mo.	11	23	34	33	12.2
6 to 12 mo.	19	17	36	29	10.9
12 to 18 mo.	14	21	35	29	11.0
18 to 24 mo.	21	18	39	32	12.3
24 to 30 mo.	26	18	44	32	12.4
30 to 36 mo.	18	21	39	35	13.0

Table 10.1 shows the number of program failures and control patients released from the hospital and readmissions (including those who had been program successes) which occurred during each six-month interval of the follow-up period. Both the amount of movement and the total number of patients involved tend to remain relatively constant. Despite the preponderance of readmissions over releases during the first six months, there is no evidence of a long-term trend in favor of readmissions.

Tables 10.2 and 10.3 contain cumulative release and readmission rates for each treatment group and for the four treatment programs. As reported in Chapter Seven, there were no significant differences among treatment programs in the release rate on completion of treatment. However, there are substantial differences in the total number released over the entire study period. Differences among treatment programs are significant at the .05 level ($x^2 = 8.64, df = 3$), primarily because of the contribution of the Maximally Structured treatment program, which had an exceptionally high "latent" release rate. It can be seen in Table 10.2 that these differences are more pronounced for male units than for female units, though neither is statistically significant by itself.

Though there were no differences in the number of patients released from the rehabilitation programs, the three programs were

TABLE 10.2

CUMULATIVE RELEASE RATES

		N	No. Released From Unit	No. Released From Ward	Total Released	% Released
	A	44	20	11	31	70
Male	B	46	20	5	25	54
Units	C	25	10	4	14	56
	D	20	6	2	8	40
	E	42	21	15	36	86
Female	F	38	25	0	25	66
Units	G	31	17	5	22	71
	H	32	13	9	22	69
	Max. Struc.	86	41	26	67	78
Trmt.	Part. Struc.	84	45	5	50	60
Prog.	Min. Struc.	56	27	9	36	64
	Cont.	52	19	11	30	58

found to be differentially successful when age and length of illness—reactivity level—are taken into account. The patients who were sent back to other wards from the Maximally Structured treatment program were largely younger, less chronic patients. The results suggest that most of these patients would have been released directly from the Rehabilitation Center had they been subjected to less social pressure. Thus the high latent release rate for the Maximally Structured treatment program is essentially a correction for a negative treatment effect. The real gain is contained in the greater proportion of older, more chronic patients helped by this program. It seems clear that, had patients been assigned to treatment programs on the basis of age and chronicity, the release rates for all three rehabilitation programs would have been substantially higher, particularly for male patients.

In Table 10.3 it can be seen that there are no significant differences among treatment programs in the number of patients read-

TABLE 10.3

CUMULATIVE READMISSION RATES

		N	No. Returned After Unit Release	No. Returned After Ward Release	Total Returned	% Returned
Male Units	A	31	8	6	14	45
	B	25	7	2	9	36
	C	14	3	1	4	29
	D	8	3	2	5	62
Female Units	E	36	11	9	20	56
	F	25	12	0	12	48
	G	22	8	4	12	54
	H	22	8	3	11	50
Trmt. Prog.	Max. Struc.	67	19	15	34	51
	Part. Struc.	50	19	2	21	42
	Min. Struc.	36	11	5	16	44
	Cont.	30	11	5	16	53

mitted to the hospital during the three-year follow-up period. In general, the pattern of differences is similar to that found in the release data. Male patients tend to return less frequently than female patients (38 per cent vs. 53 per cent, and male rehabilitation patients tend to return less frequently than male controls. The frequencies are so small in this instance, however, that comparisons are virtually meaningless.

Reactivity level continues to be an important determinant of outcome for patients in the Maximally Structured treatment program. Most of the younger patients in this program were returned to other wards on completion of treatment; those who were released to the community returned more frequently than did the older, more chronic patients (Table 10.4). As in the case of the release data, reactivity level is significant only in the Maximally Structured treatment pro-

TABLE 10.4

RELATIONSHIP BETWEEN AGE AND COMMUNITY TENURE

Treatment Program		Males		Females		Total	
		Stayed Out	Returned	Stayed Out	Returned	Stayed Out	Returned
Maximum	High Age	8	2	5	0	13	2
	Low Age	2	5	3	3	5	8
Partial	High Age	6	4	3	9	9	13
	Low Age	5	3	6	3	11	6
Minimum	High Age	4	2	6	4	10	6
	Low Age	2	1	3	4	5	5
Control	High Age	0	1	4	1	4	2
	Low Age	2	2	1	3	3	5

gram ($\chi^2 = 5.10$, $p < .05$). The slight tendency toward a reversal of this relationship in the Partially Structured treatment program is due to the return of many of the female patients who helped produce the unusually high initial release rate in group F (66 per cent). However, group F also had the lowest "latent" release rate, which suggests that the release potential for this group was virtually exhausted on completion of treatment.

The high cumulative release rate for the female control group (see Group H, Table 10.2) shows that female patients in the Partially and Minimally Structured treatment programs would have been released in comparable numbers had they not been transferred to the Rehabilitation Center. For male patients, on the other hand, transfer

to the Rehabilitation Center meant a substantial increase in the probability of leaving the hospital (61 per cent for experimental patients vs.
40 per cent for controls).

Figure 10.3 contains cumulative readmission and latent release
curves for patients in the three socio-environmental treatment programs. The readmission curve rises sharply during the first three
months, then continues to rise at a somewhat reduced rate until the
27th month, where it finally begins to level off. The rate for the first
12 months is approximately 26 per cent. The latent release curve, on

FIG. 10.3   CUMULATIVE READMISSION AND "LATENT"
RELEASE CURVES

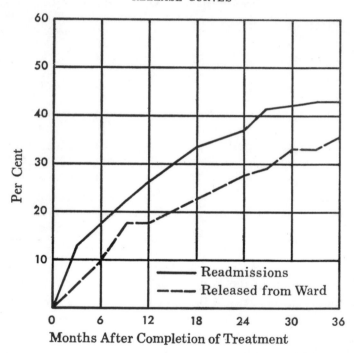

Months After Completion of Treatment

the other hand, rises less rapidly but nonetheless consistently during
the entire 3-year period. The fact that this curve is still accelerating
at 36 months is encouraging. If readmissions can be held to 45 per
cent or less while the latent release rate continues to increase, the net
gain in time spent in the community would be substantial.

Release and readmission statistics are, at best, imperfect criteria of treatment outcome. If residence in the community is the prime objective, then measures of community tenure would appear more appropriate. One problem with such measures when applied to a chronic population, however, is that they yield badly skewed distributions and thus are unsuitable for parametric analysis. In the present study, for example, if all patients selected for treatment are included in the analysis, there would be a preponderance of zero scores. If only those who reach the community are considered, the shape of the distribution is determined by the period of time selected for study.

TABLE 10.5

RELATIONSHIP BETWEEN TREATMENT PROGRAMS AND
COMMUNITY TENURE

		Months in Community		
		0	1–35	36
	Maximum	19	42	18
Treatment	Partial	30	24	20
Programs	Minimum	20	18	15
	Control	20	21	7

Table 10.5 shows the relationship between treatment programs and total months in community. The distribution of months in community had been trichotomized along arbitrary, but socially meaningful, lines. Scores of 0 represent patients who never left the hospital, Scores of 1 to 35 represent patients who spent at least part of the 3 years in the community, and scores of 36 represent those who were released on completion of treatment and remained out for at least 3 years. There are no significant differences among treatment programs ($\chi^2 = 11.51$, $df = 6$, $p < .10$).

❊ *DISCUSSION* ❊

As a general rule, readmission rates tend to correlate positively with release rates. A conservative release criterion produces a low readmission rate and a more liberal criterion a higher rate. If, for example, an investigator insists that a patient spend at least 30 days in the community before counting him as a release, the readmission rate will be reduced by the number of patients returning in the first month after placement. If the release rate is computed on a sample of first admissions, the reduction will be substantial, since the first month is still the most critical for such a population (Zolik, Lantz, and Busiel, 1965). In a chronic population, on the other hand, the effect on the readmission rate may not be as severe.

The practice of defining release in terms of a minimum number of days, weeks, or months in the community has been extended to long-term criteria of outcome as well. Some investigators define a successful treatment outcome in terms of a minimum length of time spent in the community, such as six months or a year. The difficulty with this procedure is that the patient who returns in the 7th or 13th month is not included in the readmission statistics. In view of what we now know about the shape of the readmission curve, this procedure would appear justifiable only when it can be demonstrated that the readmission curve has leveled off before the cut-off point.

A third possible source of confusion is the practice of reporting cumulative release and readmission rates over an extended period of time, say four or five years. Although the release rate is not much affected, a patient released during the first year has a much greater probability of becoming a readmission than a patient released during the fourth or fifth year. A readmission rate obtained under these conditions is probably an underestimate of the rate obtained when all patients are followed for the same length of time from the date of release. To add to the confusion, an occasional investigator will report data in terms of the number of releases or readmissions per time unit, rather than the number of patients in the sample released or readmitted.

As in the case of release, readmission can also be defined along more or less conservative lines. Some investigators require that a patient spend a predetermined number of days or nights in the hospital before counting him as a readmission. This has the advantage of eliminating the patient who returns for nonpsychiatric reasons. However, the period of time selected is necessarily quite arbitrary, and there is no general agreement among investigators as to what constitutes a reasonable length of time.

The readmission data presented in Figure 10.3 compare favorably with data from other projects concerned with the treatment of chronic psychosis. Ellsworth (1963), for example, reports a cumulative readmission rate of 43 per cent for unselected male schizophrenics treated in a "maximum structure" rehabilitation program. The treatment program was in operation for a period of 30 months, and the readmission rate is based on all patients released during this period. The readmission rate for an untreated control group was 48 per cent. These figures apply only to patients in the study sample having three or more years of previous hospitalization. Thus the sample is comparable in many respects to that employed in the present study.

Freeman and Simmons (1963) in their report on the Harvard Community Health Project state that over a third of their total sample had been readmitted within a period of 12 months from the date of release. The rate for chronic patients (2 or more years of previous hospitalization) was 44 per cent. In this instance the sample was composed of male and female patients released to live with their families from 9 state and 3 Veterans' Administration hospitals in Massachusetts. Readmission was defined as 11 or more consecutive days of hospitalization for psychiatric reasons, a much less stringent definition than that employed in the present study. Freeman and Simmons noted that the cumulative readmission curve showed no sign of leveling off during the first year. However, they had no means of determining when, or if, the curve would begin to level off. The data in Figure 10.4 provide at least a tentative answer to this question.

The readmission rate for an admission cohort of 1,250 male functional psychotics in the Veterans' Administration Hospital Psychiatric Evaluation Project (1963) was 42 per cent during the first year for patients who had been in the community for at least 30 days before readmission. By the end of the four-year follow-up period, cumulative readmission rate was 65 per cent. Again the definition of readmission was less stringent than that employed in the present study: 15 or more consecutive nights in hospital. The readmission rate for a cohort of 442 chronic patients transferred from one VA hospital to another before release and readmission was 27 per cent during the first 3 years (Veterans' Administration Hospital Psychiatric Evaluation Project, 1964). However, the patients in this sample had a minimum of 2 years of previous hospitalization as compared with the admission cohort where some of the patients in the sample had had no previous hospitalization. Apparently, the patients in the transfer cohort were more chronic than those in the admission cohort, and the release rate was correspondingly low: 28 per cent versus 89 per cent. The patients in the transfer cohort were followed for a period of 8 years. At the end of this period, the cumulative release rate was 58 per cent and the readmission rate had increased to 50 per cent. It seems probable that these patients are representative of the "hard core" chronic population rather than the broad range of chronicity included in the admissions cohort.

Lee (1961–1964) reports a cumulative readmission rate of 35.5 per cent for chronic schizophrenics treated in an experimental rehabilitation program. The sample included both males and females and was representative of a large segment of the chronic population of a state hospital. The program was in operation for a period of 30 months. The readmission rate for a comparable control group was 43.9 per cent.

Galioni (1960) reports low readmission rates for both experimental and control groups: 33 and 27 per cent respectively. However, these are offset by exceptionally low release rates for both groups. Nineteen per cent were released from the experimental and 7 per cent from the control group. The treatment program in this instance was of the "total push" variety, and it seems clear that release was not a realistic expectation for many of the patients selected for treatment.

Despite differences in the characteristics of the sample, the period of time during which data were collected, and the definitions of release and readmission, the readmission rates of the studies reviewed are remarkably similar. The two studies which are most nearly identical in these respects, the Harvard Community Health Project (Freeman and Simmons) and the Veterans' Administration Hospital Psychiatric Evaluation Project (1963), report virtually identical readmission rates: 44 and 42 per cent respectively. The patients included in these studies were drawn from many different hospitals but were not exposed to any specialized rehabilitation procedures. Consequently, the readmission rates reported in these studies probably constitute fairly good baseline estimates for the total chronic population. The readmission rates for the control groups employed by Lee (44 per cent) and by Ellsworth (48 per cent) are of the same order, though obtained over a longer period of time.

With the exception of the Galioni study, readmission rates for patients exposed to specialized rehabilitation procedures tend to be slightly lower than those for control patients, though the differences are not statistically significant. Differences in release rates between experimental and control patients are generally much greater than those associated with readmission rates. This suggests that measures of community tenure may bear little relationship to hospital treatment procedures. The results of the present study are in accord with such a conclusion, which Freeman and Simmons (1963) state explicitly: "The conclusion is clear-cut: specific therapies are not associated with a patient's chances of remaining in the community."

❁ The Use of Release and Readmission Statistics

The value of release and readmission statistics as criteria of outcome rests entirely on their relationship to more direct measures of psychiatric adjustment. In the days when the primary purpose of the mental hospital was to protect the community from the patient and the patient from himself, policies governing the release of patients were usually quite conservative. Under these conditions, it was comparatively safe to assume that a patient leaving the hospital had actually demonstrated some degree of clinical improvement, and that readmission meant reappearance of symptomatic behavior. In recent years, however, it has become increasingly difficult to interpret release and readmission statistics as evidence of clinical improvement or regression.

The factors primarily responsible for this erosion of meaning were the introduction and widespread use of the tranquilizing drugs and the success of the mental hygiene movement. The effect of the drugs was to make patients much more manageable, both in the hospital and in the community. The patient therefore presented less of a threat to those responsible for his care. The possibility of continued suppression of symptoms through drug therapy on an out-patient basis brought about a general relaxation of release policies in many hospitals. Simultaneously, basic changes were occurring in the community's understanding of, and willingness to tolerate, mental illness. It became possible to find places in the community for patients who were previously unacceptable to it.

The net result was an astonishing increase in the flow of patients to and from mental hospitals. At the Philadelphia State Hospital, for example, new admissions increased from approximately 700 in 1954 to approximately 1,500 in 1962. During this period there was no significant increase in bed capacity, nor any basic change in the nature of the patient population accepted for treatment. During 1965, admissions were running well over 2,000 a year. Bed capacity remained essentially the same. However, the geographical area served by the hospital has recently been redefined to include suburban areas, the "unit plan" has been adopted, court commitments are on the increase, and acute cases are being admitted in greater proportion. Consequently, present release and readmission statistics are not comparable to those obtained in the forties and early fifties. Since the situation at the Philadelphia State Hospital is by no means unique, one suspects that the release and readmission probabilities cited by Fuller (1930), Malzberg (1952), Kramer et al. (1956), and Lehrman (1960) may be similarly outdated.

As a temporary expedient, it may be possible to improve the validity of release and readmission statistics as criteria of outcome by applying more stringent operational definiitons. The "first significant release" (FSR) concept developed by the Veterans' Administration in the Psychiatric Evaluation Project (1963) is an example of such an attempt. In the long run, however, such efforts are doomed to failure. The custodial ethic has given way to a philosophy of rehabilitation which emphasizes social recovery and eventual return to the community. The most recent manifestation of this ideological shift is the community mental health center. With the development of small, community-based out-patient facilities offering day-care programs, family therapy, and vocational training, it will be possible for many patients to avoid hospitalization altogether. As the treatment of severe mental illness becomes less identified with total hospitalization (legal commitment), release and readmission statistics become increasingly useless as criteria of clinical improvement. Eventually we shall have to relinquish such convenient measures as "in community days," "total months in community," "consecutive months in community," etc., in favor of more direct—and expensive—indices of psychiatric adjustment.

Chapter XI

Prediction of Outcome

In most investigations of innovative treatment programs, the objective of prediction is to enable the clinician to screen out the "undesirable" patient, the patient not likely to respond to treatment. Such an objective is most attainable when the treatment under consideration is relatively specific, as with drug therapy or electroshock. In many instances, accurate prediction is almost a necessity because of the high cost of specialized therapy programs. Although socio-environmental therapy is undoubtedly more expensive than custodial care, it is not a substantial entity which can be administered in controlled dosages. Moreover, the therapeutic aspects of socio-environmental treatment are ill-defined and poorly understood. For this reason, it would seem more profitable to look beyond the practical aspects of prediction toward gaining a better understanding of the interaction between the characteristics of patients and components of the physical and interpersonal milieu.

The findings reviewed thus far and the data to be presented in this chapter suggest that relatively small differences in program content or physical surroundings can produce substantially different results, depending upon such characteristics as age, length of hospitalization, race, or the like, of the patient. However, since the treatment components employed in this investigation were by no means exhaustive, we are as yet in no position to talk about the limits of applicability of socio-environmental therapy. The addition or subtraction of one or two specific procedures could alter the picture materially. This chapter, therefore, will take as its focus the pattern of relationships between the predictor variables and the four treatment conditions.

Two criteria of outcome were employed in the present study: release on completion of treatment and total months in the community during the 3-year follow-up period. Since the distribution of scores for total months in community was found to be badly skewed, this measure was dichotomized for purposes of correlational analysis. Quite by chance, the median score fell between 12 and 13 months. Therefore, this measure is identical with the first significant release criterion employed by other investigators (FSR 1 year).

Considered separately, both criteria leave much to be desired in the way of social significance. Patients who left the hospital within a few weeks or months after completion of rehabilitation treatment were counted as failures as regards the release criterion. Yet many of these patients spent most of the three-year follow-up period in the community. On the other hand, a patient who was released on completion of treatment but survived only a few weeks or months outside was counted a success. Similarly, dichotomizing total months in the community forces assignment of the same score to the patient who is released on completion of treatment and survives in the community for just short of a year and the patient who fails to respond to treatment altogether and spends the entire follow-up period in the hospital.

To compensate to some extent for the shortcomings of these two criteria, total months in community was combined with release to form four criterion groups: patients released on completion of treatment who remained in the community for 36 months, patients released on completion of treatment who returned to the hospital at least once during the follow-up period, patients returned to other wards on completion of treatment who subsequently left the hospital, and patients returned to other wards who remained in the hospital throughout the follow-up period.

Relationships between the predictor variables and the two primary criteria were studied by means of correlational analysis. The correlations in the tables which follow are either biserial r's or *phi* coefficients, depending upon whether the predictor variable was continuously distributed or dichotomized. The correlational analysis is followed by comparison of means and percentages for the four criterion groups.

❀ PREDICTION OF RELEASE ON COMPLETION ❀ OF TREATMENT

Table 11.1 shows the correlations between the predictor variables and the release criterion. The correlations in the left-hand column are based on the total experimental sample and include all cases for whom data were available on each measure. The remaining correlations represent breakdowns of the total sample by sex and treatment program. The predictor variables have been grouped for purposes of discussion. The first group is composed of variables which describe the patient prior to onset of illness.

❀ The Significance of Race

Although none of the variables in the first group predict the release criterion for the total sample, the correlation between race and disposition for the control patients suggests that race is a factor that needs to be given special attention in the appraisal of release potential. The significant correlation of $+ .40$ means that Negroes are more likely to be released from the control wards than white patients. In the treatment conditions, there is no strong and consistent relationship. However, the relative order of magnitude of the coefficients suggests that the degree to which the treatment situation was structured to promote interaction might have something to do with the observed relationships. Thus, for patients in the combined group interaction

Table 11.1

PREDICTION OF INITIAL DISPOSITION

Variable	N	Total Sample	Max. Struct.	Partial Struct.	Min. Struct.	Cont.	Grp. Int. Prog's	No Grp. Interact.	Male	Female
Marital Status	277	.06	.08	.17	.00	−.02	.12	.01	.07	−.03
Race	278	.02	−.17	−.06	.11	.40**	−.12	.24**	−.03	.05
Education	274	.02	.01	.18	−.13	.03	.09	−.06	.06	.02
Social Competence	270	.11	.26*	.23*	.06	−.12	.24**	−.04	.13	.09
Age at 1st Hospitalization	278	.13*	.24*	.16	.13	−.06	.19*	.01	.10	.12
Length of Hospitalization	278	.00	.16	.01	.11	−.40**	.08	.12	.06	−.04
Age at Transfer to Rehab.	278	.17**	.36**	.22*	.31*	−.32*	.29**	.00	.17*	.17*
Chronicity Index	278	.06	.14	.08	.24	−.30*	.11	−.01	.09	.05
No. Previous Hospitalizations	278	.12*	.13	.15	.24	−.09	.14	.09	.03	.20*
Screening Rating	227	.10	−.05	.13	.02	.37**	.04	.19	.08	.15
Initial Psychiatric Status	193	.28**	.17	.32**	.43**		.23**	.43**	.22**	.30**
Initial Social Partic.	193	.27**	.25*	.26*	.40**		.23**	.40**	.32**	.20**
On Medication Before Transfer	278	.11	.00	.07	.11	.31*	.04	.21*	.05	.21*
History of EST or Insulin	266	.01	.14	.05	−.26	.06	.09	−.12	−.03	.01
Yrs. Since Last Shock Rx	148	.00	−.40**	−.20	.27	.51**	.30**	.43**	−.12	.22**
Hunter Problem Box	242	.17**	.30**	.09	.10	.27	.20*	.14	.21*	.15
Estimated IQ	223	.14**	.15	.24*	.15	−.19	.19	.05	.13	.22*
Occupational Check List	127	.11	.20	.13	.04	.07	.16	.02	.11	
Initial Sociometric Status	139	.07	.21	.06			.07	.20	.16	−.01
Photo Naming Test	167	.27**	.28	.31*	.20		.29**		.21	.37**
Activ. Part. Gain Score	105	.12	.17	.10	.02		.12	.02	.21	.01
Soc. Inter. Gain Score	67	.02	.08	−.02			.03		.02	

* $p < .05$.
** $p < .01$.

191

programs the race-release correlation is $-.12$, while for patients in the combined Minimally Structured and Control conditions the correlation is $+.24$. To look into this matter further, release rates were computed separately for Negroes and whites in each of the four treatment conditions. The results appear in Table 11.2.

TABLE 11.2

COMPARATIVE RELEASE RATES FOR NEGRO AND WHITE PATIENTS

Treatment Programs	N	% Negro	N	% White
Maximally Structured	6/19	32	35/67	52
Partially Structured	7/15	47	38/69	55
Minimally Structured	6/10	60	21/46	46
Control	11/15	73	8/37	22

It can be seen that for Negro patients there is an orderly relationship between the degree of social structure in the living situation and release on completion of treatment. The greater the social pressure, the less likely the Negro is to succeed. There may not be an especially complicated reason for this. To be one of approximately 80 or 90 Negroes in a 300-bed chronic ward may involve relatively little interracial difficulty. In a large chronic ward there is no requirement that patients relate to one another in any but the most superficial fashion, and the pressures of racial hostility are likely to be minimum. To be one of only 3 or 4 Negroes in a 20-bed cottage, however, is quite another matter. In the cottage living situation, patients were required to interact with one another in a meaningful manner. This requirement was most severe in the Maximally Structured treatment program where group cohesion was maintained via patient government. Inadvertently, the rehabilitation staff created a situation within which the dynamics of racial prejudice could flourish unhindered.

In an effort to determine whether the high failure rate among Negroes in the group interaction programs was due to rejection by the white majority, initial sociometric scores were examined for evidence of a relationship between race, rejection, and failure to complete the program. In the four treatment units which comprise the Maximally and Partially Structured treatment programs (groups *A*, *B*, *E*, and *F*), communal housekeeping chores were performed by teams of three or more patients. The composition of these teams was determined by sociometric choice. Patients were asked to choose at least three other patients in their own living unit with whom they would like to work. Choices were honored insofar as possible. The performance of the teams was rated each week by the nursing staff. These ratings were made public at cottage meetings, and there was an additional element of competition between cottages. Consequently, the patients' choices tended to be quite meaningful. The teams were reconstituted every two months to allow for replacement of patients released or transferred to other wards. New patients were assigned to existing teams on a temporary basis until time for the next sociometric selection.

Table 11.3 shows the mean initial sociometric scores for Negro and white patients grouped in accordance with the release criterion.

TABLE 11.3

MEAN SOCIOMETRIC SCORES FOR NEGRO AND WHITE
SUCCESSES AND FAILURES

	Negro		White	
	*N**	Mean	*N**	Mean
Released	12	53.58	73	47.79
Not released	15**	44.87	57	48.04

$t = 2.72; p < .02$

* These *N*'s represent the cumulative totals of Whites and Negroes who received initial sociometric choices upon entering the two most structured programs.

** Six patients transferred before data obtained.

These scores are standard scores based on a squared matrix. They represent the number of two-step connections or relationships available to the patient by reason of the primary choice. For example, a patient chosen by an isolate would have relatively few channels of communication with the rest of the group available to him by means of this choice. In contrast, a patient chosen by another who himself is frequently chosen has a great many potential relationships opened to him by reason of this choice. Considering the small number of Negroes in the treatment programs at the time the sociometric choices were made (2 or 3 out of 20 in each cottage), it is evident that the sociometric status of Negroes is strongly determined by the choices of white patients. The data in Table 11.3 thus indicate that release on completion of treatment is related to initial acceptance or rejection of Negro patients by whites. The sociometric status of white patients is not related to the release criterion.

❀ Implications for Socio-Environmental Therapy

The discovery of the interaction between race, social structure, and the release criterion—like most by-products of a large-scale investigation—raises more questions than it answers. What was the basis for the initial rejection? Since all Negroes were not rejected, race alone is obviously not the answer. One thing seems clear, however. It is no longer feasible to select patients for rehabilitation treatment and assign them to groups irrespective of race, as was done in this project. Since the group is the principal therapeutic vehicle in socio-environmental therapy, failure to gain admission to the group is equivalent to throwing the medication down the drain when the attendant isn't looking. In both instances there is no real contact between patient and therapy.

In a socio-environmental treatment setting, the therapist has very little control over whether the patient is "admitted to treatment." To a large extent, this is decided by the patients themselves. Simply transferring the patient from one building to another, or assigning the patient to an existing group, is not sufficient guarantee that he is experiencing the intended therapy. In fact, it is quite possible that he is experiencing just the opposite. In the present project, 80 per cent of the so-called "screening errors" (early program failures) occurred in the two treatment programs which contained group interaction therapy. In the Maximally Structured treatment program (patient government and group interaction therapy), over half the screening errors were Negroes. Clearly, socio-environmental therapy programs can contain a mixture of therapeutic and nontherapeutic forces. The extent to which these forces serve to counteract one another remains a problem for research. Presumably, because of the countertherapeutic effects of racial prejudice and rejection, the structured programs appear to have no influence upon the release rate of the combined white and Negro patient samples. However, when the samples are analyzed separately, the effects of the programs are clear and systematic. Table 11.2 shows that for the white sample alone the difference in release rates across the four treatment conditions is statistically significant ($\chi^2 = 6.54$, $p < .02$).

Social Competence and Outcome

Returning to Table 11.1, it can be seen that marital status and education, considered separately, apparently bear no relationship to the release criterion. However, both of these variables are included in the Social Competence Scale, which does have some predictive utility for patients in the Maximally and Partially Structured treatment programs. Although the correlations are not impressive, the scale is worthy of more detailed examination because of its previously reported relationship to outcome in psychiatric disorders (Zigler and Phillips, 1960). These investigators report that, in a sample of first admissions, patients with low social competence scores tend to remain in the hospital much longer than patients with high scores, and are more likely to be readmitted if released. Low scores are associated with low intelligence, early age of onset, no marital history, little education, low-level jobs, and frequent unemployment.

The results of the present study are not entirely consistent with those reported by Zigler and Phillips. None of the four items included in the social competence scale (marital status, education, intelligence, age at first hospitalization) is highly related to the release criterion. Unless the major burden of the scale is carried by the two vocational items (low-level jobs and frequent unemployment), it would seem that premorbid indices of social competence are largely irrelevant to outcome in a sample of chronically institutionalized psychotic patients. In all probability, the failure to replicate the results reported by Zigler and Phillips is directly attributable to the difference in samples. Results obtained with first admissions simply do not generalize to a chronically institutionalized population.

❀ Severity of Illness and Outcome

The variables in the second group of predictors are indicative of the course of the illness, or the patient's psychiatric condition at some point in time. Here, too, the pattern of relationships reveals the presence of significant interaction effects among treatment programs. Length of hospitalization, for example, has prediction value for patients in the control group but not for patients in the three rehabilitation programs. The correlation is negative for patients in the control group, which is consistent with the general rule that the longer a patient remains in the hospital the less likely he is to leave. The fact that the correlations are positive for the three rehabilitation programs is encouraging, since these programs were designed specifically for the long-term chronic patient. Their effectiveness in this regard is more apparent, however, in the correlation for age at transfer to the rehabilitation programs. It is interesting to consider the basic axiom of medical practice that the sooner the patient gets to treatment after the onset of illness the better his chances for recovery. In the present study, this does not hold for patients in the rehabilitation programs. In fact, it is clear that the older, more chronic patient has a better chance of leaving the hospital after rehabilitation treatment.

The Chronicity Index is a measure of the total time-span during which the patient has been subject to mental illness. It is based on the difference between age at first hospitalization and age when transferred to the Rehabilitation Center. It does not take into account periods of remission or time spent out of the hospital. Relationships with the release criterion are notably weaker for the chronicity index than for age at transfer alone. This could mean that chronological age is a more important determinant of outcome than length of illness; a 60-year-old patient who has been ill for 20 years may be a better bet for social rehabilitation than a 40-year-old patient ill for the same period of time.

The distribution of scores for number of previous hospitalizations was, of course, badly skewed. Therefore, this measure was dichotomized into none vs. one or more previous admissions. The correlations indicate that number of previous admissions is a relatively poor predictor of outcome.

The screening rating was a prognostic estimate of the patient's chances of leaving the hospital, given rehabilitation treatment. The score used here is a composite of the independent judgments of two psychologists who talked with ward personnel, reviewed the clinical record, and interviewed the patient before deciding whether or not he or she was an appropriate candidate for rehabilitation therapy. The raters were asked to indicate whether the patient had a better than average chance of leaving the hospital within a 6-to-12-month period, a 50-50 chance, a slight chance, or no chance at all. Reliability was estimated by having 5 staff members rate each of 10 patients observed in individual interview sessions (coefficient of concordance $= .73$; $\chi^2 = 32.8$, $p < .001$). The raters had no knowledge of which treatment program the patient would ultimately be assigned to. Therefore, it is of considerable interest that the only patients for whom they could predict successfully were those assigned to the control group. The $+ .37$ correlation means that patients who received a good screening rating tended to be released from the control wards. Presumably, the poor predictability for patients assigned to the socio-environmental programs was due to the understandable inability of the raters to take account of the change that was to be expected as a consequence of socio-environmental treatment. Indeed, if we look at the accuracy of screening ratings in predicting the social adjustment and participation of the patient just after transfer to the socio-environmental programs, that is, before any marked improvement could take place, the picture is somewhat better. The correlation between the screening ratings and initial psychiatric status[1] was $+ .20$ for male patients, and $+ .25$ for female patients, the latter significant at the .05 level. The correlations with initial social participation were $+.67$ and $+ .64$ for male and female patients respectively, both significant well beyond the .01 level. Of course, these latter high correlations are due not only to the absence of marked improvement at the early phase of the program but also to the relative consistency of the behavior (social participation) being predicted.

The ratings of initial psychiatric status and social participation

---

[1] Although both sets of ratings were made by the unit administrators, they were not made by the same individuals. Male patients were selected by the administrators for the female treatment units and vice versa.

predict best for patients in the Minimally Structured treatment program. This is consistent with the finding that patients changed most in these respects in the Maximally and Partially Structured treatment programs. It was most unfortunate that comparable ratings could not be obtained for control patients.[2] Had such ratings been available, one would anticipate an even greater relationship with the release criterion than that shown by patients in the Minimally Structured treatment program. Nonetheless, the relative magnitude of the available correlations provides indirect evidence of a relationship between the degree of social structure in the living situation and changes in psychiatric and social adjustment.

❀ Previous Treatment and Outcome

Accurate information concerning psychiatric treatment received a decade or more ago is extremely hard to come by in most state hospitals. A search of the records at the Philadelphia State Hospital showed that it would be possible to determine which patients had received insulin or electroshock therapy and the approximate time (months) during which these treatments were given. However, information concerning the number of treatments received, dosage level, and outcome was generally not available. Only two or three patients in the study sample had encountered the surgeon's knife. There was no mention of group or individual psychotherapy, except in a few instances in which the patient had been in a private institution before coming to the state hospital.

The tranquilizing drugs were just coming into general use when this project began. In fiscal 1957 the average monthly expenditure for drugs was less than $10,000 a month. By fiscal 1965, the monthly drug bill had increased to approximately $75,000. The difference is almost entirely attributable to the advent of tranquilizers and antidepressants. For reasons which are not entirely clear, these drugs were being administered to female patients much more frequently than to male patients. The percentage of patients selected for rehabilitation treatment who were on tranquilizing or antidepressant medication immediately prior to transfer is shown in Table 11.4. The immediate

[2] There was no opportunity to observe control patients under comparable conditions as they were scattered in numerous wards and followed schedules which made them inaccessible.

TABLE 11.4

PERCENTAGE OF PATIENTS ON ATARACTIC OR ANTIDEPRESSANT
MEDICATION PRIOR TO ASSIGNMENT TO REHABILITATION PROGRAM

	N	% Male	N	% Female	% Total
Maximally Structured	14/44	32	29/42	69	50
Partially Structured	15/46	33	28/38	74	51
Minimally Structured	6/25	24	25/31	81	55
Control	9/20	45	23/32	72	61

acceptance and rapid utilization of chemotherapy by the female treatment service is probably not unrelated to the rise in the release rate for female patients which took place during this same period.

Previous drug treatment is related to outcome for female patients in the rehabilitation programs, and for males and females in the control group. Though statistically significant, these relationships are both relatively weak and cannot be considered useful for predictive purposes. There seems little doubt, however, that social interaction treatment interferes with predictions based on previous chemotherapy in the same way that it limits the predictive value of measures of severity of illness.

A history of insulin or electroshock therapy appeared to be totally irrelevant to outcome in subsequent socio-environmental therapy. This seemed reasonable, since shock treatment is usually given shortly after the initial hospitalization, if given at all, and the majority of the patients in the study sample had been hospitalized for over five years. The possibility remained, however, that there might be a relationship between insulin or electroshock therapy and the release criterion for patients who had received such treatment in recent years. But what constitutes "recent"; where does one draw the line? Over how long a period is it reasonable to expect insulin or electroshock therapy to influence behavior? Presumably, these treatments were unsuccessful for most patients in the study sample, as they had been hospitalized continuously after receiving them. Could there be long-term negative effects?

To establish whether there was any relationship at all between elapsed time since last shock therapy and outcome of rehabilitation treatment, correlations were calculated for all patients who had received such treatment. Elapsed time was computed to the nearest year. Although the correlation for the total sample proved nonsignificant, this analysis uncovered the most striking program interaction to appear in Table 11.1. Interpreted literally, these correlations mean that recent insulin or electroshock therapy is associated with failure in programs which involve group interaction, but predicts success in programs where social pressures are minimal. Conversely, patients who received insulin or electroshock therapy in the distant past tend to do well in social interaction therapy, whereas they are seldom released from chronic wards. (Maximally Structured $r = -.40$, Control condition $r = +.51$; in both cases $p < .01$.)

The mean length of time since previous shock treatment for the 148 patients in the study sample who had been exposed to such treatment was 7.5 years. Thus "recent," in this context, means treatment received at any time during the past four or five years. This suggests the possible existence of long-term aftereffects about which little is known at present.

There are several possible explanations for the observed interaction. One of these is that patients who have not received shock therapy in recent years tend to be chronic and older. It has already been shown that this type of patient fares better in a maximally structured environment and least well in the conventional ward situation. There is also reason to believe that shock treatment in relatively recent years has been more selectively limited to patients showing affective disorders and catatonic excitement and inactivity. It is possible that the strong and persistent environmental pressures of the Maximally Structured program disturb these patients more than the unpressured ward environment.

The Initial Test Battery and Outcome

The fourth group of predictors in Table 11.1 is composed of four of the six tests administered either immediately before or shortly after transfer to the Rehabilitation Center, and the initial sociometric score obtained within the first eight weeks. The two measures which were part of the initial test battery but are not included in Table 11.1

are the W-A-Y (Who Are You) Test (Bugental and Zelen, 1950) and the Semantic Differential (Osgood, Suci, and Tannenbaum, 1957). Responses to the W-A-Y Test were never reliably quantified. The Semantic Differential proved to be too complicated for many of the patients in the study sample; some were unable to follow the instructions. In other instances, the presence of symmetrical response patterns casts doubt on the validity of the data. With the doubtful cases removed, the data were no longer representative.

The Hunter Problem Box

The Hunter Problem Box is an electrical device which requires the subject to push buttons in order to make a light come on. The object is to make as few errors as possible, which means that the subject must discover by trial and error the pattern programmed by the experimenter. Four problems were presented, the first being a simple alternation between two of the five lights on the instrument panel. The patient then progressed to three- and four-light problems, followed by a double alternation problem (two lights, each of which must be lit twice in succession) which required a change in set.[3]

The Hunter Problem Box was designed to tap those cognitive processes which facilitate modification of behavior under changing environmental demands. In essence, it can be considered a measure of learning capacity. It requires that the subject formulate a series of hypotheses, test each one, and be able to overcome the perceptual set established by the first three problems when faced with the double alternation problem. To do this, the subject must correctly perceive and interpret environmental requirements, that is, know whether he is succeeding or failing, be able to generate a new idea when faced with failure, and modify his behavior accordingly. These very same processes are presumably related to the requirements of social interaction treatment. Therefore, patients who did well on the Hunter Problem Box were expected to show most improvement. However, potential is of little or no value until actuated by appropriate stimuli. Therefore, predictive efficiency was also expected to vary in accordance with the demand for behavioral change.

The correlation of the Hunter Problem Box score with the

[3] For a more complete description of this device, see Smith *et al.*, 1963.

release criterion was significant only in the Maximally Structured treatment program. The order of magnitude of the remaining correlations is not impressive. Moreover, the correlation for the total sample was substantially lower than that reported in a previously published article (Smith *et al.*, 1963). This demonstrated that predictive efficiency had been greatly attenuated as new patients were added to the study sample.

In the published data, the correlation between the Hunter Problem Box and the release criterion was .47, $p < .01$ for the 69 male patients used in the development of the scoring index. The instrument was cross-validated on a sample of 48 male patients, and a correlation of .44, $p < .01$ was obtained. Although the scoring system had been developed on male patients only, a third sample of 71 female patients yielded a correlation of .31, $p < .02$. These findings appeared substantial enough to warrant publication. However, with each new group of patients added to the original samples, the correlation was further attenuated. The breakdown appeared complete when a sample of 68 male patients obtained long after the close of the experimental project yielded a correlation of $-.08$. The correlation, obtained concurrently, for a group of 69 female patients was $-.09$. Thus a once-promising instrument appeared headed for the trash heap.

Before the instrument was abandoned altogether, however, a post-mortem seemed in order. There were four major possibilities: a change in the way the test was administered or scored, a change in the substance of the treatment program, a change in the decision processes governing release from the hospital, and a change in the character of the patients selected for treatment.

The possibility of a change in the manner in which the test was administered or scored was checked by comparing the test protocols and index scores of patients tested by different examiners at different times. Examination of the various components of the scoring system revealed no differences in the frequency or pattern of errors. Performance was essentially the same regardless of who officiated or when the test was administered. The treatment program had in fact undergone considerable revision since the close of the experimental project. Many new ideas had been generated in the course of the project. However, changes had been held to a minimum in order to maintain the integrity of the experimental design. When the experimental phase was terminated, the minimal structure treatment program was abandoned and a new program created for patients in the other four treatment units. Since there was no way of comparing this program with the Maximally and Partially Structured treatment programs, the influence of changes in program content could not be checked. The same was true for the third possibility: changes in the criteria affecting release from the hospital. The psychiatrist in charge of the disposition staff early in the project had assumed other duties. Although the release rate remained the same, there was no assurance that patients released in later years had met the same standards as those applied to the original sample. Moreover, during the course of the experiment the Rehabilitation Center acquired a full-time social worker who facilitated prompt release at termination of treatment.

The possibility of a change in the nature of the population selected for socio-environmental treatment was the only one which could be systematically explored. This analysis led to the discovery of the importance of age and chronicity as mediating variables for predicting outcome, and ultimately to a better understanding of differential responses to treatment.

Comparison of the original samples with those most recently obtained revealed substantial differences in age for both male and female patients, and in chronicity (duration of illness) for males. These findings are summarized in Table 11.5.

The data in Table 11.5 suggested that the correlations obtained in the initial study were mediated primarily by older, more chronic patients. To test this hypothesis, the data in Table 11.1 were reanalyzed with the samples divided at the median on age and chronicity. The results of this analysis appear in Table 11.6.

The correlations for the dichotomized samples show that the predictive utility of the Hunter Problem Box is in fact limited to older patients. The predicted interaction between learning potential, as measured by the Hunter Problem Box, and demand for behavioral change emerged quite clearly in the case of the older patients. The greater the demand for behavioral change, the greater the predictive efficiency of the Hunter Problem Box.

TABLE 11.5

AGE, CHRONICITY, AND PREDICTION OF RELEASE WITH THE HUNTER
PROBLEM BOX FOR INITIAL AND RECENT SAMPLES

| | | | Age | | Chronicity | | | |
		N	Mean	Mdn.	Mean	Mdn.	r_b	p
Male	Initial	117	45.3	44.9	14.7	14.1	.45	.01
	Recent	68	38.9	36.5	8.6	4.5	−.08	n.s.
Female	Initial	71	45.3	47.2	10.3	9.1	.31	.02
	Recent	69	40.3	39.5	12.8	12.5	−.09	n.s.

But why the breakdown in prediction for the younger, less chronic patients? The explanation which comes to mind most readily is that the younger patients were somehow less well integrated, and thus less able to tolerate increased environmental pressures, particularly those of a social nature. If this were the case, it was certainly not apparent to the screening teams. There were no significant differences between older and younger patients in the screening ratings or the initial ratings of psychiatric status and social participation.

The next step was to identify the "false positives" (patients with good scores who failed to attain release) and "false negatives" (patients with poor scores who succeeded in being released) among the younger age group. The cases which upset the prediction turned out to be mostly false positives, that is, patients with good Hunter Box scores who were sent back to other wards. There were 35 false positives and only 13 false negatives for the combined male and female samples. The majority of these were male patients. Of the 13 false negatives, 6 subsequently returned to the hospital. Of the 35 false positives, 11 were "screening errors," patients who were either too ill to participate in the program on arrival or who got rapidly worse shortly after transfer to the Rehabilitation Center. Pre- and post-psychiatric status ratings were available on 18 of the remaining 24 patients. The difference between the pre and post means for these patients was significant well beyond the .01 level ($t = 6.62$), indicating that they had shown a marked increase in psychiatric symptomatology. The difference between the pre and post means for younger

Table 11.6

PREDICTION OF INITIAL DISPOSITION FOR OLDER AND YOUNGER PATIENTS

Variable	Total		Older				Younger		
	Older	Younger	Part.	Min.	Cont.	Max.	Part.	Min.	Cont.
Marital Status	.01	.08	.13	−.01	−.17	.02	.21	−.08	.17
Race	.00	.08	−.13	−.05	.33	−.04		.31	.33
Education	.10	.01	.20	.02	−.00	.22	.21	−.21	.07
Social Competence	.09	.10	.17	.21	−.17	.26	.30	−.16	.07
Age at 1st Hospitalization	.03	.17	.05	.03	−.09	.12	.27	.01	.30
Length of Hospitalization	−.02	−.07	.10	.01	.26	.00	−.21	.07	.57**
Age at Transfer to Rehab.	.13	.16	.26	.47**	−.14	.11	.28	−.06	−.25
Chronicity Index	.05	−.03	.11	.23	.00	−.06	−.02	.07	.57**
No. Previous Hospitalizations	.14	.10	.03	.45*	.04	.13	.27	.02	.17
Screening Rating	.07	.21*	.17	.24	−.05	−.05	.16	−.05	.71**
Initial Psychiatric Status	.23*	.36**	.43**	.36		−.07	.23	.57**	
Initial Social Part.	.23*	.33**	.34**	.31		.06	.19	.49**	
On Medica. Prior to Transfer	.03	.19*	.05	.02	.17	.02	.24	.09	.28
History of Shock Therapy	−.04	.12	−.18	−.20	−.12	.31*	.37*	−.30	.13
Yrs. Since Last Shock Rx.	.14	−.15							
Hunter Problem Box	.47**	.04	.44*	.40*	.22	.80**	−.10	−.01	.30
Est. Full Scale IQ	.24*	.03	.28	.32	−.06	.34*	.21	−.08	−.23
Occupational Check List	.06	.11							
Initial Sociometric Status	.05	.13							
Photo Naming Test	.44**	.17	.56**	.21		.47*	.14	.06	
Activ. Part. Gain Score	.05	.25	.02			.08	.23		
Soc. Inter. Gain Score	.19	−.19							

* p < .05.
** p < .01.

205

patients for whom the Hunter Box had predicted successfully was insignificant ($t = 1.42$).

The clinical charts of the false positives were scanned for clues to the nature of the problem which had resulted in their transfer. The most striking finding was the frequency with which content of a sexual nature appeared in the delusions and hallucinations manifested by many of these patients. This suggested that one of the primary sources of stress for younger patients may have been mixing of the sexes in the group interaction program, and the comparative freedom which male and female patients enjoyed in their casual after-hours social contacts. It is quite possible that the attempt to encourage normal relationships with the opposite sex served to activate problems for the younger patients which were no longer of great concern to the older, more chronic patients.

To check on whether younger patients were in fact more responsive to members of the opposite sex than older patients, data obtained early in treatment in the Photo Naming Test and the Spontaneous Social Interaction Scale were examined. The Photo Naming Test revealed that younger male patients were able to identify more female patients by name than could older patients, indicating that they were much more aware of their presence ($x^2 = 12.68$, $df = 2$, $p < .01$). The data from the monthly socials confirmed that younger patients also showed a higher frequency of spontaneous interaction with the opposite sex in a free social situation ($x^2 = 8.84$, $df = 2$, $p < .02$). It seems clear, therefore, that one of the sources of stress in the rehabilitation program was confrontation with the opposite sex. If older patients are less responsive to members of the opposite sex, it is possible that they are also less responsive to other sources of stress as well, and thus better able to maintain equilibrium in the face of changing environmental demands. These findings suggest that "reactivity," or the process associated with aging, may be a key factor in determining outcome in socio-environmental therapy.

The discovery of the importance of age in predicting outcome with the Hunter Problem Box suggested that other predictors might be similarly affected. Accordingly, the relationship between all predictors and the release criterion was re-examined with the sample divided at the median on both variables (see Table 11.6). With the exception of the Hunter Problem Box, most of the measures reported on thus far are not appreciably affected by age or chronicity. With respect to measures in the severity of illness category, the age dichottomy reveals that the significant correlations for the control group were based largely on younger patients. It is interesting to note that the screening team was also able to predict very well for this group ($r = +.71$), which supports the previous interpretation of the screening team's failure to predict outcome for patients in the rehabilitation programs. That is, traditional clinical criteria work very well for younger patients when there is relatively little therapeutic intervention. The older patients in the control group could not help but lower the correlation, since they had little chance of obtaining release.

❀ Intelligence and Outcome

The measure of intellectual capacity employed in the present study was based on four subscales of the Wechsler Adult Intelligence Scale (WAIS): Information, Comprehension, Block Design, and Picture Completion. Scores on these four subscales were combined and prorated to obtain an estimate of the full-scale IQ.

The over-all pattern of correlation between estimated IQ and the release criterion is similar to that obtained with the Hunter Problem Box. However, the magnitude of the correlations in Table 11.1 is rather unimpressive. It is only when the sample is divided at the median for age that intelligence appears to have any real importance. It is apparently something of an asset to older patients in the rehabilitation programs, but of little or no help to younger patients or patients in the control group. There was no difference in mean IQ between age groups. It would seem clear that these findings can be interpreted in much the same way as the data relating to the Hunter Problem Box. Positive assets such as intellectual ability are of little use in a social learning situation until the pressure of illness is somehow attenuated.

❀ Vocational Aspirations and Outcome

The Occupational Check List is a paper-and-pencil device intended to tap the patient's vocational aspirations. Thirty occupations were selected from a list of jobs which had previously been scaled on a status continuum.[4] The occupations selected were taken from the lower two thirds of the status continuum, and were approximately equidistant from each other in terms of scale values. Examples of high status occupations included in the check list are airline pilot, radio announcer, manager of a small store, and public school teacher. Low status occupations included janitor, shoe shiner, street sweeper, and filling-station attendant. The patient was asked to indicate whether, in a free-choice situation, he would like each job a lot, like it a little, dislike it a little, or dislike it a lot. This instrument was constructed because it was felt that patients with high vocational aspirations would probably have greater difficulty getting along in the community. The Occupational Check List was not expected to relate to the release criterion, and the correlations in Table 11.1 confirm that there is no relationship. Vocational aspirations will be considered in the section on prediction of community tenure.

Sociometric Status and Outcome

The initial sociometric status score (described earlier in the section entitled "The significance of race") is apparently unrelated to the release criterion for most patients in the study sample, the exception being Negro patients in the two group interaction programs as previously noted. The number of patients for whom sociometric scores were available was not sufficient to permit breakdowns into older and younger groups.

Awareness of Others and Outcome

Table 11.1 shows that awareness of others, as measured by the Photo Naming Test, is a moderately good predictor for the total study sample, and is apparently somewhat more effective with females than males. However, the true value of this instrument as a predictor did not become apparent until comparisons were made between age groups, and the release criterion was combined with community ten-

[4] The Minnesota Scale for Paternal Occupations developed at the Institute of Child Welfare, University of Minnesota, Minneapolis, Minnesota, classifies occupations, purportedly in accord with socio-economic status.

ure to form the four criterion groups described in the introduction to this chapter. The age dichotomy showed the Photo Naming Test to be a powerful predictor for older patients in the group interaction programs (Table 11.6). There was no significant difference in mean number of photographs identified by older and younger patients, indicating that both were equally aware of those in the immediate environment. Therefore, it seems probable that we are again confronted with a capacity which becomes relevant to outcome only when the patient is free to attend to stimuli other than those dictated by his illness. The absence of this capacity, however, has significance, as will be seen in the analysis of the combined criterion.

❀ Change in Social Behavior and Outcome

The failure of the two gain scores to predict the release criterion is unequivocal. There are a number of possible explanations for this failure, the most disturbing of which is that changes in social adjustment are entirely irrelevant to outcome. Since there are alternative explanations, such a conclusion would be premature. One possible difficulty lies with the gain score itself—the *beta* coefficient. Patients whose initial social behavior scores are good and presumably reflect good release potential are unable to obtain high gain scores because of the relatively low "ceiling" of the measures. This "ceiling effect" tends to reduce the relationship between the gain scores and the release criterion.

❀ *PREDICTION OF COMMUNITY TENURE* ❀

Community tenure refers to the total number of months spent in the community during the 36-month period following release or transfer from the Rehabilitation Center. For patients in the control group, the baseline date was set at 12 months from the date of assignment to control status. In order to be counted as residing in the community, the patient must have been on Indefinite Home Visit status. Temporary leaves of absence were not counted unless they were changed to Indefinite Home Visit status without the patient having to return to the hospital.

Table 11.7 shows the relationship between the predictor vari-

TABLE 11.7

PREDICTION OF TOTAL MONTHS IN COMMUNITY

Variable	N	Total Sample	Max.	Part.	Min.	Cont.	Grp. Intera.	No Grp. Inter.	Male	Female
Marital Status	255	.01	.03	−.02	.10	−.10	.01	.01	−.02	−.04
Race	256	−.07	−.06	−.07	−.03	.21	−.06	.07	−.06	.03
Education	250	.06	.02	.10	−.08	.30*	.06	.06	.10	.01
Social Competence	244	.04	.18	.04	.02	−.11	.11	−.05	.03	.04
Age at First Hospitalization	254	.02	.19	−.07	.05	−.10	.05	−.03	−.01	.03
Length of Hospitalization	254	.06	.14	.17	.11	−.32*	.15	−.06	.14	−.02
Age at Transfer to Rehab.	254	.07	.20	.13	.23	−.37**	.16	−.04	.10	.04
Chronicity Index	254	.07	−.02	.27*	.22	−.33*	.01	.02	.14	.01
No. Previous Hospitalizations	254	.08	.02	.05	.29*	−.04	.04	.15	.03	.12
Screening Rating	208	−.15*	.04	−.28*	.01	−.46**	−.11	−.21*	−.12	−.22
Initial Psychiatric Status	178	.26**	.14	.32**	.31*		.23**	.31**	.18	.30**
Initial Soc. Part.	178	.30**	.24*	.31*	.37*		.27**	.37**	.26*	.32**
On Medica. at Transfer	250	.00	.14	−.14	.17	.10	.00	.14	−.00	.10
History of EST or Insulin	243	.05	.09	.07	−.17	.31*	.08	.02	.01	.08
Yrs. Since Last Shock R_x	137	.14	−.07	.07	.04	.46*	.01	.28	.00	.30
Hunter Problem Box	216	.17*	.28*	.18	.03	.12	.23**	.05	.26**	.09
Estimated IQ	203	.11	.06	.18	.06	.08	.12	.09	.12	.13
Occupational Check List	116	−.09		−.21			−.17	.07	−.09	
Initial Sociometric Status	122	.04	.23	.44**	.62**		.04		.17	−.08
Photo Naming Test	151	.28**	.13				.31**	.62**	.38**	.13
Activ. Part. Gain Score	91	.06	.05	.07					.06	.06
Soc. Int. Gain Score	58	−.02								
Post. Psychiatric Status	171	.59**	.55**	.56*	.67**		.56**	.67**	.59**	.60**
Post. Social Part.	171	.59**	.40**	.64**	.79**		.53**	.79**	.61**	.58**

* $p < .05$.
** $p < .01$.

210

ables and community tenure. Generally speaking, the pattern of correlation is very similar to that shown in Table 11.1. This is not surprising, since the correlation between the two criterion measures was .73 for the total sample. The correlations for the demographic variables are generally lower than their counterparts in Table 11.1. All of the correlations which were significant in Table 11.1 are now not significant. The data suggest that education may be of some importance to members of the control group $(r = + .30)$ once they reach the community, whereas it was of no value in effecting their release from the hospital.

The correlations for many of the predictors related to psychiatric condition held up remarkably well. Age at first hospitalization and age at transfer to the Rehabilitation Center are no longer relevant. However, the screening ratings and the ratings of initial psychiatric status and social participation predict community tenure only slightly less well than the release criterion. The postprogram ratings of psychiatric status and social participation correlate significantly with community tenure. However, the importance of these ratings as predictors are minimized because the ratings were made after the disposition of the case had been decided.

The previously observed interaction between years since last shock therapy and the four treatment conditions is no longer present. The significant relationship for the control group, however, persists. The view that relatively recent shock treatment can have beneficial effects in an environment which lacks systematic pressure for social interaction is thus still tenable.

The pattern of correlations for the Hunter Problem Box is very similar to that in Table 11.1, except that the order of magnitude of the correlations for male and female patients is reversed. The Hunter Problem Box predicted the release criterion at approximately the same level for both sexes, but is correlated with community tenure for male patients only. This may be attributable to the higher release and readmission rates for female patients. Again, as can be seen in Table 11.8, age is a critical factor. The Hunter Problem Box data are the first clear indication of the persistence of treatment effects beyond the treatment situation itself. They suggest that the learning potential activated by the various treatment programs was put to use in the posttreatment environment. The fact that a measure of learning capacity can predict survival in the community is extremely encouraging, even if it does so only for patients in the older age group. It demonstrates that the capacity to learn is a relevant variable in a social treatment situation when sufficient stimulation and support are provided.

Estimated IQ, vocational aspirations, and initial sociometric status are apparently not related to community tenure.

The Photo Naming Test is only a moderately good predictor of community tenure for the study sample as a whole. However, the data in Table 11.8 show that the instrument predicts very well for patients in the older age group in all three treatment programs. As with the Hunter Problem Box, prediction of outcome for the younger age group is disrupted by some factor associated with age or chronicity. The order of magnitude of the three program correlations in Table 11.7 suggests that the predictive value of initial awareness scores is dependent upon a minimum of therapeutic intervention. The greater the impact of the treatment program on the patient's awareness of others (see Chapter Five), the less the predictive power of initial awareness scores. Thus, the Photo Naming Test is clearly not a measure of potential or capacity in the sense that the Hunter Problem Box is. In all probability, it is indicative of the strength of the bond between the patient and external reality, that is, the extent to which he dares to be aware of the interpersonal environment. The truly withdrawn patient seeks to depersonalize his environment insofar as possible. Consequently, he cares little for labels which convey the unique identity of another human being.

❀ PREDICTION OF THE COMBINED CRITERION ❀

In view of the shortcomings of both the release criterion and the measure of community tenure, it seemed advisable to employ a more comprehensive measure of outcome. This was accomplished by combining the release criterion with total months in the community to form four criterion groups. Group I $(N = 60)$ consists of all patients released on completion of treatment who remained out continuously for the three-year follow-up period. Group II $(N = 59)$ is composed of all patients released on completion of treatment who

TABLE 11.8

PREDICTION OF TOTAL MONTHS IN COMMUNITY FOR OLDER AND YOUNGER PATIENTS

Variable	Total Older	Total Younger	Older Max.	Older Part.	Older Min.	Older Cont.	Younger Max.	Younger Part.	Younger Min.	Younger Cont.
Marital Status	−.07	.10	−.21	−.04	.09	−.20	.15	.10	.14	−.10
Race	−.04	.02	−.02	−.23	−.03	.14	.05	−.01	.05	−.10
Education	.14	.01	.10	.07	.12	.46*	−.02	.09	−.18	.07
Social Competence	.08	−.01	.05	.06	.13	.19	.09	.05	−.04	−.26
Age at First Hospitalization	−.01	.07	−.01	−.06	−.00	.20	.20	−.01	.16	−.21
Length of Hospitalization	.08	.02	.02	.25	.17	−.20	.40*	.02	−.11	−.35
Age at Transfer to Rehab.	.12	.06	.03	.28	.33	−.10	.29	.14	.18	−.43*
Chronicity Index	.08	−.01	.03	.26	.18	−.29	.03	.17	.07	−.25
No. Previous Hospitalizations	.04	.04	−.02	.03	.24	−.07	−.10	.01	.26	.07
Screening Rating	−.23*	.04	−.03	−.44*	−.24	−.30	.22	−.05	.31	−.30
Initial Psychiatric Status	.26*	.33**	.21	.25	.28		.12	.44**	.48*	
Initial Social Part.	.39**	.30**	.32	.36*	.44*		.20	.25	.47*	
On. Medica. Prior to Transfer	−.00	.14	.06	−.33*	.10	.22	.17	.05	.26	−.10
History of EST or Insulin	−.01	.26**	.19	−.13	−.26	.17	.12	.40*	.05	.53**
Yrs. Since Last R$_x$	.01	−.14								
Hunter Problem Box	.29**	−.06	.53**	.37*	.04	(−.18)	−.14	.05	−.14	(.09)
Estimated IQ	.22*	−.07	.16	.19	.15		−.13	.08	−.01	
Occupational Check List	.10	−.21								
Initial Sociometric Status	−.12	.23								
Photo Naming Test	.61**	−.02	.58**	.69**	.57**		−.18	.32**	−.13	
Activ. Part. Gain Score	−.02	.25	−.01	−.10			.07	.43		
Soc. Int. Gain Score	−.08	.01								
Post. Psychiatric Status	.54**	.62**	.57**	.37**	.71**		.42*	.69**	.72**	
Post. Social Part.	.58**	.59**	.48**	.52**	.81**		.18	.70**	.87**	

( ) = based on less than 25 cases.

* $p < .05$.
** $p < .01$.

213

TABLE 11.9

COMPARISON OF FOUR CRITERION GROUPS ON PREDICTOR VARIABLES

Variable	I	II	III	IV	Statistic	df	p Value
			Criterion Groups				
Marital Status (% married)	52	54	51	57	$\chi^2 = .67$	3	n.s.
Race (% Negro)	17	27	24	20	$\chi^2 = 2.15$	3	n.s.
Education	8.57	8.88	9.28	8.13	$F = 2.29$	246	n.s.
Social Competence	48.46	47.69	49.73	50.73	$F = 1.16$	243	n.s.
Age at 1st Hospitalization	32.40	34.35	29.61	31.86	$F = .02$	250	n.s.
Length of Hospitalization (mos.)	133.19	77.45	87.03	116.78	$F = 5.26$	250	.01
Age at Transfer to Rehab.	47.96	45.15	40.67	44.05	$F = 4.29$	250	.01
Chronicity Index	15.57	10.80	11.06	12.19	$F = 3.65$	250	.025
Previous Hospitalization (% none)	25	20	33	40	$\chi^2 = 7.95$	3	.05
Screening Rating	4.93	5.97	6.02	5.36	$F = 2.57$	201	.06
Initial Psychiatric Status	8.00	5.95	7.64	9.99	$F = 9.36$	172	.001
Initial Social Participation	7.03	6.28	7.42	10.00	$F = 8.44$	172	.001
On Medica. Prior to Transfer (%)	46	73	58	45	$\chi^2 = 12.57$	3	.01
History of EST or Insulin (%)	51	64	56	55	$\chi^2 = 1.92$	3	n.s.
Yrs. Since Last Shock R_x	6.76	7.60	6.32	8.17	$F = 1.36$	133	n.s.
Hunter Problem Box	49.02	49.22	51.86	53.04	$F = 2.57$	215	.06
Estimated IQ	93.44	92.34	92.03	86.65	$F = 2.04$	200	n.s.
Occupational Check List*	51.21	43.95	49.30	51.21	$F = 2.66$	110	.06
Initial Sociometric Status	48.35	48.66	46.27	48.57	$F = .33$	121	n.s.
Photo Naming Test	48.29	49.17	48.57	57.09	$F = 7.99$	149	.001
Activ. Part. Gain Score	49.39	51.09	46.94	47.64	$F = .74$	89	n.s.
Social Int. Gain Score	50.57	47.76	50.00	50.06	$F = .21$	56	n.s.
Post Psychiatric Status	5.08	4.77	11.73	12.39	$F = 90.80$	169	.001
Post Social Participation	4.47	4.57	9.12	11.74	$F = 55.96$	169	.001

* The higher the score, the lower the aspiration level.

returned to the hospital at least once during the follow-up period. Group III ($N = 46$) consists of patients sent back to other wards on completion of treatment but who subsequently left the hospital at least once during the follow-up period. Group IV ($N = 89$) consists of treatment failures who remained in the hospital for the entire follow-up period. The four criterion groups were compared with respect to the predictor variables as shown in Table 11.9. Means and F ratios are given for variables with continuous distributions, percentages and *chi* squares for those which were dichotomized.

As in the preceding correlational analyses, the variables which describe the patient's condition prior to onset of illness are rather poor predictors of outcome. The most surprising finding among the variables in the first group is the high percentage of married patients in Group IV. According to Zigler and Phillips (1960), marriage is indicative of a relatively high level of psychosexual adjustment, a supposedly favorable prognostic sign. It would seem reasonable, therefore, to expect fewer married patients in Group IV, the least successful group. On the other hand, the Social Competence Scale itself, of which marital status is but one component, does not predict very well for a chronic population. It may be, therefore, that the predictive value of this instrument is limited to first admissions or acute cases.

Beginning with measures of psychiatric adjustment, some rather clear-cut differences emerge among the four criterion groups. In fact, it is possible to draw a composite picture of each group which differentiates it from the others. Group I, the most successful group, had been hospitalized the longest and was the oldest at the time of selection for treatment. This group was accorded the best chance of leaving the hospital by the screening team, but was considered relatively sick by the unit administrator shortly after transfer to the Rehabilitation Center (control patients are not included in the latter ratings). Social adjustment, on the other hand, was judged to be somewhat better than psychiatric condition, indicating that withdrawal was less of a problem. Although residual symptoms of the psychotic process were very much in evidence, the patients in this group were apparently socially more accessible, which may account for the favorable impression they made on the screening team. The means for the Hunter Problem Box, estimated IQ, and Photo Naming

Test suggest that cognitive functions were relatively intact in this group, as compared with Group IV, for example. Vocational aspirations were modest.

Group II, the "successes" who eventually returned to the hospital, presents a somewhat different picture. The patients in this group had been hospitalized only half as long as those in Group I. Seventy-three per cent were on tranquilizing medication when selected for rehabilitation treatment, and there was a tendency for more patients in this group to have had electroshock or insulin therapy. Eighty per cent had had one or more previous hospitalizations. Apparently, Group II had been the object of considerable therapeutic attention. Although the screening team was not particularly impressed with the potential of the patients in this group, the unit administrators felt that they were in pretty good shape, both psychiatrically and socially. Mean scores on the Hunter Problem Box, estimated IQ, and Photo Naming Test indicate that Group II was also in relatively good shape cognitively. The measure which most clearly differentiates them from the other three groups, however, is the Occupational Check List. The patients in Group II apparently had unusually high vocational aspirations, which may account in part for their eventual return to the hospital. There is no manifest support for such aspirations in the form of higher means in education or estimated IQ. Therefore it seems probable that these aspirations were unrealistic and thus a potential source of difficulty. The postprogram ratings of psychiatric status show that Group II presented the best aggregate picture on leaving the hospital.

Group III resembles Group II more closely than either of the other groups does. The characteristic which most clearly differentiates this group is the low mean age, which suggests that Group III contains a large number of screening errors and program failures from the Maximally Structured treatment program. A check of the cases in this group revealed that over 50 per cent of the patients in Group III were indeed from the Maximally Structured treatment program. The patients in this group had not been hospitalized as long as those in the other three groups, and tended to have fewer previous hospitalizations than the patients in Groups I and II. Group III also appeared to be in relatively good shape on measures of cognitive performance.

However, the ratings of psychiatric status and social participation indicate that they were both sicker and more withdrawn than the patients in Group II. Group III, then, is composed of younger patients who proved to be extremely unstable under pressure. Evidence of continued instability is contained in the fact that 58 per cent of the patients in this group were readmitted to the hospital within the 3-year follow-up period.

Group IV is clearly differentiated from the other three groups on a number of measures. The patients in this group were slightly younger than those in Group I, but had been hospitalized almost as long. Forty per cent of the patients in Group IV had had no previous hospitalizations. The fact that many of these patients were hospitalized continuously since their first admission indicates that they failed to respond to treatment from the outset. Although the screening team felt that the patients in Group IV had reasonably good exit potential, the unit administrators considered them to be among the sickest and most withdrawn patients in the program. The latter impression is confirmed by the relatively low mean scores on the measures of cognitive performance, and by the Photo Naming Test in particular. Group IV patients are largely unaware of those in their immediate environment. The dual predictive significance of the Photo Naming Test is now clear. High scores predict success for patients in the older age group, but are inconclusive for younger patients. Low scores, on the other hand, predict failure irrespective of age. These are the patients so well insulated from the interpersonal environment that they are virtually impervious to socio-environmental therapy. They may go through the motions, but they never become involved at a personal level. This is the hard core of the chronic population, the patients for whom a new approach to treatment must be devised.

❀ DISCUSSION ❀

The present study afforded a unique opportunity to observe the interplay between structured social pressures and individual assets and liabilities. Had there been but one treatment program, the findings would have contributed little to what was already known. Only 3 of the 22 measures employed would have merited consideration as predictors, and the major conclusion to emerge would have been that the best predictor of outcome is the patient's condition on entering treatment. The use of social structure as a treatment variable revealed both the complexity of the prediction problem and the importance of differences in program content in determining outcome. As a result, the findings of the present study have both theoretical and practical significance, as well as providing a number of promising leads for future research.

❀ The Concept of Chronic Psychosis

It seems clear that a major revision in the concept of chronic psychosis is in order. The traditional picture of the chronic psychotic as an apathetic, deteriorated, withdrawn nonentity is a gross over-simplification. Differences among chronic psychotics are probably as great, if not greater, than those between so-called "acute" and chronic patients. In fact, the term "acute" is both confusing and inappropriate when used to refer to the early stage of a psychiatric illness. This usage is a holdover from the medical concept of infectious disease and has no place in the field of mental illness. If used at all, the term should be employed to describe the sudden increase in frequency or severity of symptomatology, which can occur at any time in the course of a psychiatric illness.

The results of this study demonstrate clearly that many chronic patients not only retain positive assets and abilities but are able to put them to good use when appropriately stimulated. Of greater importance, however, is the discovery that this positive activity can occur in the presence of manifest psychotic symptomatology, especially in older, more chronic patients. With younger patients, on the other hand, psychotic processes are much more apt to interfere with utilization of positive assets. Generally speaking, the patients in criterion groups I, II, and III can be characterized as responsive or accessible to a socio-environmental approach. The effect on the patient was not always of a positive nature. Consequently, it is not at all clear that social interaction therapy is the appropriate treatment for many of these patients. Nevertheless, they did expose themselves to the treatment situation; there was actual confrontation between patient and treatment. The patients in Group IV, on the other hand, who represent roughly one third of the total study sample, were apparently not accessible to the treatment techniques utilized. It is not clear whether the patients in this group were incapable of responding or were rendered inaccessible by defense mechanisms which precluded involvement at an interpersonal level. The data from the Photo Naming Test suggest that the latter alternative is worthy of exploration.

❀ Implication for Treatment

The differential response of older and younger patients to the variable of social structure argues strongly for maintaining the traditional distinction between "treatment" and "rehabilitation" as a basis for development of more effective therapeutic programs. As Rapoport (1960) points out, the terms "treatment" and "rehabilitation," once clearly separable with respect to goals, procedures, and personnel, have come to be used almost synonymously when applied to psychiatric illness. Jones (1953), for example, asserts that "the whole of a patient's time spent in hospital is thought of as treatment." Thus, in a therapeutic community, treatment includes both the handling of the patient's neurotic problems and the teaching of social and vocational roles. This implies that all elements of the therapy program can serve both goals equally well, whereas in reality these goals are frequently in conflict.

Rapoport suggests that the term "treatment" be employed only with respect to measures which have as their principal immediate aim "the alteration of the individual personality toward better intra-psychic integration." The term "rehabilitation," on the other hand, would be used in conjunction with all measures which have as their immediate objective "the fitting of a particular personality to the demands of an ongoing social system." The findings here are entirely in accord with this distinction. The emphasis in all three treatment programs was on preparation for community living rather than improved intrapsychic adjustment. This approach worked comparatively well with patients who had managed to achieve some sort of internal stability, but failed with those who had not yet come to terms with their illness. Clearly, the problem with the younger chronic patient is one of treatment rather than rehabilitation. Until the psychotic process is isolated, abolished, or otherwise contained, rehabilitation procedures will be of little or no avail.

This state of affairs means that therapeutic procedures must be geared to the needs of the individual patient. Some patients can be assigned immediately to rehabilitation-type programs. Others will need a preliminary program in which the emphasis is on resolution of internal conflicts and personality reintegration. These programs need not be mutually exclusive. A certain amount of overlap is probably desirable to facilitate the transition from treatment to rehabilitation. However, the primary aim of each program component must be clearly spelled out in advance.

In view of the findings on interaction with the opposite sex, it would seem advisable to begin the treatment phase on a segregated basis. When mixing of the sexes does occur, as it must in a social rehabilitation program, it should be in a task-centered context with ample opportunity for continued group or individual therapy on a segregated basis. This arrangement would provide a safety valve in case of initial difficulty in adjusting to the opposite sex.

If Negroes are to be included in the therapy program, the problem of racial prejudice must be faced within the context of the program itself. Prejudicial attitudes toward minority groups are the legitimate concern of any therapeutic program which aspires to social rehabilitation. This is especially true when the environment the patient is expected to return to is organized along minority group lines. Prejudice should be exposed as soon as possible, preferably in the treatment phase. If the emotional underpinnings of prejudice can be dealt with in this phase, it should be possible to introduce a series of planned positive experiences with minority group members in the rehabilitation phase.

The findings with respect to vocational aspirations suggest that, for some patients, survival in the community may depend more on *de*motivation than on *re*motivation. In retrospect, it would appear that finding a job received altogether too much emphasis in this program. Seeking employment in a competitive job market is part of the terminal stage of the rehabilitation process. For most of the patients in the study sample, release from the hospital was probably closer to the half-way mark in this process. Our inability to provide continued service to patients in the community doubtless contributed to the effort to find employment for as many as possible before leaving the hospital. In most instances, however, employment might better have been deferred until the patient had made the initial adjustment to life in the community.

✸ Implications for Selection of Patients

The failure of the screening teams to predict outcome for patients assigned to the three rehabilitation programs suggests that many promising candidates may have been inappropriately rejected. This suspicion was partially confirmed when it was discovered that many patients who were initially rejected on psychiatric grounds were later admitted to treatment. Forty-seven such patients had been selected at random early in the experiment to provide a baseline group for validation of measures of psychiatric status. Of this number, 45 per cent were subsequently admitted to treatment after the close of the experiment. It is possible, of course, that these patients had improved in the interval between the first and second screenings, but, if so, the improvement must have been quite dramatic, since 57 per cent were released from the hospital on completion of treatment. The release rate for "rejects" compares very favorably with that for the study sample as a whole.

It is evident that traditional clinical and demographic criteria do not provide an adequate basis for selection of patients for rehabilitation therapy. Once identified, variables such as recent shock therapy, age, race, length of hospitalization, and the like, can be employed in routine actuarial fashion by the clinician who wants to improve his batting average. In the long run, however, the problem of prediction is basically a research responsibility. Age and race are merely superficial indications of more dynamic variables now concealed from view. All Negroes were not rejected, nor were all younger patients program failures. Arbitrary use of such gross categories can only lead to denial of service to appropriate patients.

Effective prediction in a social rehabilitation setting depends to a large extent on an accurate appraisal of the stimulus situation of the demands made upon the patient by the therapy program. Some variables cut across differences in program content while others are extremely sensitive to such differences. Age, for example, was equally effective as a predictor in all three rehabilitation programs. The predictive efficiency of race and recent shock therapy, on the other hand, depended entirely on the quality and intensity of the social pressures brought to bear on the patient. The screening teams were asked to make their predictions on the assumption that all patients would be assigned to the Maximally Structured treatment program. Thus, the failure to predict for patients actually assigned to this program is extremely significant. Our data suggest that those responsible for selecting chronic patients for rehabilitation programs would do well to concentrate on evidence of functional disability rather than manifest symtomatology. The latter may be entirely irrelevant to the patient's capacity to look out for himself, which is the key to survival in the community.

❀ The Strategy and Tactics of Prediction

It seems clear that it would be difficult, if not impossible, to replicate many of the findings of the present study in any other setting. The results with respect to age should generalize to any hospital in which there is a comparable chronic population. However, the various program interactions could be obtained only if the three rehabilitation programs were reconstructed in their original form. It is doubtful that this could be done, even at the Philadelphia State Hospital. Aside from the problem of generalization, the results of the present study suggest certain guidelines for the conduct of future research on selection of patients and prediction of outcome.

Rehabilitation has been described as a multistage process. For maximum effectiveness, prediction should be closely related to the various stages of this process. The immediate aim of prediction is to anticipate the patient's response to the next stage in the process. This means establishing a series of criteria based on identification of the behaviors relevant to each stage. Exclusive reliance on relatively long-range criteria such as release from the hospital or total months in the community may lead the investigator to overlook significant changes in behavior which fall short of these goals. It is quite likely that the various components of the therapy program will not be the same from stage to stage. Consequently, the contribution (or lack of contribution) of any single element will remain obscure if only long-range criteria are employed.

Since we are interested in predicting the patient's progress through the various stages of a rehabilitation program, we must have criterion measures which reflect behavioral change rather than attainment of ultimate goals. Such measures are notoriously difficult to come by. They require both identification of relevant variables and specification of the sequence in which these behaviors are expected to change. The attempt to construct such measures, however, can have a very beneficial effect on vaguely defined therapeutic procedures.

On logical grounds alone, one would expect that prediction of behavioral change would require instruments which tap the patient's capacity for change. However, our experience with the Hunter Problem Box indicates that one must also take into account factors which may limit the free expression of this capacity. Once established, the change measures themselves may become the best predictors of outcome. Jones (1953) states that "it is the capacity of the individual for change, rather than the severity of his illness, which is the important factor in estimating prognosis." If this is the case, then the goal of prediction is to identify the patient who will be able to modify his behavior when exposed to a particular therapeutic program. The most suitable instruments for this purpose may be psychomotor tasks in which the patient is presented with a miniature problem-solving situation. Verbal requirements should be held to a minimum, since verbal skills suffer from disuse in a chronically institutional population.

The distinction between treatment and rehabilitation also contains important implications for the problem of prediction. If treatment is the goal, then measurement must be aimed at detecting changes in intrapsychic processes. Observations of social behavior on the ward are of secondary importance, if relevant at all. Conversely, changes in psychiatric symptomatology may not become relevant in a social rehabilitation program until the last stage of the rehabilitation process—perhaps long after the patient has left the hospital. In any event, there is no point in looking for positive changes in manifest symptomatology during the early stages of such a program, though negative changes may be very much in evidence. The customary pre-post mean decrement in measures of psychiatric status need not be a source of embarrassment. Substantial improvement is rarely observed in chronic psychosis, whereas spectacular regression is quite common. Since psychiatric symptomatology tends to increase when environmental pressures increase, postprogram means will typically be lower than baseline measures obtained in the relatively benign atmosphere of the chronic ward.

PART FOUR

THE FOLLOW-UP STUDY

Chapter XII

Description of
the Follow-Up Study

The primary purpose of the follow-up study was to assess the relative contribution of the three social treatment programs to the patient's ability to adjust to life in the extramural community. The initial plan called for three interviews, to be conducted at 2, 6, and 12 months from the date of release. There was no plan for interviewing patients who remained in the hospital, the assumption being that such patients were unimproved and would probably remain hospitalized indefinitely. The focus was entirely on the community. Interest centered on the relationship of the performance of the patient to the training received at the Rehabilitation Center. Success would be indicated by prolonged survival outside the hospital, failure by return.

The apparent objectivity of release and return rates as criteria of adjustment was initially quite appealing. It seemed reasonable to equate release from the hospital with clinical improvement and readmission with exacerbation of illness. The decision to follow patients for a full 12 months seemed adequate, as it was widely held that patients who returned to the hospital generally did so within the first two or three months after release. It soon became apparent that relatively sick patients could leave the hospital if community factors were favorable, and that patients sent back to other wards as "unimproved" could leave the hospital within a matter of weeks. Moreover, patients began to return for essentially nonpsychiatric reasons, and the expected build-up of readmissions during the first few months after placement failed to materialize.

By the end of the first year, the initial aim of evaluating the long-term effects of three socio-environmental treatment programs seemed much too narrow. A number of important questions had arisen. If patients returned to the hospital in large numbers after six or more months in the community, what was the significance of rehospitalization? Was readmission indicative of treatment failure, or evidence of a malignant environmental situation? If so-called treatment failures were able to leave the hospital shortly after transfer from the Rehabilitation Center, did this reflect an error in clinical judgment or a delayed treatment effect? What were the problems actually encountered by the patient in the community? Did they bear any resemblance to those he was being prepared to face? Did growth stop when active treatment ceased, or were there progressive changes in the course of time? For community patients only, or hospital patients as well?

In order to obtain answers to these and similar questions, two major modifications were introduced in the design of the follow-up study. First, the study was broadened to include all patients treated at the Rehabilitation Center except the so-called "screening errors" (see Chapter Seven, note 3). Second, the length of time during which patients were followed was extended from one to three years, with additional interviews scheduled at 18, 24, and 36 months. The two-month interview was omitted for patients remaining in the hospital, since little change was anticipated for these patients within so short a period. Patients released from the hospital were to be interviewed in the community at the next regularly scheduled interval.

The increased scope of the follow-up study necessitated recruitment and training of additional interviewers. Before the expanded schedule of data collection could be fully implemented, many of the projected interviews with hospitalized patients were lost with expiration of the critical time interval.[1] The number of interviews obtained at each significant time is shown in Table 12.1. In general, the interviewers were fairly successful in their efforts to schedule and complete interviews; 80 per cent of the interviews called for by the expanded design were completed. The loss of data was particularly heavy at 6 and 12 months, for the decision to interview hospitalized patients was not made until after many had passed their 6- and 12-month anniversary dates. Thus, of the 86 interviews listed in Table 12.1 as "missed" at 6 months due to expiration of the time limit, 79 represent hospitalized patients who could have been interviewed had the decision been made in time. If the projected total (1,376) is reduced by the number of deaths plus the number of interviews missed by reason of the change in experimental design, interviews obtained would be 93 per cent.

Of the 136 patients released directly to the community, only 13 had returned before the scheduled 2-month interview. The majority of those listed as missed because of expiration of the time limit at 2 months were control patients released from other wards of the hospital. Channels of communication had not yet developed to the point where research personnel were routinely informed of the release of such patients.

✤ Obtaining the Patient's Cooperation

The fact that there were only 12 occasions on which a patient refused to be interviewed suggests that the procedure developed for contacting patients, scheduling interviews, and maintaining a positive relationship over a 3-year period was fairly effective. This procedure began while the patient was still participating in the rehabilitation

[1] With the exception of the two-month community interview, interviews had to be obtained within plus or minus four weeks of the anniversary date to be considered representative of a particular time interval.

TABLE 12.1

NUMBER OF FOLLOW-UP INTERVIEWS OBTAINED

AT EACH ANNIVERSARY DATE

	Months						
	2	6	12	18	24	36	Total
No. Obtained	105	154	189	208	226	220	1102
No. Missed							
Died	0	1	1	4	6	13	25
Moved Away	3	5	6	8	6	7	35
Could Not Locate	2	1	4	5	5	5	22
Refused	0	1	0	5	3	3	12
Too Ill	1	0	1	1	0	0	3
Time Limit							
Expired	12	86	47	17	2	0	164
Returned to Hosp.	13						13
	31	94	59	40	22	28	274
Original N	136	248	248	248	248	248	1376

program. The interviewer arranged to attend one of the program discussion groups having to do with preparation for community living.
During this session she talked with the patients about her role in the
project. The patients were reminded that the program was in fact
quite new, and that the only way staff could be sure it was genuinely
helpful was to know something about how well patients were able to
get along after leaving the hospital. For this reason, they were being
asked to participate in an effort to evaluate the long-term effects of
the project. It was explained that the information obtained in the
study would be used to improve the rehabilitation program for those
who followed them, and that the staff wished to be available in the
event help was needed after the patient left the hospital. In short, the
interviewer attempted to enlist the patient's cooperation in a joint ven-
ture in which the patient could both give and receive. The interviewer
made it quite clear that, although she was a social worker, she herself
would not be able to offer any of the services ordinarily provided by
the Social Service Department. Her function was simply to collect
information. She could, however, help the patient reach an appropri-

ate person or agency when this seemed indicated. The procedure for contacting the patient by letter was described, and the interviewer tried to answer any questions raised during the session.

Appointments for the initial interview were made by letter. Control patients released from other wards presented a special problem. In this instance, there was no preliminary personal contact, nor any connection with the Rehabilitation Center to fall back on. Letters to such patients went out through the clinical directors of the male and female treatment services.

The original plan called for the interviewer to visit the patient at his own residence. However, this had to be abandoned, as the number of interviews due to be completed each month increased rapidly after the change in experimental design. Trips into the community proved very time-consuming; the hospital is located some 17 miles from the area of the city in which most of the patients reside. Eventually, most patients were asked to come to the hospital for interviews. Whenever possible, interviews were scheduled to coincide with visits to the out-patient clinic. Arrangements were made for the patient to have lunch at the Rehabilitation Center dining room, and bus tokens were made available to insure that the trip to the hospital would not be a financial hardship. Patients who worked were interviewed in the evening or on their day off if this occurred during the regular work week. Appointments were frequently scheduled in conjunction with the monthly meeting of the "Alumni Club," an ex-patient social club for Rehabilitation Center "graduates."

❊ The Interview

The interview itself can best be described as semistructured. The information desired was specified in advance. However, the method of obtaining it was left to the interviewer. For the community interview, the major content areas were economic adjustment (use of income, provision for food, clothing, and shelter), work adjustment, use of leisure time, interpersonal relationships (including family, relatives, friends, and functional relationships), attitude toward hospitalization, physical condition, and psychiatric adjustment. Using the information obtained in these areas as a basis, the interviewer prepared a summary of the patient's current needs and problems and was encouraged to make specific recommendations for services which, if available, would help to alleviate these problems. In addition, the interviewer rated the patient's total psychiatric condition and social adjustment. Community interviews usually required at least two hours.

Hospital interviews tended to be of somewhat shorter duration, averaging about an hour. The content of the interview for hospitalized patients was, of necessity, more restricted. The major content areas were freedom of movement, work adjustment, use of unscheduled time, participation in specialized therapy programs, interpersonal relationships, motivation to leave the hospital, attitude toward the hospital and the Rehabilitation Center, physical condition, and psychiatric status. Ratings of psychiatric and social adjustment were also made in conjunction with hospital interviews.

The problem of deciding whether to confine the inquiry to the patient himself or to seek additional information from persons in the immediate environment was resolved for us by the patient. In the course of developing the initial interview protocol, it was discovered that many patients elected to conceal their previous relationship with the hospital from landlords, employers, and neighbors. Since relatively few patients lived with their own families, there seemed little to be gained by introducing data which could not be obtained directly. The patient himself was by all odds the most important informant and everything depended on securing and maintaining his cooperation. Therefore, no attempt was made to verify from other sources information obtained from the patient. In the case of hospitalized patients, on the other hand, information obtained from the patient was supplemented by data obtained from ward personnel and work supervisors.

Within each major content area there were certain kinds of information which could be coded in advance. This was particularly true of relatively objective data such as type of housing, hours of work, or preparation of meals. However, in many instances it was impossible to establish response categories in advance. Therefore, the patient's comments on such topics as budgeting, attitudes toward others, future plans and aspirations, were recorded verbatim. Although this procedure was relatively time-consuming, it proved a necessity when additional interviewers had to be recruited and trained.

❋ The Interviewers

As mentioned previously, the staff member who participated in the development of the interview protocol, established the interviewing procedure, and did most of the initial interviewing was a trained social worker. The interviewers who subsequently participated in the follow-up study varied widely in experience and academic background. Three had Ph.D.'s in clinical psychology, but one had no graduate training whatsoever. Two had masters' degrees in psychology but little interviewing experience and almost no familiarity with mental patients. Still another was an experienced school psychologist. With such diversified talent, the problem of maintaining quality control became of critical importance. Interviews conducted by inexperienced personnel were routinely reviewed to insure that information was properly recorded. The interviewer took extensive notes during the interview, then summarized these on the interview protocol immediately afterward. This material was reviewed in detail with an experienced staff member. Relevant material brought out during these supervisory conferences was included in the final write-up. If the information appeared sketchy or not readily interpretable, the interview was returned to the interviewer with the supervisor's comments. Inexperienced interviewers were supervised for at least six months.

❋ Treatment of Data

The information recorded on the original interview protocol was later coded in its entirety. A detailed manual of instructions containing the necessary definitions for handling subjective data was developed on a selected sample of six-month interviews. By this time, it was apparent that the data obtained at six months would not be sufficiently representative to be included in the final analysis. Therefore, these data were utilized freely for developmental purposes.

The final abstract of the interview protocol was the handiwork of a production line. Relatively objective information was abstracted by clerical personnel. Information concerning employment was abstracted by a psychologist utilizing the code employed in the *Dictionary of Occupational Titles: Volumes I and II* (1949). The section on interpersonal relationships was coded by the social worker. The assessment of current needs and problems made by the interviewer was reviewed and coded consensually, with at least two experienced interviewers participating. Many protocols contained little in the way of recommended services, as the inexperienced interviewers were unfamiliar with existing or potential community resources. Therefore, all interviews were reviewed by experienced personnel, and specific recommendations were formulated on a consensual basis.

Since the evaluation of current needs and problems required that each case be reviewed in detail, the abstractors were also asked to rate the patient on total psychiatric and social adjustment. These ratings, though based on secondary source material, are less subject to differences in familiarity with psychiatric illness, and thus possibly more accurate than those made by the original interviewers.

When the abstracts were completed, the information was transferred to IBM cards for automatic data processing. The community interview contained 252 items of information; the hospital interview contained 143. The number of scorable items in each individual protocol was often substantially less. This was particularly true in cases where there was no employment history or where the patient had no known relatives.

Chapter XIII

The Patient in the Community
Two Years After Completion
of Treatment

This[1] chapter reviews the adjustment of the study sample in the community two years after completion of treatment. Interview data gathered 24 months after treatment ended was available for 101 patients residing in the community. Of this community sample, 31 had experienced the Maximally Structured socio-environmental program, 28 the Partially Structured Program, and 19 the Minimally Structured pro-

[1] This chapter was written in collaboration with Wayne Leese.

235

gram; 23 were from the Control groups. Five areas of adjustment were evaluatied with respect to the interview data: living situation, work, leisure time, interpersonal relations, and psychiatric condition.

The demographic characteristics of these 101 patients were quite similar to those described for the total sample in Chapter Four. The average age was 47 years, the average length of hospitalization before experimental treatment was 9 years, and the average illness duration was 17. These individuals were in a low socio-economic position, as reflected by limited educational backgrounds and occupational abilities, which were generally at the unskilled level.

❀ The Living Situation

Few follow-up studies of chronic mental patients have dealt with a population characterized by as long a period of hospitalization as that of the community sample in this study. Comprehensive follow-up studies conducted by Freeman and Simmons (1963) and the Veterans' Administration Hospital Psychiatric Evaluation Project (1965) considered patients who had been hospitalized less than one and two years respectively. The majority of patients in both studies returned to live with parents, spouse, or siblings. In the current study, however, the long duration of continuous hospitalization severed patients' close ties even with relatives living in the community. Less than 25 per cent of the community sample in the current study went to live with first-order relatives (see Table 13.1); the great majority were living without supervision by relatives. The patients living with family members tended to be in poorer psychiatric condition than those who were not living with relatives. These two groups showed mean scores on the Psychiatric Status Scale (described later in this chapter) of 8.4 and 5.8 respectively. The difference between the two means was significant ($t = 3.68, p < .001$).

Since most of the community sample in this study did not return to sheltered familial settings, any evaluation of their adjustment to the community should take into account degree of independence. One measure of independence is how much economic responsibility is assumed by a given patient. Such a measure was derived from the degree of financial responsibility exercised by a patient in providing housing for himself and the degree of his responsibility in obtaining

TABLE 13.1

DISTRIBUTION OF PATIENTS* ACCORDING TO TYPE OF PERSONS
AVAILABLE FOR ASSOCIATION IN THE LIVING SITUATION

	N
Living with Immediate Family	
Spouse	6
Children	2
Parents	16
Living with Others	
Other Relatives	9
Employer	3
Others Available: Patient had Choice of Approaching or Avoiding Others	
Employees	7
Boarders	17
Roomers	5
Alone	36

* N — 101 — approximate %.

and preparing food. The maximum score of 8 was given when a patient assumed complete responsibility in each of these areas; for example, a patient who lived alone in an apartment and who purchased food and prepared his own meals was assigned a score of 4 in each area, for a total score of 8. The minimum total score of 2 was assigned in a situation where other people took full economic responsibility for a patient; for example, a patient who lived with his parents and had no responsibility for providing food and shelter was assigned a score of 1 in each area, for a total score of 2. The distribution of scores on the economic responsibility measure (see Table 13.2) indicates that over 50 per cent of the patients living in the community were assuming more than minimal responsibility for their own basic needs.

It is obvious that assuming economic responsibility for basic needs does not in itself constitute financial efficiency in establishing the best possible living situation. Funds must be used for a wide array of essentials for community living. A patient's discretion in expenditure of funds is of particular importance to his community adjustment

TABLE 13.2

DISTRIBUTION OF ECONOMIC RESPONSIBILITY SCORES

	Score	N^*
None	2	8
to	3	1
Minimal	4	33
Moderate	5	8
to	6	24
Full	7	21
	8	5

*No information was available for one subject.
$N = 100 = \%$.

when financial support is limited. Table 13.3 shows that the financial resources of the community sample were sufficient only to permit subsistence at a minimal level. More than half were receiving public assistance or pensions. Weekly income ranged from none to $66, with

TABLE 13.3

PRIMARY SOURCE OF SUPPORT AND MEAN WEEKLY NET INCOME
FOR PATIENTS IN THE COMMUNITY

Primary Source of Support	% of Patients Receiving Support	Mean Weekly Net Income
Public assistance	39	$16.69
Employment	29	34.02
Family	15	6.69
Pensions and benefits	14	23.54
Other (savings, charity, estate)	3	—

a mode of $15. Clearly, the judgment exercised in utilizing these funds becomes an important indicator of adjustment to the community.

Judgment was defined in terms of appropriateness of decision regarding expenditure of funds and the benefits derived from such expenditure. On the basis of follow-up interview data, a patient was rated as showing "Good," "Fair," or "Poor" judgment. Good judgment was said to be used by 42 per cent of the community sample, fair judgment 35 per cent, and poor judgment 23 per cent. Thus, 77 per cent of the total sample were viewed as making decisions and choices which were generally appropriate and advantageous.

❀ Work Adjustment

The vocational situation of a former mental patient is often posited as a crucial factor in his general adjustment to the community. On the basis of the poor premorbid histories of patients in this study (low educational levels, lack of occupational skills, and unsatisfactory work records), favorable posttreatment work adjustment is unlikely. Moreover, the long period of hospitalization without meaningful employment and the concomitant deterioration of work skills, as well as decreased desirability in the employment market due to advancing age, further diminish the significance of vocational status as a factor in community adjustment.

Table 13.4 summarizes the employment status of the 101 patients living in the community 24 months after completion of treat-

TABLE 13.4

EMPLOYMENT STATUS OF COMMUNITY PATIENTS*

	N
Full-Time Job**	19
Lives-In Job	11
Part-Time Job	8
Training	2
Unemployed	61

* $N = 101$ = approximate %.
** Worked more than 24 hours per week.

ment. It should be noted that 30 per cent held full-time positions. This finding is similar to that reported by the Veterans' Administration Hospital Psychiatric Evaluation Project (1965) for patients with a much shorter duration of illness.

The mean net weekly salary for the 19 full-time workers was

$38.07, the range $12.00 to $66.04. The average hourly wage for
both males and females was $1.12, below the $1.25 minimum level
prevailing during this period. Patients with live-in jobs averaged
$16.19 per week. The average cost of room and board ($16.06)
added to this amount yields a total weekly salary of $32.25 for a
46-hour work week. Patients with part-time jobs received a mean salary of $7.20 for 15¾ hours of work. None of these part-time workers
attained an hourly wage of $1.00. Clearly, the remuneration received
by these ex-patients was below the poverty level. Thirty-two per cent
of this sample expressed dissatisfaction with their jobs, usually on the
basis of inadequate salaries.

To determine whether the low-level, posttreatment employment status of the sample was commensurate with the premorbid employment level, the prehospitalization and posttreatment job skill levels
were coded according to the procedure outlined by the United States
Employment Service (United States Department of Labor). This code
is based on the amount of preparation required to master the essentials
of a given job. Table 13.5 categorizes the 101 community patients
according to level of vocational preparation required for the position
of longest duration prior to hospitalization and that held 24 months
after completion of treatment. Before hospitalization, 87 of these patients were employed, but only 38 were employed 24 months after
completion of treatment. The mean of the skill level of patients' employment, 3.54 prior to hospitalization, had fallen to 2.21 when evaluated 24 months after completion of treatment. The skill level required
in jobs held by most patients in this sample is considerably lower than
that of their premorbid employment. In addition, individual comparisons of premorbid and posttreatment vocational preparation indicate a decline in vocational situation for 71 per cent of the community
sample, no change for 19 per cent, and an improvement for only 10
per cent.

The fact that the vocational skill level of most persons in this
sample had declined below that of their premorbid level need not be
attributed to environmental factors such as lack of job opportunities
and prejudice against mental patients. These people had spent many
years in the hospital, which offers patients few opportunities to exercise
job skills. A survey of work assignments for patients at the Philadel-

TABLE 13.5

PREMORBID AND POSTTREATMENT EMPLOYMENT LEVELS OF
COMMUNITY PATIENTS, COMPARED ON THE BASIS
OF VOCATIONAL PREPARATION REQUIRED

| | Number of Patients | |
| | | 24 Months After |
Level of Vocational Preparation	Premorbid	Treatment
0. Unemployed or in training	14	63*
1. Only short demonstration required	16	14
2. Up to 30 days preparation	21	16
3. 30 days to 3 months preparation	9	1
4. 3–6 months preparation	8	0
5. 6–12 months preparation	18	7
6. 1–2 years preparation	6	0
7. 2–4 years preparation	7	0
8. 4–10 years preparation	2	0

* Two patients in training.

phia State Hospital, conducted in May, 1964, revealed two major types of assignment: industrial therapy and ward housekeeping. The industrial therapy assignments, which are of a higher level than the ward assignments, provide varied work experiences in all areas of the hospital. However, only 7 per cent of the 830 patients employed in industrial therapy assignments were placed in jobs requiring more than 3 months of training for minimal proficiency. The vast majority of patients performed work which offered little opportunity for retention of premorbid skill levels or for the learning of higher-level vocational skills.

According to Table 13.4, 60 per cent of the community sample were unemployed 24 months after completion of treatment. Abstractors reviewed the 24-month interview protocols of these 61 unemployed patients and rated them in terms of employability potential. The specific status of a given patient was determined by agreement between two of three judges. The rating categories, which ranged from "Employable" to "Unemployable," required judgments about how far a patient was incapacitated and if he had the ability to assume the responsibility of a regular job. The distribution of ratings is presented in Table 13.6. Forty-nine per cent of the unemployed patients were considered to be unemployable. Physical disability was the cause of this judgment in only 5 of these cases. An additional 25 per cent were evaluated as "Probably Unemployable." These pessimistic ratings were based primarily on psychiatric incapacitation. Only 6 per cent of the unemployed patients were classified as "Employable," and 18 per cent

TABLE 13.6

EMPLOYABILITY STATUS OF UNEMPLOYED PATIENTS,
24 MONTHS AFTER TREATMENT

	N	%
Employable	4	6
Marginal	11	18
Probably unemployable	15	25
Unemployable	30	49
Cannot judge	1	2
Total	61	100

were rated "Marginally Employable." Thus, 76 per cent of unemployed patients in this sample were judged to be unemployable or probably unemployable.

Since unemployability is associated with psychiatric debilitation, employed patients were expected to manifest the most effective adjustment in other areas of community life. The measure of economic judgment described earlier was used to evaluate this expectation. The economic judgment exercised by employed and unemployed patients was compared. Patients supported by their families were eliminated from this analysis, since many of them had no opportunity to exercise judgment in economic affairs and thus could not be rated. Employed patients were characterized by economic judgment superior to patients receiving public assistance or pensions ($\chi^2 = 16.97$, $df = 4$, $p < .01$).

Not all of the patients judged to be unemployable or probably unemployable had reconciled themselves to continued unemployment. Sixteen of the 61 unemployed patients mentioned job-seeking behavior in the month preceding the interview; 22 voiced an interest in employment but mentioned no specific job-seeking behavior; 23 said they were not interested in finding employment.

The poor employment potential of these patients makes their continued employment aspirations unrealistic and possibly maladaptive. Accordingly, the vocational judgment of the jobseekers was compared to that of the nonjobseekers. Abstractors reviewed the 24-month interview protocols for all patients in order to evaluate patients' judgment regarding vocational aspiration, self-evaluation for employment, and job-seeking behavior. A rating of "Good," "Fair," or "Poor" was assigned to a patient's judgment only when agreed upon by two out of three raters. The following definitions were used:

GOOD: The decisions and choices made by the patient are by and large consistently appropriate and potentially beneficial.

FAIR: The decisions and choices made by the patient are generally appropriate and tend to have a beneficial effect; however, he is unable to function consistently to his own best advantage.

POOR: The decisions and choices made by the patient are sometimes quite inappropriate and thus detrimental to his welfare.

Analysis revealed that unemployed patients who did not seek employment manifested better judgment. All of the 18 patients not available for employment (5 could not be rated) were considered to exercise good or fair judgment. Only 36 per cent of the 14 job-seeking patients (2 could not be rated) were rated as "Good" or "Fair." In summary, the bulk of the unemployed patients were rated as unemployable, and better judgment was shown by those patients who accepted their unemployability and did not seek employment.

❀ Leisure-Time Activities

Since the majority of the community sample did not have full-time employment, a considerable amount of free time was available to them. The use of their leisure time reflects to some extent their adjustment to the community. These 101 persons engaged in an aver-

TABLE 13.7

LEISURE-TIME ACTIVITIES OF THE COMMUNITY SAMPLE

	% of Sample
Television and radio	92
Reads	75
Takes walks	61
Visits others	46
Movies	42
Church	41
Writes letters	26
Naps	24
Games with others	21
Shops (including window-shops)	21

age of 5.9 leisure-time activities; only 1.8 of these activities involved other people. Table 13.7 presents the most frequent leisure-time activities of the community sample and the percentage of patients who engaged in each activity.

These 10 activities account for 77 per cent of all leisure-time activity of the community sample. The largely nonsocial character of these pursuits suggests an unusually barren and isolated existence, especially in view of the average age for the people involved of 47 years. Male and female patients did not differ in leisure-time patterns except for church attendance: more than twice as many females as males attended church.

The economic situation of the patients undoubtedly affects their choice of leisure-time activities. A tally showed that 55 per cent were free, 21 per cent involved a nominal cost (like carfare or a small donation), 9 per cent were ambiguous, and only 15 per cent required more than a nominal cost (such as admission to a movie or refreshments for entertaining others). Apparently the type and range of leisure-time activities in which the community sample engaged were largely determined by their limited financial resources.

❀ Interpersonal Relations

Since socio-environmental treatment was specifically designed to increase social interaction, the long-range effects of the programs on interpersonal relations are of primary importance in evaluating this type of treatment. Family relationships, number of friends, group affiliations, social orientation, and total social participation were areas of social behavior investigated in the follow-up interview.

Evaluation of family relationships was restricted to reviewing the number of contacts with, and attitudes toward, first-order relatives (parents, siblings, spouse, and children) who were outside a patient's immediate living situation. The contacts could be initiated either by the patient or the relative and included visits, letters, and telephone calls. Ninety-three of the 101 subjects in the community had at least one family member with whom a contact could be made. Information on family contacts was available for 86 patients, 43 males and 43 females. Forty-eight per cent had contact with relatives at least once each week; 20 per cent had had no contact during the entire year preceding the interview. Significantly more females than males had weekly contact with family members (65 and 30 per cent, respectively: $\chi^2 = 10.48$, $df = 1$, $p < .01$).

The interview protocols of the 93 patients with family members in the community were also utilized to determine patients' attitudes toward family. This attitude was rated as positive, negative, or indifferent. The categorization of attitude toward family members was based on the attitude most frequently noted. Five cases classified as indifferent were eliminated from the analysis, and another 14 cases could not be categorized because of insufficient information. Sixty-nine per cent of the remaining 74 subjects (33 males and 41 females) were rated as having generally positive attitudes toward family members. Thirteen of the 16 male patients who lived with their families (81 per cent) were characterized by positive attitudes toward relatives, as were 10 of the 11 female patients (91 per cent) who lived with their families. Seventy-three per cent of the 30 females who lived away from their families also indicated positive attitudes. However, only 35 per cent of the 17 males not living with their families maintained generally positive attitudes toward family members. Thus, males and females who lived away from their families differ significantly in attitude toward family members ($\chi^2 = 9.98$, $df = 1$, $p < .01$).

The significantly greater expression of negative attitudes by male patients living away from home is presumably related to male-female differences in community adjustment. Males and females were compared on the problem areas encountered in the community and on psychiatric adjustment.[2] The 47 patients who did not live with relatives showed no sex differences, either in number of problem areas or in psychiatric adjustment. However, males who expressed positive attitudes toward family members exhibited fewer problems in community adjustment (Fisher's Exact Probability Test, $p < .005$) and better psychiatric adjustment than their counterparts who expressed negative attitudes (means of 6.0 and 13.6 respectively, $t = 4.72$, $p < .001$). Comparable relationships did not emerge among female patients.

The negative attitudes of the poorly adjusted males living away from their families may be associated with such factors as psychopathology, frustration of dependency needs, or rejection by family. Some clarification of the major precipitant of these negative attitudes is provided by data on individuals who were in the hospital at the time of the 24-month interview. Data on family attitude were available for 82 of the 125 comprising the in-hospital group. Seventy-seven per cent of the 36 in-hospital male patients held positive attitudes toward their families, compared to only 35 per cent of the 17 males in the community sample. The attitudes of hospitalized males are thus significantly more positive than those of community sample males living away from their families ($\chi^2 = 7.34$, $df = 1$, $p < .01$).

The hospitalized group was significantly more psychiatrically debilitated than the community group living away from home who expressed negative attitudes. Therefore, these negative feelings cannot be attributed to the presence of more severe psychopathology. Rejection by family can also be eliminated as a causative factor in negative attitudes, since there is no greater rejection than being left in, or returned to, the hospital. The most reasonable explanation for the negative attitudes of the poorly adjusted males who lived away from home

[2] These two measures will be described below in the section on Psychiatric Adjustment.

is their frustrated dependency needs. Such poorly adjusted patients apparently resent their families for not caring for them. Within the sheltered situation of the hospital there is gratification of dependency needs and little resentment toward family members.

Females in the hospital at the time of the 24-month interview did not differ in attitudes from females in the community living away from their families. Fifty-nine per cent of the 46 females in the hospital and 73 per cent of the 30 females in the community showed positive attitudes toward their families. Females tend to express positive attitudes toward their families whether it is merited or not. This suggests a general reluctance among females to express negative attitudes, which may in turn explain the absence of significant relationships between expressed attitude and measures of community adjustment. It should be recalled that the poor initial response of females to the Maximally Structured treatment program (which included group therapy) was also attributed to their desire to avoid the expression of negative feelings.

The number of friendships developed by former patients in the community sample is an important indicator of their social anchoring in the community. In investigating friendships, community members whom the patient could name and with whom he had regular contacts were considered "friends"; excluded from this category were people with whom regular contacts occurred in functional relationships (for example, co-workers, landlord, employer). There was a striking inability to establish friendships. Thirty per cent could name no friends at the two-year follow-up interview. Twenty-five per cent coud name only one friend, and 45 per cent could name two or more friends.

A further indicator of sociability was the number of groups with which the patient was affiliated. The patients in the community attended only a few group activities on a regular basis. These included church social groups, "Y" activities, card-playing groups, activities for former mental patients conducted by such organizations as Hopetown and Horizon House, and the Rehabilitation Center's Alumni Club. If the Alumni Club is eliminated as not being an entirely indigenous community group, only 27 per cent of the sample attended some type of community group. Clearly, then, the chronic mental patient in the community tends to have few friends and limited group contacts and cannot be considered to have attained assimilation.

Since the Alumni Club was organized to facilitate the transition from the Rehabilitation Program to community membership and to provide the former patients with a supportive group during the transition period, the ex-patient's social affiliation with this organization warrants special attention. The Alumni Club provided an opportunity for continued contact with hospital staff and other project patients. Patients were invited to each monthly meeting, which was held at the hospital,[3] and transportation expenses were provided where the need was indicated. Patients attending the Alumni Club meetings were free to initiate and participate in whatever activities they preferred; no formally organized activities were available, but games and music were provided. Most popular was the refreshment period toward the end of the meeting. At least two psychologists and a social worker were present at each session to give support and guidance to those who sought this service.

The importance of the Alumni Club to the former patient is reflected in the high degree of attendance. Forty-one per cent of the community sample[4] attended at least one meeting during the six months preceding the 24-month interview, compared to 27 per cent who attended all other community groups combined. It was expected that Alumni Club meetings would be attended most frequently by patients in the early phase of their community tenure, and by those who were making a poor community adjustment and required the continued support of this group affiliation. Data on attendance of Alumni Club meetings were analyzed to test this prediction. For this analysis, the experimental patients[5] released to the community were divided into two groups: those who left the hospital and remained in the com-

[3] The Alumni Club meetings are now held in a Hopetown Association facility in central Philadelphia.

[4] The Control group was eliminated from this tabulation because the Alumni Club was restricted to former Rehabilitation program patients.

[5] Data on the experimental sample were supplemented by the inclusion of preexperimental patients and several patients who had experienced the socioenvironmental treatment program but were not included in the experimental sample.

munity for 24 months, and those who left the hospital but returned within 24 months. Males and females were studied separately.

The proportion of patients who attended an Alumni Club meeting was derived by dividing the actual number of patients present by the total number of patients invited. Curves showing the percentage of patients attending were plotted along a time axis, divided into two-month intervals following initial release to the community. These curves (Figure 13.1) are limited to the first 12 months following release from the hospital. After this period, the number of patients remaining in the community in the Return to Hospital Group decreased rapidly. It should be noted that the possible number of Return to Hospital patients available to attend the Alumni Club meetings decreased at each time interval subsequent to the initial disposition. The possible number of Remained Out patients who could attend meetings of course did not change.

Contrary to expectation, female patients who remained out of the hospital for the 24-month period attended Alumni Club meetings in significantly greater numbers than their counterparts who required rehospitalization during the 24-month follow-up period. In addition, the percentage of Remained Out females who attended meetings stays relatively constant, in contrast to a marked decline in attendance for the Return to Hospital group. It is possible that the females who most needed the continued support of this group affiliation took least advantage of it. Male patients tended gradually to reduce their contact with the Alumni Club, regardless of their adjustment in the community. However, males who made a poor adjustment (that is, those who returned to the hospital during the 24-month period) tended to make greater use of the Alumni Club than their Remained Out counterparts. It should be recalled that the data on family relationships—the poorly adjusted males who lived away from family had negative feelings toward relatives while those who remained in, or returned to the hospital, had positive feelings—led to the hypothesis that dependency needs and gratification of these needs represent core problems for males who are experiencing difficulty in adjustment to the community. The Alumni Club attendance findings support this viewpoint.

The general social orientation of the community sample was

FIG. 13.1   ALUMNI CLUB ATTENDANCE OF MALE AND FEMALE
PATIENTS WHO REMAINED IN THE COMMUNITY OR RETURNED
TO THE HOSPITAL DURING THE 24-MONTH FOLLOW-UP PERIOD

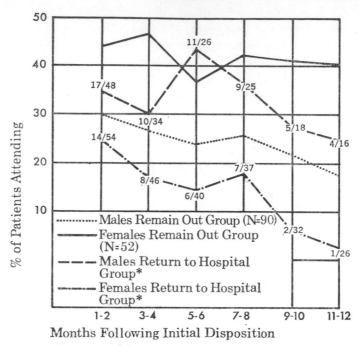

Months Following Initial Disposition

* The number of patients available to attend the Alumni Club meetings decreased at each time interval because of returns to the hospital. At each time
interval on the curves, the number of patients still remaining out of the hospital
is indicated in the denominator; the number of patients attending the Alumni
Club is indicated in the numerator.

ascertained on the basis of information from the interview protocols
regarding attitudes toward others. Each patient was assigned to one
of four categories which described his general way of dealing with
people. "Moves toward others" characterized those who generally
sought the company of other people, regardless of the maturity level
of the seeking behavior. "Indifferent toward others" described patients
who did not initiate contact with others and made no effort either to
sustain or to avoid relationships initiated by others. The category
"Moves away from others" included patients who may have had one

or two close relationships but tended to avoid all other contacts. "Moves against others" portrayed patients who manifested hostility toward others. Since only 3 of the 101 patients in the sample fell into this last category, they were omitted from this evaluation. Thirty-eight per cent of the community sample were categorized as "Moves toward others," 25 per cent as "Indifferent toward others," and 37 per cent as "Moves away from others." Sixty-two per cent are thus, at most, indifferent.

In addition, patients were rated[6] on their social participation in the community. The 15 intervals on the Social Participation Scale were collapsed into 3 inclusive categories (see Figure 13.2). Ten per cent of the 101 patients demonstrated essentially normal social participation; 61 per cent showed limited participation; and 29 per cent were essentially withdrawn. The findings on social orientation and social participation indicate that apathy or withdrawal continues to characterize the interpersonal behavior of the majority of the community sample 24 months after completion of treatment.

✸ Psychiatric Adjustment

Normal adulthood presumes an ability to satisfy personal needs and to deal effectively with people involved in daily life. In meeting these requirements, the adult must make provision for food, clothing, housing, personal care and household items, recreation, employment, interpersonal relations, physical health, and his mental and emotional state. The inability to gratify needs in these areas is evidence of the existence of a problem or a potential problem in adjustment.

Table 13.8 summarizes data on the number of patients who manifested difficulties in certain potential problem areas. These data were abstracted from the follow-up interview protocols. Interpersonal relations, whether with a relative or nonrelative, whether in the residence or outside, clearly represents the most crucial problem area for patients in the community. More patients have interpersonal difficul-

[6] Two abstractors assigned each patient a scale rating based on the information in the interview protocol. The two ratings were averaged for the final score. The interjudge reliability of the ratings assigned to male and female patients is .75 and .87 respectively.

Fig. 13.2   Social Participation Scale

General: This scale is designed to tap a fundamental attitude toward people. Basically, it is the attitude of moving toward or away from people, of maximizing or minimizing interaction with others. The term "participation" here implies a mutuality of relationship, either in a group setting or in individual contacts. It is the difference between talking *with* and talking *at*. Thus, a person who does a lot of talking is not necessarily participating in a relationship. Note that both an absence of participation and inappropriate participation are grounds for a low rating on this scale. Both asocial and antisocial behavior are considered inappropriate for purposes of this scale.

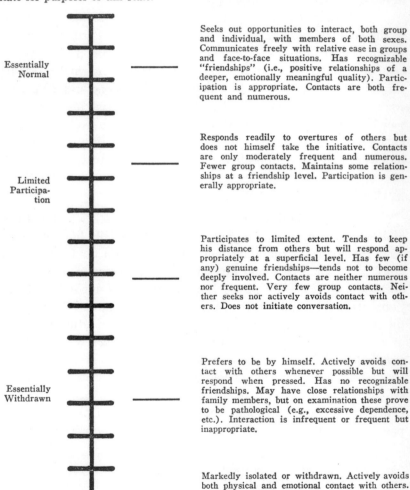

Essentially Normal — Seeks out opportunities to interact, both group and individual, with members of both sexes. Communicates freely with relative ease in groups and face-to-face situations. Has recognizable "friendships" (i.e., positive relationships of a deeper, emotionally meaningful quality). Participation is appropriate. Contacts are both frequent and numerous.

Responds readily to overtures of others but does not himself take the initiative. Contacts are only moderately frequent and numerous. Fewer group contacts. Maintains some relationships at a friendship level. Participation is generally appropriate.

Limited Participation — Participates to limited extent. Tends to keep his distance from others but will respond appropriately at a superficial level. Has few (if any) genuine friendships—tends not to become deeply involved. Contacts are neither numerous nor frequent. Very few group contacts. Neither seeks nor actively avoids contact with others. Does not initiate conversation.

Essentially Withdrawn — Prefers to be by himself. Actively avoids contact with others whenever possible but will respond when pressed. Has no recognizable friendships. May have close relationships with family members, but on examination these prove to be pathological (e.g., excessive dependence, etc.). Interaction is infrequent or frequent but inappropriate.

Markedly isolated or withdrawn. Actively avoids both physical and emotional contact with others. Interaction which does occur tends to be inappropriate.

ties (from 46 to 77 per cent) than recreational (41 per cent) or employment (41 per cent) problems. This pattern confirms previous findings regarding the poor social adjustment of the chronic mental patient in the community. It should be noted that 84 per cent of the sample living in the community were judged to have problems deriving from their mental and emotional state. The interview protocol was studied by two abstractors, each of whom rated each patient on the Psychiatric Status Scale (see Figure 13.3); the average of these two ratings constituted the psychiatric status score. When the 15 intervals on the original scale were collapsed into 3 gross categories, 31 per cent of the community sample were characterized by essentially normal psychiatric status, 44 per cent showed limitations, and 25 per cent were judged to be essentially abnormal. Apparently the mental and emotional state of the former patients remains a major limiting factor in their adjustment.

Findings regarding the adjustment of the chronic patients who were in the community 24 months following completion of treatment suggest that performance of instrumental acts is extremely limited. Although more than half of the community sample assumes better than minimal responsibilities for food and housing and exercises adequate economic judgment, the majority is unemployed and dependent upon welfare grants or social security benefits. Even the few individuals who have obtained full-time employment are able to earn only submarginal wages. These employed patients fill their leisure time with activities which reflect almost no involvement with others and which contribute little to the community; their interpersonal contacts are highly curtailed and group affiliations are practically nonexistent. In fact, interpersonal relations constitute one of the major problem areas for most of the community sample. Their social participation and psychiatric adjustment are also limited. This bleak description of the community adjustment of the former patients indicates that, if effective instrumental functioning were necessary for continued stay in the community, the majority would have to be rehospitalized. Their continued residence in the community is apparently determined by their remaining inconspicuous, avoiding demanding situations, and being satisfied with functioning below their premorbid level.

TABLE 13.8

FREQUENCY OF OCCURRENCE OF PROBLEMS FOR THE COMMUNITY SAMPLE

Problem Area	Male N	Female N	Total N	Sample for Which Data are Potentially Available	% of Sample Represented by Total N
Food	6	4	10	98	10
Clothing	4	10	14	95	15
Housing	7	4	11	100	11
Personal care and household items	7	6	13	96	14
Recreation	23	18	41	101	41
Employment	22	18	40	98	41
Interpersonal relations					
Family—Live with	11	9	20	30	67
Family—Not live with	22	26	48	82	59
Other—Live with	10	6	16	35	46
Other—Not live with	45*	30*	75	97	77
Physical health	16	20	36	94	38
Mental and emotional state	43	38	81	97	84

* χ^2 Males ($N = 50$) vs. Females ($N = 47$) : 8.04, $df = 1$, $p < .01$.

254

FIG. 13.3   PSYCHIATRIC STATUS: DEGREE OF IMPAIRMENT

General: This scale is designed to measure the extent to which the patient's ability to carry out the basic responsibilities of everyday living is impaired by psychiatric illness. In determining where on this scale a patient should be rated, consider the patient's ability to:

(*a*) assume complete responsibility for personal hygiene;
(*b*) provide adequate food, clothing, shelter, and medical attention, either directly or through seeking appropriate help;
(*c*) manage money and/or personal property in a responsible manner;
(*d*) establish and maintain adequate functional relationships (e.g., landlady, work supervisor, agency personnel, hospital attendant, etc.);
(*e*) use leisure time constructively;
(*f*) find and/or hold a job, when applicable;
(*g*) assume the responsibilities of marriage, children, etc., when applicable.

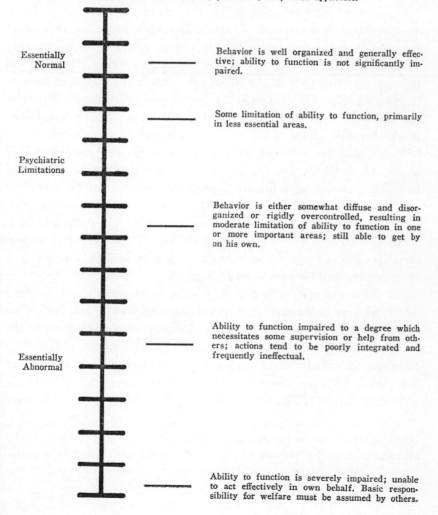

Essentially Normal

Behavior is well organized and generally effective; ability to function is not significantly impaired.

Some limitation of ability to function, primarily in less essential areas.

Psychiatric Limitations

Behavior is either somewhat diffuse and disorganized or rigidly overcontrolled, resulting in moderate limitation of ability to function in one or more important areas; still able to get by on his own.

Ability to function impaired to a degree which necessitates some supervision or help from others; actions tend to be poorly integrated and frequently ineffectual.

Essentially Abnormal

Ability to function is severely impaired; unable to act effectively in own behalf. Basic responsibility for welfare must be assumed by others.

❀ Effects of the Study Variables

Up to here, this chapter has been concerned with the entire community sample, regardless of socio-environmental treatment program, reactivity level, and sex, that is, the major study variables involved in this project. The effects of these variables on all areas of community adjustment, except leisure-time activities,[7] will be considered in this section.

Although ability to perform instrumental acts is not necessarily a requirement for continued stay in the community, level of performance is certainly a measure of community adjustment. In the current project the socio-environmental treatment programs provided training in instrumental behavior relevant to community living. Although less training was provided in the Minimally Structured condition than in the two more structured conditions, it still greatly surpassed any training available to patients in the Control condition. An important issue is whether the effects of this training differential are reflected in the community adjustment of patients 24 months after completion of treatment. Both the age (reactivity level) and the sex of the patient have been shown to influence immediate response to the treatment programs. Therefore, any meaningful consideration of previous treatment must include these two additional variables. Furthermore, it is reasonable to anticipate age and sex differences in community adjustment because of diverse community expectations for younger and older persons and for males and females.

Living situation is the only area of community adjustment which was not influenced by previous treatment program. No differences emerged for the two measures of degree of independence in the living situation: economic responsibility and judgment in handling economic affairs. However, on the latter measure older patients were considered to show better judgment than younger ($x^2 = 15.56$, $df = 2$, $p < .001$). Sixty-four per cent of the older individuals were

---

[7] The survey of leisure-time activities indicated that the patients occupied themselves with nonproductive activities which had little bearing on their instrumental behavior. Because of the inconsequential nature of these activities, it was decided not to relate them to the experimental variables.

rated as "Good" compared to only 21 per cent of the younger individuals. No sex differences were noted for either of these measures, but male-female differences were found in terms of type of living situation. Twenty-seven per cent of the males and only 4 per cent of the females lived with parents, which suggests that males are generally more dependent on their families than are females.

Previous socio-environmental treatment was a significant factor in the area of vocational adjustment. Table 13.9 presents the distributions of ratings of vocational judgment for the four treatment conditions. Those who had experienced the two more structured pro-

TABLE 13.9

RATINGS OF VOCATIONAL JUDGMENT* CATEGORIZED BY PREVIOUS
SOCIO-ENVIRONMENTAL TREATMENT CONDITION

	Ratings		
	Good	Fair	Poor
Maximally Structured	14	6	4
Partially Structured	13	8	5
Minimally Structured	4	10	5
Control	3	15	1

Over-all: $\chi^2 = 18.49$, $df = 6$, $p < .01$

Maximally and Partially Structured vs. Minimally Structured
and Control: $\chi^2 = 14.09$, $df = 2$, $p < .001$

* Thirteen patients were eliminated from this analysis because their vocational judgment could not be rated.

grams were rated as having significantly better judgment than those in the Minimally Structured and Control conditions. Apparently the two programs which provided educational content—job-seeking behavior and work conduct—had a significant impact on posttreatment vocational judgment, even if it was the negative one of dissuading the patient from seeking work.

Further analysis of these data in terms of the two other relevant experimental variables (sex and age) revealed a sex difference but no age difference in vocational judgment. Females were considered to show better judgment than males in the vocational area ($\chi^2 = 7.54$, $df = 2$, $p < .05$). This superiority in vocational judgment may reflect the ability of females to limit their employment aspirations; unemployment is culturally more acceptable for females than for males.

Since differences in vocational judgment were attributable to socio-environmental treatment programs, a relationship between post-treatment employment rates and type of program was also anticipated. The employment rates for the four conditions were 48 per cent for the Maximally Structured condition, 37 per cent for the Partially Structured, 42 per cent for the Minimally Structured, and 23 per cent for the Control condition; the Maximally Structured condition showed twice as high a rate as the Control condition. Employment rates were not influenced by either age or sex.

The social adjustment of the community sample was also influenced by type of previous treatment. The distribution of friendships dichotomized at the median (0-and-1 versus 2-or-more) revealed significantly more friendships in the community for patients who had experienced the socio-environmental programs than for patients in the Control condition ($\chi^2 = 6.86$, $df = 1$, $p < .01$). Although the former patient in the community generally tends to have a limited number of friendships, his contacts with others would be even more curtailed without the experience of socio-environmental treatment. Sex or age did not relate to number of friendships in the community.

Group affiliation appeared to be affected by a program-age interaction. The poorest attendance at group activities occurred in the younger patients who had experienced the Control and the Minimally Structured treatment conditions. None of the 25 younger patients in these two groups attended community group activities, compared to 37 per cent of the 30 younger patients in the Maximally and Partially Structured conditions. The social experiences provided by the two more structured programs apparently influenced the group affiliation behavior of the younger patients.

The ratings of social participation conformed with findings regarding number of friendships and attendance at community group activities. For the most part, patients who were in the Control condition manifested the poorest social participation. The mean rating for the Control group was 9.61, whereas the comparable ratings for the three socio-environmental treatment groups ranged from 7.41 to 8.04 (the higher the mean score, the poorer the social participation). The difference among the programs approaches significance ($F = 2.20$, $p < .10$) and is attributable to the poor social participation of those in the Control group. The social participation ratings also revealed age and sex differences. Older patients showed a definite superiority over younger patients (the mean ratings are 7.38 and 9.04 respectively, $F = 7.09$, $p < .01$), and females tended to surpass males (the mean ratings are 7.69 and 8.72 respectively, $F = 2.81$, $p < .10$).

Although females tended to surpass males only on the Social Participation Scale, their social orientation more clearly reflected their greater sociability. On the social orientation measure significantly more females were categorized in "Moves toward others," while males dominated the "Indifferent" and "Moves away from others" categories. This difference was significant ($x^2 = 8.68$, $df = 2$, $p < .02$). No program or age differences were found on this measure.

Besides influencing the vocational and social adjustment of the community sample, type of previous treatment affected psychiatric status evaluated 24 months after completion of treatment. An analysis of Psychiatric Status Scores (see Table 13.10) revealed better psychiatric condition for patients who had experienced the three socio-environmental treatment programs than for those who had been in the Control condition. A significant age difference also emerged: younger patients were generally more psychiatrically disabled than older patients, and the younger patients in the Control condition showed the most marked disability. The poor scores of the younger Control patients contributed heavily to the significant difference in psychiatric status scores attributable to previous treatment.

Another indicator of psychiatric condition is the number of areas in which patients experienced adjustment problems and the degree of stress precipitated by such problems. Previous treatment showed no relationship with total number of problems. There was no sex difference in the total number of problem areas. However, significantly fewer females than males had interpersonal problems with others outside the living situation (64 and 90 per cent respectively; see Table 13.8).

Age is the only study variable related to number of problem areas encountered in the community. Older patients had problems in

TABLE 13.10

MEAN PSYCHIATRIC STATUS SCORES OF OLDER AND YOUNGER
PATIENTS CATEGORIZED ACCORDING TO PREVIOUS SOCIO-
ENVIRONMENTAL TREATMENT CONDITION

	Maximally Structured		Partially Structured		Minimally Structured		Control		Over-all	
	M	N	M	N	M	N	M	N	M	N
Older	5.94	17	5.50	12	6.00	12	6.44	9	5.94	50
Younger	7.10	14	7.34	16	6.22	7	9.82	14	7.80	51
Total	6.47	31	6.56	28	6.08	19	8.50	23	6.88	101

F sex $= .68$, $p =$ n.s.

F age $= 8.85$, $p < .01$

F programs $= 2.72$, $p < .06$

significantly fewer areas than younger patients (the means are 3.30 and 4.71 respectively, $F = 11.39$, $p < .01$).

The amount of stress and tension experienced by patients in the various problem areas was also evaluated. The abstractors who reviewed the follow-up interview protocols for potential problem areas also rated on a four-point scale the degree of stress noted in each of these areas. A total stress score was computed for each patient by adding the individual stress scores in each problem area. Analysis of variance of the total stress scores yielded results similar to those noted in analyzing the total number of problem areas. Total stress scores did not vary according to treatment condition or sex, but differences attributable to age did emerge. Older patients had significantly lower stress scores than younger patients ($F = 13.24$, $p < .01$).

❀ SUMMARY AND DISCUSSION ❀

The general effects of socio-environmental treatment were still apparent in patients' community adjustment 24 months after release from the hospital. Patients in the Control condition had the poorest adjustment; they were characterized by inadequate vocational judgment, low employment rates, minimal relations with other community members and social groups,[8] and poor psychiatric adjustment.

Patients from the Maximally and Partially Structured programs, which provided specialized training in some of the instrumental behaviors required in the community (such as cooking, sewing, budgeting, and applying for employment), tended to show a community adjustment comparable to that of patients in the Minimally Structured program, which offered no such training. The similarities in community adjustment of patients who experienced socio-environmental treatment, regardless of program structure, can be attributed to the impact of group-living experiences and the variety of social organizations which were common elements in all three socio-environmental programs. Living in a therapeutic social milieu apparently teaches patients to make the accommodations necessary to minimize interpersonal stress and to avoid potentially disturbing situations. In this study, patients exposed to such a hospital milieu made a more adequate community adjustment than patients who experienced the traditional regimens of hospital wards.

These findings should not be interpreted to mean that experience in a therapeutic social milieu alone is sufficient, and that special training in instrumental behavior is unwarranted. Patients in the two more-structured programs did surpass those in the Minimally Structured condition in vocational judgment and number of group affiliations (the latter a result of the poor group attendance of younger patients in the Minimally Structured condition).

[8] It was the younger patients in the Control condition who showed no group affiliations.

The community adjustment of chronic mental patients can be enhanced by training in instrumental acts, but certain factors limit the efficacy of such training. Eighty-four per cent of the community sample still had psychiatric problems 24 months after completion of treatment, and 69 per cent were rated either as abnormal or limited in their ability to function due to psychiatric symptoms. Certainly one major determinant of general community adjustment is psychiatric condition. The limitations posed by poor psychiatric condition must be considered in helping patients establish realistic expectations for themselves and in delimiting their range of community activities.

Because the older patients manifested better psychiatric adjustment at completion of treatment, it was expected that they would be capable of a more favorable community adjustment than younger patients. At the 24-month interview these older patients not only showed better psychiatric adjustment, but also were superior to the younger patients in practically all areas of community adjustment. They showed superior economic judgment, comparable employment rates, higher-level social participation, fewer problem areas, and less stress associated with community living. It is conceivable that the reduction in drive level and the concomitant enhanced ability to withstand stress, which helped the older patients respond so successfully to socio-environmental treatment, also facilitated a more satisfactory community adjustment. Lowered aspirations and acceptance of limitations, which also accompany reduction in drive level, undoubtedly are factors enhancing the adjustment of older patients to the community.

It should be recalled that, at completion of treatment, the response of females to socio-environmental treatment was not influenced by the degree of program structure. One reason advanced for this finding was that despite their chronic mental illness females are generally socially oriented and require either a more intensive and demanding socialization experience or a program directed toward personality factors other than sociability. Twenty-four months after completion of treatment, females continued to surpass males with respect to social functioning. In general, females had more weekly contact with relatives and fewer interpersonal problems with others outside their immediate living situation. Unlike males, who tended to avoid or be indifferent to others, females initiated contact with others. Females also surpassed males in vocational judgment, probably a function of the greater cultural acceptance of limited employment for women.

Chapter XIV

Patterns of Change in Adjustment: A Thirty-Six-Month Longitudinal Study

Little is known about the long-term adjustment pattern of the chronic mental patient who is released from the hospital at completion of treatment and manages to function in the community. Does such a patient manifest progressive growth as a result of previous treatment? Or, without the mainstay of hospital treatment, does he remain at a static level or even regress?

     Chapter Eleven discussed the characteristics of the successful chronic mental patients in this study, that is, those who remained in

264

the community for 36 months following release. This chapter[1] will emphasize patterns of change in adjustment among this sample. The longitudinal study of these patients was also designed to yield information on the effects of the study variables (previous treatment, age, and sex) on the patterns of community adjustment with the passage of time.

Data were available on 58 of the 60 patients who remained in the community for the full 36-month period. All analyses were based on this sample of 58 patients. To determine the patterns of change, the 12-, 24-, and 36-month interview data were analyzed for each of the five areas of adjustment: living situation, work, leisure time, interpersonal relations, and psychiatric condition. Baseline data regarding the living and work situations of the community sample at the time of release from the hospital were available from each patient's Disposition Records. Interview data at completion of treatment were unsuitable for a baseline measure[2] of three areas of adjustment: leisure time, interpersonal relations, and psychiatric condition; consequently, the 12-month interview data were taken as the baseline for these adjustment measures. The instruments used to measure adjustment in each of the five areas were described in the preceding chapter. Data for each measure were based on behavior manifested during the six-month period preceding each of the follow-up interviews.

The living situation of the former patient in the community involves not only the kind of setting in which he lives, but also the degree of responsibility which he assumes within it. Source of support is taken as an indicator of degree of responsibility.

Table 14.1 summarizes the living situation of the 58 patients who remained in the community for the full 36 months. The four living situation categories—With family, With employer, With others in a boarding house, and Alone—are mutually exclusive. The per-

---

[1] This chapter was written in collaboration with Wayne Leese.

[2] Data gathered two and six months following completion of treatment were available for a restricted sample of patients. These data were used to provide information regarding the social participation and psychiatric condition of the community sample shortly after completion of treatment. However, because of the many revisions made during the early phase of the follow-up study, these early interview protocols could not be abstracted to yield reliable information regarding other measures of adjustment.

TABLE 14.1

LIVING SITUATION OF THE COMMUNITY SAMPLE ($N = 58$) AT COM-
PLETION OF TREATMENT AND AT TWELVE, TWENTY-FOUR, AND
THIRTY-SIX MONTHS FOLLOWING COMPLETION OF TREATMENT

	With Family	With Employer	With Others in Rooming or Boarding House	Alone
	%	%	%	%
At Completion of Treatment	28	5	28	40
12 Months	28	9	22	41
24 Months	26	9	19	47
36 Months	29	7	16	48

centage distributions for these four categories at release from the
hospital and at the three subsequent follow-up periods reveal very
little change in living situation. Further analysis discloses that previous
treatment, age, and sex do not affect type of posttreatment living situation.

With respect to source of support, Table 14.2 shows that the
number of patients in the community sample able to assume their
own support does vary in time ($Q = 16.73$, $df = 3$, $p < .001$). At
completion of treatment only 17 per cent of the 58 patients were supporting themselves primarily through employment. This figure increases to 29 per cent at 12 and 24 months, and to 36 per cent at 36
months. A concomitant of this increased self-support is decreasing
dependence on public assistance and family support. Additional analyses reveal that, for the community sample, long-term change in employment as a source of support is not related to previous treatment,
age, or sex.

Employment status is a commonly used indicator of the level
of adjustment to the community. Employment data presented in
Table 14.2 are incomplete, however, since a number of patients not
reported in this table did work but did not earn enough to be self-
supporting. Thirty-five, 42, and 46 per cent of the sample were employed, either on a full- or part-time basis, at 12, 24, and 36 months

TABLE 14.2

SOURCE OF SUPPORT OF THE COMMUNITY SAMPLE $(N = 58)$ AT
COMPLETION OF TREATMENT AND AT TWELVE, TWENTY-FOUR,
AND THIRTY-SIX MONTHS FOLLOWING COMPLETION OF TREATMENT

	Public Assistance	Employment	Family	Pension Savings, etc.
	%	%	%	%
At Completion of Treatment	50	17	14	19
12 Months	43	29	10	17
24 Months	45	29	12	14
36 Months	38	36	5	21

respectively. At the time of the 36-month interview, almost all of the 27 former patients in the community who were judged to be employable held some type of employment. Only 1 of the 31 unemployed ex-patients was judged to be employable.

An evaluation of the ex-patients' vocational adjustment was derived from the follow-up interview data. The abstractors rated each patient as "Good," "Fair," or "Poor" with respect to the appropriateness of his vocational aspirations and job-seeking behavior. They also rated him on the dependability of his job performance and employment-seeking behavior. Employed as well as unemployed patients in the community sample were rated. Patients who chose not to seek employment because they were incapacitated were considered to show "Good" vocational judgment.

Table 14.3 presents the proportion of community patients rated as having good vocational judgment. It should be noted that at the time of the 36-month interview the majority of the community sample had achieved a vocational adjustment in accord with their limitations. Although there was significant change in vocational judgment[3] $(Q = 6.72, df = 2, p < .05)$ as time passed, Table 14.3 shows that this change is due entirely to the improvement manifested by the older

[3] The results presented in this section are based on comparisons of patients in the "Good" category with the combined number of those in the other two categories.

TABLE 14.3

PERCENTAGE OF OLDER AND YOUNGER COMMUNITY SAMPLE PATIENTS
$(N = 52)$* SHOWING "GOOD" VOCATIONAL JUDGMENT AT TWELVE,
TWENTY-FOUR, AND THIRTY-SIX MONTHS FOLLOWING
COMPLETION OF TREATMENT

	12 Months %	24 Months %	36 Months %
Older $(N = 33)$	42	42	70
Younger $(N = 19)$	53	42	42
Total $(N = 52)$	46	42	60

* Six cases were eliminated from this study because interview data on their vocational judgment could not be rated.

patients $(Q = 9.00, df = 2, p < .02)$. The younger patients show no comparable improvement. This improvement in vocational judgment ratings for the older patients is apparently related to their ability to accept their limitations and to lower their aspirations. This process is facilitated by cultural acceptance of decreased productivity in older individuals, and by the energy diminution which accompanies aging.

As the former patient becomes more established in the community, a change in the pattern of his leisure-time activities is expected to occur. As he becomes more aware of the variety of activities available in the community, he is likely to find some that reflect his interests. Thus, with time, the number of activities in which he engages can be expected to increase. Another relevant factor is the effect of differences in level of adjustment on leisure-time activities. For example, compared with the unemployed patient, the employed patient, who has more funds but a limited amount of free time, may utilize his time differently. He may show either an increase in the number, or a change in the type, of activities in which he participates.

The type and number of leisure-time activities in which the community sample engaged has been described in Chapter Thirteen. These activities were relatively few in number and tended to be non-social and sedentary. Most frequently reported were watching television and listening to the radio, reading, taking walks, visiting others, going to movies, and attending church. The sample of 58 patients who remained in the community over a 36-month period shows a small but significant increase in number of leisure-time activities ($F = 4.85$, $p < .01$). The mean number of activities at the 12-, 24-, and 36-month intervals are 5.55, 6.34, and 6.43 respectively. Although this increase is statistically significant, it is much smaller than one might expect for a two-year period in the community following release from the hospital. Females tend to engage in more leisure-time activities than males ($F = 8.36$, $p < .01$). Age and type of previous treatment have no bearing on the increase in number of leisure-time activities.

There is apparently no relationship between number of leisure-time activities and differences in level of community adjustment as determined by employment status. Thirty-six months after completion of treatment there is no difference in the number of leisure-time activities characterizing employed and unemployed individuals in the community sample. In addition, although obtaining employment after having been unemployed is not associated with an increase in the number of leisure-time activities, there is evidence that employed and unemployed patients engage in different types of leisure-time activities. Employed females engage in more activities involving some cost, even if only a nominal one such as carfare ($\chi^2 = 5.39$, $df = 1$, $p < .03$). This difference is not found for employed and unemployed males. Thus, compared with males, females apparently engage in a greater number of leisure-time activities and the pattern of their activities is also more amenable to change.

One obvious dimension of community adjustment is interpersonal relations. Patterns of change in interpersonal relations were analyzed by using two measures: group memberships and social participation. Because the people in the sample were affiliated with very few community groups, the number of group memberships proved to be an inadequate measure of interpersonal relations. An informal measure was substituted—whether the patient attended any community-group meeting. Social and recreational groups conducted by local "Y's," churches, and organizations for former mental patients[4] (for

---

[4] Attendance at the Alumni Club was not included in this measure

example, Horizon House, Hopetown) are examples of the type of group meetings included in this informal measure. Table 14.4 shows no difference in attendance with the passage of time for the total community sample. However, a fairly consistent difference in affiliation differentiates patients who had experienced any socio-environmental therapy from patients who had been in the Control condition. This latter group showed the poorest group affiliation. Neither age nor sex influenced attendance patterns.

TABLE 14.4

ATTENDANCE AT COMMUNITY GROUP FUNCTIONS BY THE COMMUNITY
SAMPLE, CATEGORIZED BY PREVIOUS TREATMENT

	Attendance 12 Months %	Attendance 24 Months %	Attendance 36 Months %
Maximally Structured (N = 18)	61	61	61
Partially Structured (N = 18)	56	61	56
Minimally Structured (N = 14)	57	43	50
Control Condition (N = 8)	0	25	13
Total (N = 58)	50	52	50

Another measure of social adjustment in the community is the patient's social participation: the frequency, diversity, and appropriateness of his interpersonal relations. As described in Chapter Thirteen, abstractors rated each patient's social participation on the Social Participation Scale (Figure 13.2) from interview data gathered at 12, 24, and 36 months after completion of treatment. The mean ratings for the whole sample are surprisingly stable from the 12- to the 24- to the 36-month interview (see Table 14.5). Furthermore, baseline data from interviews of a reduced sample of 43 community patients 2 months after release are comparable to data obtained through-

because attendance at Club meetings was not open to patients from the Control condition.

out the 36-month follow-up period and indicate no temporal changes in the pattern of interpersonal behavior.

The study variables (type of treatment, age, and sex) do not influence change in social participation during the 36 months in the community. However, sex and age differences are noted throughout the follow-up period. According to Table 14.5, females are significantly more social than males. A similar finding is made for older patients.

TABLE 14.5

SOCIAL PARTICIPATION SCALES: MEANS* FOR THE COMMUNITY SAMPLE
AT TWELVE, TWENTY-FOUR, AND THIRTY-SIX MONTHS FOLLOWING
COMPLETION OF TREATMENT CATEGORIZED BY SEX AND AGE

	12 Months	24 Months	36 Months
Total Sample ($N = 58$)	7.85	7.88	7.78
Sex			
Males ($N = 30$)	8.83	8.99	8.62
Females ($N = 28$)	6.79	6.70	6.89

$$F \text{ (sex)} = 11.74, \, df = 1, \, p < .005$$

Age			
Older ($N = 36$)	7.52	7.32	7.25
Younger ($N = 22$)	8.39	8.80	8.66

$$F \text{ (age)} = 2.89, \, df = 1, \, p < .10$$

* The lower the score, the better the social participation.

It is generally assumed that a patient's psychiatric condition influences his community adjustment. The Psychiatric Status Scale described in the preceding chapter (see Figure 13.3) was used by abstractors to evaluate each patient's psychiatric condition at 12, 24, and 36 months following completion of treatment. The Psychiatric Status Scale is essentially a measure of the degree to which the patient's psychopathology impairs his ability to perform daily life activities. Data based on the Psychiatric Status Scale indicate that the psychiatric adjustment of patients remaining in the community for 36 months does not change during that period. The same finding is made for the restricted sample of 43 patients for whom 2-month interview data are also available. There are no changes in psychiatric status attributable to the study variables.[5]

❈ Mental Health and Adaptation to the Community

A very striking characteristic of the community sample is the absence of progressive changes in interpersonal relations and psychiatric condition, two crucial areas of community adjustment. The static nature of patients' adjustment in these two areas, usually a reflection of their mental health, does not result from their functioning at an optimal level. Deficiencies in instrumental social behavior and psychiatric adjustment are noted throughout the 36-month study period. For example, 36 months following completion of treatment only 9 per cent show essentially normal social participation; 67 per cent manifest limited, and 24 per cent essentially abnormal, participation. A comparable situation prevails with respect to psychiatric status: 12 per cent are rated as essentially normal, 74 per cent as showing psychiatric limitations, and 14 per cent as essentially abnormal. These distributions remain relatively constant throughout the period.

Although a large proportion of the community sample continue to show social and psychiatric difficulties, they do not have to return to the hospital and are able to make some basic accommodations to their environment. There is a progressive increase in the number of patients who support themselves through employment, and almost all patients rated as having employment potential were actually working at the time of the 36-month interview. Furthermore, the improved vocational judgment ratings suggest that in the course of time patients are able to achieve a more realistic evaluation of their vocational limitations and their abilities to meet job requirements. Although there is little evidence of a marked change in their partici-

---

[5] Differences attributable to previous treatment were not found because of the small number of cases in the sample of successes from the control condition who remained in the community for 36 months. The mean Psychiatric Status rating for the 8 Control group patients in the community is 8.6, 7.6, and 8.1 at 12, 24, and 36 months following completion of treatment respectively. For the 50 community patients who had experienced the socio-environmental programs, the mean rating is 6.0 for all 3 comparable time periods.

pation in community activities, there is a small increase in the number of their leisure-time activities. Thus, though chronic mental patients do make progressive adaptations to the community, this is not necessarily accompanied by a concomitant change in the usual indices of mental health.

�֎ The Influence of the Study Variables

Differences in the level of adjustment attributable to the study variables (previous treatment, sex, and age) are found during the early phases of the follow-up. Socio-environmental treatment results in greater attendance at community group meetings than treatment given in the Control condition; females have more numerous leisure-time activities and higher ratings of social participation than males; older patients tend to surpass younger patients in level of social participation. These differences are maintained throughout the 36-month period. With one exception, there are no increments or decrements in the measures of adjustment related to the study variables. The one exception is noted for the older patients who show progressive improvement in vocational judgment.

Previous treatment. Previous socio-environmental treatment was expected to effect differential improvement in community adjustment, so that patients who experienced the Maximally Structured program would manifest the greatest degree of growth on all indices. It is evident, however, that previous treatment has little or no bearing on patterns of change in adjustment in the community sample, although socio-environmental treatment in general seems to produce greater attendance at community group meetings than do traditional ward treatment programs. The chronic mental patient who is released from the hospital may continue to require the application of components of socio-environmental treatment (such as a high degree of structured demands, pressures, and supports for appropriate interaction) for his continued improvement in social and psychiatric adjustment.

Age. Older patients were expected to show progressive improvement in community adjustment on the basis of their superior response to socio-environmental treatment and their better adjustment to the community 24 months following completion of treatment. It was felt that, because of their reduced drive level, older patients were less disturbed by psychotic symptoms, had a greater tolerance for interpersonal stress, and were more capable of learning new modes of adaptation. However, this learning necessitated that the environment be structured to elicit social behavior through the application of impelling social stimuli and demands. Such a high degree of stimulation was considered necessary to overcome the withdrawal of the chronic psychotic and to counteract the process of disengagement associated with aging. The older patients in the community do maintain the level of social and psychiatric adjustment achieved as a result of treatment. This fact suggests that the stimulation provided by the community is adequate to "engage" these patients and to permit them to make continued accommodations in other areas of adjustment. An environment devoid of stimulation will apparently exacerbate the disengagement and withdrawal of the older chronic psychotic and lead to regression. Older patients who failed in treatment and remained in the hospital throughout the 36-month follow-up show this pattern of regression. These patients consistently manifest significantly poorer social participation[6] than the younger treatment failures ($F = 11.51$, $df = 1$, $p < .005$). They are also characterized by progressive psychiatric deterioration and consistently poorer psychiatric status[7] than the younger patients (F Age $= 4.90$, $df = 1$, $p < .05$; F Time $= 3.63$, $df = 1$, $p < .05$). The younger patients exhibit some regression, followed by a comparable degree of recovery; therefore, there is little change on the whole in their psychiatric condition.

Thus, it is significant that the older patients who are released from the hospital are able to maintain in the community the social and psychiatric gains achieved during treatment. It is reasonable to assume that socio-environmental treatment, which was responsible for

[6] The mean Social Participation Scale scores of the older patients ($N = 25$) at 12, 24, and 36 months after treatment are 10.86, 11.88, 11.78 respectively. The means for the younger patients ($N = 16$) at the same time periods are 8.59, 9.18, and 8.43. (The higher the score, the poorer the social participation.)

[7] The mean Psychiatric Status Scale scores at 12, 24, and 36 months after treatment are 11.74, 12.74, and 13.14 respectively for the older patients ($N = 25$), and 10.97, 12.12, 10.91 respectively for the younger patients ($N = 16$). (The higher the score, the poorer the psychiatric status.)

enhancing their adjustment in the hospital, also provided them with the preparation to sustain this level of adjustment in the community. However, the small number of control group patients who were able to remain in the community for 36 months does not permit meaningful comparisons between the posttreatment adjustment of the control and experimental groups. Nevertheless, the treatment success rate for older patients (that is, the percentage of older patients released from the hospital and remaining in the community for 36 months) reveals that the success rate for the Control condition is markedly lower than that characterizing the experimental programs. Only 14 per cent of the 28 older patients in the Control condition were successes, compared to a 28 per cent success rate for the 114 older patients in the three socio-environmental treatment conditions. These findings imply that the antecedent treatment conditions not only influenced the patients' adjustment at completion of treatment, but also had some effect on the survival rate during the 36-month follow-up period.

There is more direct evidence indicating that socio-environmental treatment influences the social and psychiatric condition of older patients during the posttreatment period. Significant correlations are found between improvement in verbal interaction during the course of treatment (VIS *beta*) and the Social Participation Scale and Psychiatric Status Scale scores at the end of the 36-month follow-up period. The correlations are .34 ($p < .05$) and .38 ($p < .08$) respectively. The first correlation is based on data for the entire sample of older patients; the second is based only on data for older male patients. No significant relationships are noted for the younger patients.

It appears that certain benefits are derived from the socio-environmental treatment experience which enable older patients to maintain themselves in the extramural community. A relationship exists between level of improvement achieved during treatment and adjustment status at the end of the 3-year period following treatment. The improvement attained during treatment is conceivably a reflection of the older patient's acquired ability to cope with interpersonal situations in a more realistic manner. It is these learned social responses which are viewed as sustaining such patients in their community adjustment.

Chapter XV

The Problem of Rehospitalization

The fact that more than 40 per cent of the patients released on completion of treatment were readmitted to the hospital within the three-year follow-up period is just cause for concern. Is this indicative of the inadequacy of socio-environmental treatment, or does it reflect the exercise of poor judgment on the part of those responsible for the release of the patient? Were the patients who returned "borderline risks" at the time of release, or were they in fairly good shape, with symptoms recurring only after a period of relatively good adjustment? In short, what brings patients back to the hospital?

The mean postprogram psychiatric status ratings reported in Table 11.9 indicate that the patients who returned (Group II) were no sicker at the time of release than those who managed to stay out

(Group I). In fact, the data suggest that those who returned had been in slightly better shape than those who remained out. Aside from length of hospitalization, the only predictor in Table 11.9 which clearly differentiates Group I from Group II is the measure of vocational aspiration. This suggests that the patient's response to vocational realities in relation to aspirations may be an important determinant of community tenure.

Mistakes in clinical judgment at a disposition staff meeting are usually rectified by the patient himself shortly after release. Yet only 13 per cent of those released returned within the first three months, and only 26 per cent returned within the first year. Figure 10.3 indicates that approximately 40 per cent of all readmissions took place more than a year after release. This suggests that community factors not present at the time of release may play an important part in the patient's return. It is also possible that the socio-environmental programs provided some immunization to community stress which took time to break down.

Although the variable of social structure appeared to have some effect on release rates (see Tables 10.2 and 11.2), there was no evidence of a comparable effect on readmission rates (Table 10.3). Apparently, what happens to the patient in the hospital is largely irrelevant to community tenure. It seems reasonable, therefore, to seek an answer to the problem of rehospitalization by examining what happens to the patient after he reaches the community.

❀ THE READMISSION INTERVIEW ❀

Patients who returned to the hospital during the period of the follow-up study were interviewed as soon as possible, generally within a week of readmission. The purpose of the interview was to determine how and why the patient returned to the hospital. In retrospect, the latter goal turned out to be too ambitious; the patient's version of the reasons for his return was often highly distorted, and without supplementary information from outside sources it was usually impossible to reconstruct the sequence of events which culminated in readmission. In most instances, however, the interviewer was able to evaluate the patient's attitude toward rehospitalization, identify the person or agency who initiated the return, determine what precipitated this action, and identify the areas of adjustment in which the patient encountered the greatest difficulty. In cases where additional information was readily available through previously established channels, the interviewer telephoned the potential informant. However, limitations of time and money precluded expansion of the study in this direction.

Readmission interviews were obtained with 75 of the 87 patients in the original study sample who returned to the hospital at least once during the three-year follow-up period. This includes patients released from other wards as well as those released directly from the Rehabilitation Center.[1] Readmission interviews were also obtained with 53 patients who were not part of the original study sample but who were treated at the Rehabilitation Center either before or immediately after the experimental period. Although the content of the treatment programs differed somewhat for these patients, the differences were no greater than those existing among the three experimental programs. Since there was no evidence of a relationship between treatment programs and readmission, the additional cases were combined with those from the original study sample. In all instances the data represent the first readmission after rehabilitation treatment.

❀ Attitude Toward Return

Table 15.1 shows the patient's attitude toward rehospitalization. Contrary to expectation, more than half the patients expressed positive attitudes toward return. Only 6 per cent appeared angry and resentful. There is little doubt that the positive feelings exhibited were as genuine as the anger and resentment. The scoring criteria were quite conservative, as evidenced by the high percentage in the "Could not judge" category. Patients scored for "Strong desire to return" usually did return on their own initiative. Patients who expressed a desire to return, but qualified this with an expression of regret or reluctance, were scored "Best thing to do under the circumstances."

---

[1] There were no significant differences attributable to origin of release except those related to differences in the initial placement situation. For example, patients released from other wards were more frequently placed with families. Therefore, family members were more frequently instrumental in the process of rehospitalization for patients in this category.

TABLE 15.1

ATTITUDE TOWARD REHOSPITALIZATION

	f	%
Strong desire to return	35	27.3
Best thing to do under the circumstances	36	28.1
Indifferent	4	3.1
Mild protest	23	18.0
Angry and resentful	8	6.2
Could not judge	22	17.2

❈ Initiation of Return

The interviewer also attempted to identify the person or agency who initiated the sequence of events culminating in return to the hospital. The data in Table 15.2 are consistent with the attitudinal data in Table 15.1 in that almost one third of the returns were self-

TABLE 15.2

PERSON OR AGENCY WHO INITIATED REHOSPITALIZATION

	f	%
Self	41	32.0
Family or relative	30	23.4
Employer	11	8.6
Friend	4	3.1
Landlord-landlady	12	9.4
Police	14	10.9
P.S.H. clinic	4	3.1
P.S.H. caseworker	1	0.8
Community agency	5	3.9
Other	3	2.3
No information	3	2.3

initiated. Only 11 per cent were forcibly returned after an encounter with the police. Returns under "employer" usually meant that the patient had lost his job; those under "landlord or landlady" meant that the patient's behavior was not acceptable. When this occurred, the landlord or landlady might contact the hospital, call the police, or simply ask the patient to leave, depending upon the circumstances.

It is of interest to note that only 8 per cent of all readmissions were initiated by representatives of the hospital or personnel affiliated with community agencies. Despite the fact that all of the patients in the study sample were on out-patient status and thus technically under the supervision of the hospital, in the majority of cases rehospitalization was initiated by nonprofessional members of the community.

Table 15.3 shows who accompanied the patient on the trip back to the hospital. Note that more patients returned unaccompanied than initiated their own return (see Table 15.2). A relatively large

TABLE 15.3

MANNER IN WHICH PATIENT RETURNED TO THE HOSPITAL

	f	%
Returned accompanied by:		
Family	26	20.3
Friend	5	3.9
Employer	1	0.8
Police	32	25.0
Caseworker	4	3.1
Other hospital personnel	10	7.8
Other	3	2.3
Returned unaccompanied	47	36.7

proportion is escorted by the police because police departments in large urban centers are often called upon to transport disabled persons to both general medical and psychiatric hospitals. Landlords, boarding-house operators, and low-income families without other means of transportation frequently avail themselves of this service.

❀ Critical Factor

In addition to ascertaining who initiated the patient's return, the interviewer attempted to discover what caused that person to take whatever action was taken at the time. The first two categories in Table 15.4 account for most of the cases in which the return was initiated by the patient himself. In the majority of such cases the patient reported that he began to feel "ill" (physically or mentally) and decided to return before matters got worse. Sometimes it was clear that the patient had no desire to remain in the community. As far as could be determined, there was nothing particularly wrong: the patient just decided to give up.

TABLE 15.4

CRITICAL FACTOR LEADING TO REHOSPITALIZATION

	f	%
Self-initiated:		
1. No desire to stay out	10	7.8
2. Began to feel ill	27	21.1
Other initiated:		
3. Bizarre or unusual behavior	52	40.6
a. Dangerous to self	7	5.5
b. Dangerous to others	7	5.5
4. Poor judgment	10	7.8
5. Burden to others	12	9.4
6. Physical condition	2	1.6
7. Cannot judge	1	0.8

Patients in the third category exhibited bizarre or unusual behavior which brought them to the attention of others in the immediate environment. Approximately 20 per cent of the patients in this category were judged to be dangerous either to themselves or to others just before readmission. The fourth category contains those patients whose return was clearly attributable to the consistent exercise of poor judgment in the conduct of everyday affairs, generally in the bad management of financial resources, the selection of inappropriate living quarters, unreasonable demands on friends, relatives, tradespeople, etc. Patients in this category were trying to get along on their own, but simply weren't up to it. Patients in the fifth category were usually living in dependent or semidependent circumstances. Although they exhibited no bizarre or unusual behavior, they required a great deal of attention and care. Eventually those responsible decided that the burden was too great and initiated return to the hospital. Categories six and seven are self-explanatory.

These data suggest that in the majority of cases the immediate cause of rehospitalization was recurrence of psychiatric symptomatology. More than 70 per cent of all readmissions were classified in categories two and three. This conclusion is strongly supported by information recorded in the clinical charts. At least 60 per cent of the sample were determined to be overtly psychotic at the time of readmission on the basis of behavioral descriptions filed by nurses, psychiatrists, and social workers. This does not, however, provide an answer to the question of what precipitated recurrence of symptomatology. In an attempt to shed some light on this problem, a frequency tabulation was made of the various difficulties and complaints mentioned by the patient in his own account of why he returned to the hospital. These data appear in Table 15.5. More than half the patients reported difficulties with persons other than family members.

TABLE 15.5

FREQUENCY OF DIFFICULTIES REPORTED IN MAJOR PROBLEM AREAS

Problem Area	f	%
Economic Adjustment	32	25.0
Recreation	6	4.7
Employment	46	35.9
Interpersonal—family	47	36.7
Interpersonal—other	70	54.7
Physical condition	38	29.7
None	12	9.4

Problems with family members and difficulties in the employment area were also prominently mentioned. Physical complaints were frequent, though seldom considered crucial to the patient's return. One fourth of the sample complained of difficulties in the economic area.

In at least 17 per cent of the sample there had been a major change in the medication schedule just before readmission. In most instances medication had been discontinued on the recommendation of the clinic physican. In a few cases the patient himself had decided to stop taking the prescribed medication, or the dosage had been reduced to a minimum.

The high frequency of problems in the interpersonal area suggests that the social treatment approach is not entirely inappropriate. By the same token, however, it is apparent that the training in interpersonal relationships received at the Rehabilitation Center provided little protection against the development of interpersonal problems in the community. Actually, the data in Table 15.5 contribute little to an understanding of why some patients return to the hospital but others do not. Economic, vocational, and interpersonal problems are a dime a dozen in most households. The key question is whether or not they occur with greater frequency or severity in the lives of those who eventually return to the hospital. If this could be demonstrated, a possible link with recurrence of symptomatology would be established, though much would remain to be done to determine that the relationship was causal rather than fortuitous.

❈ PREDICTION OF REHOSPITALIZATION FROM ❈ COMMUNITY INTERVIEW DATA

The fact that many of the patients who returned to the hospital had been interviewed in the community before their return suggested that the antecedents of rehospitalization might be discovered in an examination of these data. Accordingly, data obtained from patients who subsequently returned to the hospital were compared with data collected at comparable intervals of time from patients who remained in the community for at least three years.

Since the purpose of this inquiry was to uncover differences which might be related to readmission, it seemed advisable to base the analysis on data obtained just before the date of readmission. However, community interviews were available for only 40 of the 60 patients who returned after placement from the Rehabilitation Center.[2] Half of these had been interviewed three or more months preceding readmission. Fortunately, comparison of interviews obtained within two months of readmission with those obtained three or more months before readmission revealed no significant differences. Thus, the analysis which follows is based on a total of 80 patients, 40 of whom were readmitted to the hospital within the 3-year follow-up period. The remaining 40 serve as controls in that they remained out of the hospital for at least 3 years. The groups were equated for sex and time of interview. Matching for age or chronicity was impossible as both are correlated with community tenure. Partial equivalence of treatment programs was maintained by restricting cross-program pairings to the combinations of Maximal structure and Partial structure and Minimal structure and Controls.

✾ Attitude Toward Interview

Neither of the items which reflect the patient's attitude toward the interview differentiated readmissions from controls at a statistically significant level. However, there was a marked tendency for patients who remained out to be more cooperative and more deeply involved in the interview situation. There was, in other words, much less resistance on the part of those who were able to adjust to life in the community. This relationship is actually stronger than the available data indicate, since those who displayed most resistance were not interviewed at all and thus are not included in the analysis. Additional evidence of a difference in basic outlook is contained in the patient's expressed attitude toward living in the community. Thirty-seven per cent of the patients who eventually returned indicated that they were less than satisfied with life in the community, whereas only 20 per cent of those who remained out shared this opinion.

[2] The relative shortage of community interview data on readmissions was due to two factors: first, a number of patients were readmitted before the date of the first scheduled interview; second, most of the patients who "disappeared" once they reached the community, or refused to cooperate with the interviewer, eventually turned up in the readmission group.

❀ Living Situation and Source of Support

Table 15.6 shows the relationship between outcome and living situation and source of support before readmission. The statistically significant relationship between source of support and outcome indicates that patients who are self-supporting (employed) or entirely dependent upon their families are more likely to return to the hospital than patients who are maintained by various welfare agencies. Since there was no apparent reason why source of support should exercise a direct influence on outcome, it seemed reasonable to assume that this relationship was mediated by some other variable. If the unknown variable proves to be a situational (environmental) factor, then there should be differences in the frequency of problems or amount of stress associated with the four categories of support. If it is a personality factor, then one should expect no differences in these respects, and the observed relationship with outcome should obtain at the time of release from the hospital as well as immediately before return. This would not be true of a situational factor, the effects of which would become manifest only after a period of time.

Analysis of problem and stress scores revealed no differences associated with living situation or source of support. The data in Table 15.7, however, show that both living situation and source of support predict whether the patient will remain in the community or return to the hospital. Patients who reside with their families or live where they are employed tend to return to the hospital much more frequently than patients who live alone or share quarters with others in rooming or boarding houses. Patients who work or are supported by their families are also more likely to return.

There is, of course, considerable overlap in the scoring categories for living situation and source of support. It is not surprising, therefore, that these two variables should yield similar results. The relatively few changes in status of living situation and source of support which took place in the interval between release and readmission tended to reduce the relationship of both variables with outcome. Thus, it is clear that living situation and source of support just before readmission are quite irrelevant. The data in Table 15.7 indicate that the observed relationships are mediated by systematic differences

TABLE 15.6

RELATIONSHIP BETWEEN LIVING SITUATION AND SOURCE OF
SUPPORT BEFORE READMISSION AND OUTCOME

Living Situation

	With Family	With Employer	Boarding or Rooming House	Alone
Remained Out	9	5	11	15
Returned	13	6	5	16
	—	—	—	—
Total	22	11	16	31

$$\chi^2 = 3.12, \ df = 3, \ p = \text{n.s.}$$

Source of Support

	Public Assistance	Employment	Family	Savings or Pensions
Remained Out	20	6	5	9
Returned	11	15	10	4
	—	—	—	—
Total	31	21	15	13

$$\chi^2 = 10.06, \ df = 3, \ p < .02$$

among the patients in the various response categories. Further investigation revealed that age was the critical factor in determining outcome, both within and between categories.

Patients in the "family" category on either variable were significantly younger than patients in the other categories. Twelve of the 14 patients placed with their families and who eventually returned to the hospital were in the low age group. The effect of age on outcome for patients who were self-supporting (employed) was just the opposite. Most of those who returned were in the older age group. All of the patients who returned from live-in jobs were in the older age group. Older patients who were neither self-supporting nor dependent

TABLE 15.7

RELATIONSHIP BETWEEN LIVING SITUATION AND SOURCE OF
SUPPORT AT TIME OF RELEASE AND OUTCOME

Living Situation

	With Family	With Employer	Boarding or Rooming House	Alone
Remained Out	9	3	13	15
Returned	14	6	3	17
	—	—	—	—
Total	23	9	16	32

$$\chi^2 = 8.44, \ df = 3, \ p < .05$$

Source of Support

	Public Assistance	Employment	Family	Savings or Pensions
Remained Out	23	6	3	8
Returned	15	14	9	2
	—	—	—	—
Total	38	20	12	10

$$\chi^2 = 11.48, \ df = 3, \ p < .01$$

upon families had a very high survival rate if placed in boarding or rooming houses. Those who lived alone, on the other hand, had only a 50–50 chance of remaining out for at least three years. These results suggest that employment may be inadvisable for older patients, especially jobs which require that the patient live on the premises.

❀ Over-all Economic Adjustment

There were no differences between readmissions and controls in the amount of responsibility assumed in the areas of food, clothing, and shelter. However, a curious difference emerged on an item concerned with savings. Patients who eventually returned to the hospital

were attempting to save part of their income, whereas those who remained out were not $(x^2 = 3.96, df = 1, p < .05)$. This difference
is apparently not related to income level. The median weekly income
for patients who returned was only slightly higher than that for the
controls ($16.82 vs. $15.90). When the interviewer asked why they
were saving, most patients replied that they had no specific objective;
they were merely saving in preparation for a "rainy day." This fits
in with responses to another question in which it was observed that
patients who remained out tended to evidence aspirations and positive
expectancies regarding the future, whereas those who returned were
fearful of the future and preoccupied with security, that is, protection
against loss. These results suggest greater anxiety on the part of those
who eventually returned, an interpretation which receives additional
support from observations in the psychiatric area.

❊ Work Adjustment

The pattern of differences of indices of vocational adjustment
was quite consistent, but the magnitude of these differences was dis-
appointingly small. Generally speaking, patients who returned to the
hospital held more jobs, made more of an effort to find work, received
slightly higher pay when employed, worked longer hours, and held
on to jobs slightly longer than those who remained in the community.
The number of patients holding jobs was essentially the same in both
groups (17 returnees and 16 controls). These findings are consistent
with the difference in level of vocational aspiration previously noted
(see Table 11.9).

❊ Use of Leisure Time

There were no significant differences between readmissions and
controls in leisure-time activities with the exception of frequency of
attendance at organized group functions. Although the number of
patients affiliated with community organizations was essentially the
same in both groups (20 returnees and 19 controls), those who eventually returned to the hospital attended much more regularly than
those who remained out $(t = 3.15, p < .01)$. In general, returnees
tended to be more active and to do more things alone than in the

company of others. Those who remained out were considered to have more problems in the recreational area, possibly because of the general lack of activity of any sort.

❀ Interpersonal Relationships

On theoretical grounds, the interpersonal area should be the most fertile for detecting meaningful differences between readmissions and controls. In actuality, it proved a complete disappointment in this respect. There was no evidence of a difference in attitude toward family members, nor in frequency of contact with friends or relatives. Patients who remained in the community tended to avoid others slightly more, whereas patients who returned were more frequently viewed as indifferent to those in the immediate environment. However, none of these differences approached statistical significance. The abstractors felt that patients who eventually returned to the hospital tended to have more problems with family members and others they did not live with than did the controls. However, this impression was not confirmed by any of the objective indices of social behavior, nor was it supported by any of the ratings made by the interviewers.

❀ PHYSICAL CONDITION AND MEDICAL SERVICES ❀ RECEIVED WHILE IN THE COMMUNITY

Patients in the control group tended to make greater use of medical or dental services available in the community than did those who returned to the hospital. The number of patients utilizing such services was also greater in the control group (18 controls compared with 11 readmissions). Psychiatric services were provided by the out-patient clinic of the Philadelphia State Hospital. Approximately half the patients in both groups were attending out-patient clinic at the time the interview data were obtained. Physical complaints were more frequent among the control group, though the incidence of physical problems, as judged by the abstractors, was no greater. Most of the complaints were relatively mild. Only two patients, one in each group, were judged to have physical symptoms which were genuinely incapacitating.

❀ Psychiatric Adjustment

The psychiatric area presents a fairly consistent picture, though the differences between the two groups were not as great as anticipated. The over-all rating of psychiatric disability failed to discriminate between the two groups at a statistically significant level ($t = 1.57$, $p < .15$), although those who returned were more disturbed. The symptomatology scale was only slightly more discriminating ($t = 1.66$, $p < .10$). Examination of the six subscales revealed that the trend apparent in the total symptomatology score was due primarily to differences in characterological and affective symptoms. The incidence of excessive dependence, according to the abstractors' estimate, was higher among returnees, and patients in this group exhibited greater conflict over the expression of dependent needs. The affective symptoms which distinguished the returnees from the controls were anxiety and fearfulness. The incidence of psychiatric problems, as judged by the abstractors, however, was greater among the controls ($\chi^2 = 5.30$, $df = 1$, $p < .05$). Almost two thirds of the controls were judged to have psychiatric problems, so both groups can be considered relatively "sick" by normal standards.

The differences in symptomatic behavior reported by the interviewers are reflected in the extent to which psychiatric services were recommended by the abstractors. The data in Table 15.8 show both the difference between the returnees and the controls in this respect and the overwhelming importance of the psychiatric area in comparison with other problem areas. Unfortunately, the interviewers were unable to translate their behavioral observations into meaningful clinical predictions. Table 15.9 shows the distribution of responses to the question: "Will the patient be able to remain in the community until the time of the next scheduled interview?" It seems clear that periodic interviews of the type utilized in the present study cannot be depended upon to provide warning of impending regression.

❀ SUMMARY AND IMPLICATIONS ❀

Information obtained from the patient shortly after readmission, supplemented by reports from hospital personnel and those who

TABLE 15.8

FREQUENCY OF SERVICES RECOMMENDED BY MAJOR PROBLEM AREAS

Problem Area	Stay Outs			Returns		
	M	F	Tot.	M	F	Tot.
Economic Adjustment	0	1	1	0	5	5
Recreation	1	0	1	0	0	0
Employment	3	2	5	1	1	2
Interpersonal Relationships	2	4	6	2	0	2
Physical Condition	1	1	2	1	5	6
Psychiatric Condition	12	14	26	21	29	50

TABLE 15.9

INTERVIEWER'S PREDICTION OF SURVIVAL UNTIL NEXT
SCHEDULED INTERVIEW

	Returned	Remained Out
Unqualified *yes*	27	24
Qualified *yes*	8	9
Uncertain	2	4
Qualified *no*	1	2
Unqualified *no*	2	1
	—	—
	40	40

knew the patient in the community, indicate that the immediate cause of rehospitalization in most instances is recurrence of psychiatric symptomatology. Psychiatric problems are clearly apparent when patients are interviewed in the community before readmission, but differences between returnees and controls are minimal. The community interviews yielded no evidence of the economic, interpersonal, and physical problems which patients reported shortly after readmission. This suggests that such problems may materialize rather quickly, which would account for the absence of significant differences in psychiatric symptomatology at the time the community interviews were obtained. Since both groups showed evidence of psychiatric impairment, with the difference between groups already favoring the controls (those who remained out), it seems clear that very little in the way of additional stress would be required to precipitate further exacerbation of symptoms, culminating in return to the hospital.

Beyond this, it seems useless to speculate. The etiology of the specific problems encountered by patients who eventually returned remains obscure. Only a microscopic, day-by-day analysis of interpersonal transactions and decision processes could pinpoint the critical incidents which lead to rehospitalization. The end result is clearly the product of the interaction between the patient and the immediate environment. On the patient's side, one of the factors which apparently plays an important part in determining outcome is age. Younger patients are more apt to fall prey to the difficulties of life in the community than older patients. The tendency for patients who returned to the hospital to score higher on measures of activity level and vocational performance is probably attributable to the age factor. In any event, the combination of greater activity and relatively high vocational aspiration in a context of existing psychiatric disability can only amplify the probability of unfavorable encounters with the environment. The safest thing to do under the circumstances would be to settle down, establish a fixed routine, and avoid excessive stimulation. This is the pattern adopted by the older chronic patient who is left to his own devices.

PART FIVE

SUMMARY AND CONCLUSIONS

Chapter XVI

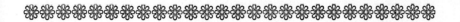

Summary and Implications

A major portion of this report has been devoted to investigating the rationale underlying socio-environmental therapy, namely, that social interaction can be induced and enhanced by increasing the opportunity and demand for social functioning, and that a direct attack on the chronic schizophrenic's social symptomatology and deficits in such functioning can bring about improvement in his general psychiatric status. It was expected that a strong stimulus would be required to compel the chronic schizophrenic to modify his established patterns of apathy and withdrawal.

It was hypothesized that the greater the external demand for interaction the more favorable the outcome. This expectation was tested by comparing the effectiveness of three socio-environmental treatment conditions structured to demand different degrees of inter-action—Minimally, Partially, and Maximally Structured conditions. A control condition, in which patients remained in regular wards, permitted comparisons between socio-environmental treatment and conventional programs.

The improvement sequence within each of the three socio-environmental programs, as well as posttreatment social adjustment, was analyzed in terms of global social behavior and of three specific social responses which were assumed to represent a hierarchy of social initiative: awareness of others, followed by interaction in structured situations, and culminating in spontaneous social behavior.

The impact of the three socio-environmental treatment con-ditions on psychiatric status was evaluated in terms of posttreatment symptomatology and release rates. The relationship between improved social behavior and posttreatment psychiatric status served as a test of the rationale underlying socio-environmental therapy.

Socio-environmental therapy has been shown to produce im-proved social adjustment and psychiatric status in some patients, but exacerbation of symptomatology in others. These divergent results were assumed to stem from the interaction between degree of struc-ture in a given socio-environmental treatment program and the pa-tient's "reactivity level," which is a construct involving measures of age and duration of illness. In this study, this interaction was most evident among male patients: the older patients and those with a longer duration of illness—the low reactivity level patients—mani-fested the most favorable social response and the most positive psychi-atric adjustment in the Maximally Structured treatment condition. The less structured treatment programs also tended to benefit low reactivity level male patients, but the effects were not as marked. In contrast, traditional ward programs were entirely ineffective with this type of patient.

Younger male patients and those with a shorter duration of illness—the high reactivity level patients—generally showed a less favorable response to socio-environmental treatment. Although some benefited from such treatment, a number of these patients were ap-parently disturbed by the interpersonal intimacy with members of both sexes demanded by socio-environmental treatment.

Similar findings were not noted for female patients. Although socio-environmental treatment was somewhat more effective than the control condition, neither degree of treatment structure nor age and length of illness produced statistically significant effects. Differences in treatment outcome for male and female patients may have derived from the greater social responsiveness of females and from the reported sex differences in response to aging and institutionalization.

A 36-month follow-up study subsequent to completion of treatment indicated that the effects of socio-environmental treatment persisted in posttreatment adjustment. Patients who experienced such treatment, regardless of degree of structure, were characterized by a more adequate community adjustment than those who underwent traditional types of treatment. Furthermore, in several areas of adjustment, patients who experienced the two more structured socio-environmental programs surpassed those who participated in the Minimally Structured condition. These findings were independent of sex and age differences.

The superior level of social and psychiatric adjustment achieved by older patients at completion of treatment was also noted in evaluations of community adjustment 24 months after treatment terminated. Indeed, older patients surpassed younger patients in practically all areas of community adjustment. Although there were no differences between age groups in return rates during the 36-month follow-up period, significantly fewer older than younger patients who had experienced the Maximally Structured condition returned to the hospital. Thus, in this study, older patients, traditionally regarded as having the poorest recovery potential, manifested the best treatment outcome in the Maximally Structured socio-environmental therapy and sustained this improvement in their community adjustment.

Younger patients released from the hospital following socio-environmental treatment also showed some enduring effects. At the time of the 24-month follow-up interview, these patients were in better psychiatric condition than their counterparts who left the hospital after traditional ward treatment.

❀ CHRONIC SCHIZOPHRENIA—A NONUNITARY ❀ SYNDROME

In view of these findings, chronic schizophrenia should no longer be viewed as a unitary entity, characterized by progressive apathy, withdrawal, and alienation. Two reactivity level subgroups were distinguished in this study, each responding differently to socio-environmental treatment. The low reactivity level male chronic schizophrenics showed the most favorable social and clinical outcomes when exposed to Maximally Structured treatment. These patients who had undergone a reduction in drive level, as a consequence either of the aging process or of the length of their hospitalization, were better able to tolerate and adjust to the stresses and demands of an intensive social learning program. High reactivity level male patients, however, tended to respond to social stress with increased defensiveness and psychopathology, and were consequently unable to learn appropriate social behaviors.

The role of reactivity level—age and length of illness—as a determinant of differential response to socio-environmental treatment can be further clarified by considering findings from the predictor study. Performance on measures of cognitive functioning—Photo Naming, WAIS subtests, Hunter Problem Box—early in treatment was related to over-all treatment outcome for the older, but not for the younger, male patients.[1] Among older patients, the greater the degree of program structure the greater the relationship between cognitive functioning and clinical outcome. Thus, the Maximally Structured condition permits the greatest prediction and the Control condition the least.

If the Photo Naming series, the WAIS subtests, and the Hunter Problem Box are considered measures of cognitive functioning, then intact thinking indicates good treatment outcome for the older male patient. Adequate cognitive functioning clearly becomes most important when the patient is confronted with strong pressures to change his behavior and to integrate more appropriate instrumental responses. The older male patient whose cognitive functioning is relatively in-

[1] Age was the only index of reactivity level utilized in the predictor study.

tact can endure the stress imposed by the Maximally Structured condition and can benefit from this intensified group learning experience. In this instance, cognitive functioning is of greater significance in determining outcome than either the social or the psychiatric status of the patient. In fact, initial social or psychiatric status has little relevance to treatment outcome for the older male patient in the Maximally Structured condition. For this type of patient, psychiatric adjustment has reached a state of equilibrium so that it interferes very little with his coping behavior or his ability to learn new social responses.

Performance on measures of cognitive functioning are of little value in predicting the outcome of treatment of younger male patients. Intactness of thinking should predict ability to learn, particularly in the Maximally Structured condition, which involves a considered demand for learning new social behaviors. The younger male patient is comparatively more volatile emotionally; as a result, his functioning tends to be disrupted by the social and interpersonal demands inherent in a heterosexual situation. Thus, in socio-environmental therapy, initial level of cognition is of little importance in determining outcome for this type of patient.

❁ ENHANCING EFFECTIVENESS OF SOCIO- ❁ ENVIRONMENTAL TREATMENT

Differential findings for reactivity level and sex subgroups suggest ways to improve the effectiveness of socio-environmental treatment. A factor limiting the response of high reactivity level male patients is their inability to adapt to radically new and challenging situations, such as making the transition from a traditional ward situation to the more independent and socially demanding existence in the socio-environmental conditions. Careful pacing of demands and more gradual introduction to potentially stressful situations may be indicated for these patients. The findings further suggest that, since the chronic mental patient is better able to interact with others in task-centered activities, the introduction to socio-environmental treatment should be made through task-centered rather than discussion-centered activities. Helping the patient adapt to socio-environmental treatment through pacing of demands and a gradual introduction to discussion activities requires a longer time in treatment.

The intensified group experiences in the Maximally Structured condition, particularly the group therapy component of this program, may have had a suppressing effect on initial social response among female patients. Although this inhibition was surmounted by completion of treatment, it is questionable whether group therapy as utilized in this program was of maximum value for these patients. It has been suggested that the inhibiting effect of group therapy among females derives from their reluctance to express negative or hostile feelings. If group therapy was phased into the program after the female patients had had an opportunity to define a role for themselves in the unit and to resolve some of their dependency needs, they might be more easily able to express hostility and thus to obtain fuller benefit from the group therapy experience.

Results of this study raise doubts about whether social interaction is a major variable in the treatment of female chronic mental patients. Since females involved in this study manifested a relatively high degree of social interaction before they became involved in socio-environmental therapy, there may have been no need to include them in a program directed toward overcoming social withdrawal. Socio-environmental treatment would possibly be more effective with females manifesting a degree of withdrawal comparable to that of male patients. The critical treatment variable has not yet been uncovered for the female patients in this study.

The alleviation of some of the tensions associated with racial problems might well enhance the effectiveness of socio-environmental treatment. It has been shown that the greater the degree of structure in the living situation the less likely is the Negro patient to attain release at completion of treatment. This pattern is attributed to the Negro's inability to gain acceptance as a member of the white patients' social community. Although the program requires him to interact with his fellow patients, he may be excluded from such interaction because of rejection by the white patients. Socio-environmental therapy, which provides patients with considerable autonomy in determining patterns of interaction, should take cognizance of the dynamics of racial prejudice. Such prejudice can be counteracted by introducing appropriate educational content and maintaining in the program activities a sufficiently large number of minority group members to reduce individual vulnerability to rejection.

❁ *A NEW TREATMENT MODEL* ❁

Clearly, socio-environmental treatment offers hope of release and community adjustment to a large group of chronic mental patients previously destined to spend their remaining years in mental hospital wards. Despite this fact, the implementation of socio-environmental therapy has met with considerable resistance in the traditional mental institution. Chapter Three listed some of the problems encountered by the authors in initiating such an innovative program of treatment in a large state hospial. Limited budget, multiple subordination, autonomous functions, vested interests, and custodialism perpetuate institutionalization and block the establishment of such programs. However, the primary limitation is an attitude of total adherence to a model of general medical care which precludes the implementation of other treatment models and the full application and actualization of their potential.

The model for general medical care underlying the organization and structure of the mental hospital has a demonstrated utility in treating acute psychotics. However, this model is not conducive to the development and dissemination of programs based on social-psychological principles with demonstrated therapeutic value for older and long-term chronic patients. If social-psychological principles are to be utilized more broadly and in greater depth, the structure and organization of the mental hospital must undergo drastic modification. Such reorganization was implied in the Joint Commission report (1961) which recommended for the chronic mental patient that the "techniques of socialization, relearning, group living, and gradual rehabilitation or social improvement . . . be expanded and extended . . ." Although the report recognized the utility of social-psychological principles, it did not specify the need for an appropriate model to follow in designing treatment centers for chronic patients.

In reviewing problems inherent in establishing an innovative socio-environmental treatment program in a traditional mental hospital, we noted (Chapter Three) that the organization and leadership of the traditional hospital was not consistent with the general goals and practices of a treatment program which emphasized educational and social-psychological techniques. If such treatment is to be used effectively for chronic patients, the institutional setting should be re-organized to conform to a social-educational model (similar to the one conceptualized on the basis of experiences in the current project).

The traditional medical model has as its goal the repair of the mentally disabled individual. This model emphasizes symptom removal through restoration of intrapsychic balance or through chemical suppression of disruptive affect and drives. The accepted therapeutic agents are chemical (ataractic drugs), physical (somatic therapies), and psychological (individual and group psychotherapies). These essential types of treatments encompassed by the medical model are viewed as falling within the purview of the physician—the psychiatrist. Logically, this model requires that the psychiatrist head the organizational structure and supervise personnel trained in the application of these treatments. Some decision-making powers are also vested in the other disciplines, proportional to the utilization of their specialized services in the treatment armamentarium.

Although those on the treatment staff, particularly the psychiatrists, wield a major portion of the authority and decision-making power, treatment encompasses only a minor portion of the patient's hospital time. As is true in a general hospital, the care and management of patients during the time they are not in treatment is the concern of a varied group of nonprofessional personnel. These staff members, who constitute the bulk of hospital employees, serve in a variety of discrete service roles ranging from basic custodial care to rehabilitation assistance in the recuperation process. Too often their services are viewed only as management procedures to facilitate treatment rather than as an integral part of the treatment process itself.

The current decade has witnessed an important innovation in the medical model, the Unit Plan, which has resulted in more effective deployment of all disciplines, including those formerly involved in patient management. Service personnel are becoming increasingly involved in the treatment process. Their skills are now more directly utilized in implementing and conducting individualized treatment programs. Such programs are designed to deal with each patient's psychological needs and problems through a direct and coordinated attack on his psychopathology or by supporting the residual healthy components of his personality. This increased use of all hospital personnel in the treatment process is expeditious to the goal of the medical model in that it holds greater promise for restoring the patient to his premorbid level of functioning.

In contrast to the medical model, which aims primarily at reduction of psychopathology, the social-education model emphasizes training and rehabilitation in order to overcome social deficits and prepare patients to cope with the requirements of daily living. This model provides a conceptual basis for the development of socio-environmental treatment programs, the utilization of staff members in new roles, and the structuring of the organization to achieve its treatment goals.

A socio-environmental treatment program can be considered to include three essential elements. The first is a special community which replicates for the patient the extramural community to which he must return. Such a context is required to provide meaningful life experiences, to offer opportunities for testing newly acquired behavior, and to insure that such behavior conforms to community standards. The social community derives from the establishment of a group-living situation which requires the patient to participate in decision-making processes and to assume responsibility for himself and others. Patient government, involving the election of individual patients to designated roles and functions, presents the patient with prescribed modes of behavior for this participation in decision-making and assumption of responsibilities.

The second ingredient is an education program which teaches skills necessary for survival, initially in the intramural community and ultimately in the extramural community. In this educational program, tasks are utilized to elicit patient interaction and provide social skills necessary for the generalization of appropriate social behavior.

The third essential element in a socio-environmental treatment program is the use of social-psychological techniques to insure participation in the program and instill new learning. In addition to the demand for interaction provided by the structured aspects of the social environment and the educational program, personnel within this program must provide sustained pressures necessary to shape and modify social behavior. Simultaneously, they provide the support which helps the patient endure the stresses involved in the interaction program, they offer feedback regarding deviant behavior to be corrected, and they reinforce the integration of appropriate social behavior.

Staff roles within the social-educational model require some specialization of function in order to provide the patient with a variety of educational content. However, the educational methods, namely, the social-psychological techniques, are common to all roles within this model. Unlike the medical model, which uses specialists from different disciplines, each with a set of particular institutionalized roles, in the social-educational model all staff members serve in similar social-educational roles. Few distinctions are made between an elite staff of specialists which provides treatment for the patient and a general staff which engages in management of the patient. Since all staff members within this model serve in similar social-educational roles, there is less chance for vested interests and interdisciplinary rivalries to develop and more opportunity for the integration of new types of manpower into the staff organization.

Chemical, physical, and psychological therapies are also utilized within the social-educational model, but they are applied by consultant specialists—psychiatrists, nurses, psychologists, and social workers —on a referral basis. Although these specialists are not members of the social-educational staff, they are available and freely consulted when symptom reduction is a necessary precondition for social education.

The organizational structure required for the social-educational model must still be evolved. It is clear, however, that the structure should be under the direction of a person who is conversant with social-psychological theories, systems, and techniques, who has an understanding of educational principles, and who is an able administrator. A social psychiatrist, a social scientist, or a social-systems clinician could, with some administrative training, fill this role. Obviously, the psychiatrist who views the mental hospital as a variant of the general medical hospital cannot adequately establish and direct a social-educational organization. The administrator of an institution based on the traditional medical model is primarily concerned either with providing a series of coexistent but discrete services or with coordinating such services to meet the individual patient's needs. In both instances preference is given to medical-psychiatric treatment. The social-educational model requires an administrator who can conceptualize and implement an institutional society which parallels the extramural community, and who can establish within this society a "core curriculum" to teach all patients the behaviors necessary for community living. The organizational challenge lies in determining the type of structure most conducive to achieving these goals.

In brief summary, the social-educational model focuses on the social and interpersonal rather than on the somatic and intrapsychic. It concerns itself with retraining rather than with reintegration, and it concentrates on actions rather than on reactions. Social-educational treatment resembles academic training in its emphasis on preparing the chronic patient for life in the extramural community. The traditional mental institution, like the general medical hospital, is designed to repair the damaged portions of an acutely disturbed individual.

The ideologies underlying the two models have been contrasted in an attempt to highlight the resultant differences in program goals, treatment procedures, and organizational structure. Each of these models has very definite utility for a different psychiatric population: the medical model for the acutely disturbed, and the social-educational model for the chronically disabled. Social-educational treatment is not more widely utilized because its goals have been obscured and its procedures subordinated; in addition, the organizational structure necessary for its implementation has been debarred by adherence to the medical model as a predominant ideology in treating all mental patients.

❀ IMPLICATIONS FOR INSTITUTIONAL ❀ TREATMENT

Socio-environmental therapy, demonstrably superior to traditional methods for treating chronic mental patients, can best be implemented in a setting devoted exclusively to chronic patients, staffed by personnel cognizant of social-educational ideology, and headed by

an administrator skilled in the application of social-psychological principles. The Joint Commission report has noted that centers for the
treatment of chronic patients do not require personnel with highly
specialized psychiatric skills like psychiatrists, psychologists, or social
workers. Such specialists are already in short supply, and their skills
are in greater demand for the treatment of the acutely disturbed. The
social-psychological and educational techniques necessary for the treatment and rehabilitation of chronic patients can easily be taught to
graduates of high school and of two- and four-year college programs.

The Psychology Department of the Philadelphia State Hospital
took college graduates from a wide variety of liberal arts fields, novices
to the mental health field, and trained them to provide therapeutic
services for chronic mental patients (NIMH Grant Number 8210:
Training New Workers for Social Interaction Therapy). This project
demonstrated that one year of hospital-based didactic and practicum
training could provide such new personnel with sufficient skill to re-
structure ward environments and to conduct group programs directed
toward enhancing the social behavior of chronic mental patients and
preparing them to return to the community (Hunter, Goldman, and
Smith, 1966). The didactic training given in the one-year program
(Sanders, 1967) included courses in Personality Theory, Psychopathology and Treatment, Group Dynamics, and Social Institutions. A
course entitled Activity Skills was also offered, designed to provide
trainees with the general skills necessary to conduct group activities
and develop group projects. Sensitivity toward group dynamics and
the group process was instilled through an ongoing "T-Group," composed of the trainees themselves.

The content of this type of training is integrated and applied
by having trainees actually conduct social interaction therapy with
chronic mental patients, under close supervision by the training staff.
The conduct of such treatment groups continues throughout the year
of training. Graduates of this training program are currently employed not only at the Philadelphia State Hospital, but at other institutions throughout the Commonwealth of Pennsylvania.

Community colleges are offering two-year programs to prepare
high school graduates to perform psychiatric technician services. Many
of these programs emphasize group interactive processes pertinent to
the conduct of a therapeutic community (Atty, 1966; Southern Re-

gional Education Board, 1966). Graduates of these programs will be very valuable in conducting socio-environmental treatment with chronic patients. However, since they have been trained only to provide a generalized therapeutic service, there is the danger that, in an institutional setting dominated by the medical model, the established disciplines will subordinate them and restrict their treatment role to acting as aides in existing specialties. This danger will be minimized in institutional settings utilizing the socio-educational model.

❀ IMPLICATIONS FOR COMMUNITY TREATMENT ❀

The current emphasis on depopulating the large mental hospitals often results in "dumping" mental patients into the community or avoiding the responsibility of providing extramural therapeutic services. The findings of the current study make it evident that, although hospital-based socio-environmental programs effect a remission of symptoms and are valuable in preparing chronic patients for community life, these programs frequently are not in themselves sufficient to insure the patient an adequate community adjustment. Despite successful efforts of hospital-based treatment, the chronic patient's residual limitations in flexibility and adaptability can only be surmounted by continued guidance and assistance in adjusting to actual community life situations. Such guidance can regulate the patient's exposure and interaction with his environment, in accordance with his particular personality resources and variations in his tolerance for stress. A community-based rehabilitation service is needed, both to help patients with everyday living problems and to assist them directly in attaining greater individuation and self-sufficiency in the community.

Community mental health centers offer great hope of establishing community-based treatment programs for mental patients. The establishment of such centers has as its impetus the concept that early and intensive treatment in the community can prevent long-term hospitalization and intractable chronicity. Cumming and Cumming (1965) have examined this rationale. They have concluded that the community-care model is particularly inadequate for chronic mental patients, most of whom are handicapped by deficits requiring long-term rehabilitation, protection, and supervision. According to these authors, community mental health centers have not yet developed a plan for the rehabilitation and maintenance of the chronic mental patient in the community. Such centers will probably redefine their task in order to concentrate on the more hopeful, acutely disturbed patients and delegate the tedious, chronic patients to whatever asylum they can locate.

In reality it seems impossible for the community mental health centers to obtain the necessary professional staff to answer the long-term treatment needs of chronic mental patients. However, this task will remain impossible only if community mental health center personnel concentrate on traditional counseling and psychotherapeutic services for their patients. If they reserve these services for the acutely disturbed and allocate time to train community members to serve in a therapeutic capacity with chronic mental patients, the task becomes surmountable.

The present authors are currently engaged in a project[2] to train community members, indigenous to the catchment area in which the chronic patient is placed, in the techniques of socio-environmental therapy. These community members provide supervision and therapeutic service for chronic patients in the community. In many instances, the patients live in apartments and are visited regularly by neighboring community members trained to provide these services. Under the supervision of professional staff these community members learn to structure the patient's home environment to be conducive to social interaction, to provide training in the instrumental behavior necessary for survival in the community, and to coordinate the patient's activities so that he fully utilizes community service agencies.

The social-educational model provides guidelines for the training and utilization of such new personnel, as well as for their interrelationship with professional staff. If this model is adopted, community mental health centers will require social psychiatrists or other social-systems clinicians both to direct the training of these new personnel and to supervise their use of social-psychological techniques and educational principles in treating chronic mental patients.

[2] Supported by NIMH Grant MH 1953: Community Treatment of Hospitalized Chronic Patients. April, 1965—March, 1968.

Appendix

Interaction Activity Program:
Outline of Content

IA   Town Pass
    Goals:
       a. Provide basic information required for trips into the community
       b. Obtain feedback regarding patient's experiences and problems in visiting the community
       c. Help patients deal with problems encountered
    Topics Discussed:
       a. Requirements for obtaining town pass and the purposes for which it may be used

1. Requirements: time on unit, behaviors expected, staffing procedure
2. Purpose of town pass
3. Procedure for obtaining pass and funds
4. Time and distance limits for town pass

b. Problems of transportation and communication
1. Public transportation system: obtaining maps, reading maps, knowing bus stops, fares and transfer points
2. Asking for information: use of telephone, how to ask for information, what to do if lost

c. Feelings about town visits
1. Fears: being lost, rejection by community members, being questioned by police
2. Supportive information: use of a "buddy," orientation to the changing city scene
3. Appropriate behavior: dress, conduct on buses and in restaurants

d. Social and recreational resources
1. Free entertainment: free films, museums, parks, concerts
2. Budgeting funds: low cost entertainment, places to eat
3. Facilities for ex-mental patients: Horizon House, Hopetown

e. Practica: three group visits to various community facilities

1B Trial Visit Seminar
Goals:
a. Provide information necessary for community adjustment
b. Assist patients in making the transition from hospital to community

Topics Discussed:
a. Financial Support
1. Public Assistance
2. Social Security
3. Pensions
4. Family Support
5. Employment—full and part-time

b. Living Situations
1. Private homes
2. Rooming houses and apartments
3. Boarding homes

4. Live-in jobs
5. Sheltered settings: Horizon House; Rebecca Gratz Club

c. Selection of living quarters
1. Location
2. Housekeeping opportunities and responsibilities
3. Availability of telephone
4. Relationship with landlord and tenants

d. Budgeting
1. Inexpensive food: food stamps, thrift shops
2. Inexpensive clothing and furniture: Salvation Army, Goodwill Industries
3. Inexpensive services: laundromats, drycleaning machines, barber schools, beauty schools
4. Planning a budget

e. Leisure-time activities
1. Free entertainment
2. Points of interest
3. Library, Horizon House, museums, Hopetown, Golden Age Club, city recreational centers, Alumni Club
4. Night school
5. Hobby groups

f. Employment
1. Requirements: hours, demands, compensation, interpersonal problems, previous work experience, promptness, neatness, ability, skills, jobs available
2. Types of employment: appraising one's limitations and assets, deciding on a suitable job
3. Job benefits: fringe benefits, hospitalization, sick leave, vacations, unemployment benefits, holidays, insurance, deductions from pay, union membership

g. Job-seeking behavior: want ads, state and private agencies, telephone inquiries (actual use of phone with teletrainee equipment), letter writing (sample letter of application, business letters), job application forms (review of sample application form), personal interview (role-playing)

h. Mental health in the community
1. Community attitudes: when to reveal your ex-patient status, whom to tell about it, the influence of inappropriate behavior and dress

    2. Exercising citizenship responsibilities: voting, use of police and fire services

    3. Church attendance

    4. Health services: community clinics, hospital out-patient clinic

II   Social Skills

    Goals: Enhance social participation and interpersonal skills in a variety of situations

    Types of Situations

      a. General Conduct

        1. Behavior in a group: joining a group, sharing facilities, eliciting cooperation, conversing with others (the meaning of silence, small talk, appropriate conversation)

        2. Entertaining others: in the hospital, in the community

        3. Behavior in public: dress, conduct, interaction with the opposite sex

      b. Dining Behavior

        1. General: table etiquette (use of utensils, passing dishes, serving self a fair portion), appropriate conversation, excusing oneself when leaving, cleaning up

        2. Restaurant and cafeteria behavior: ordering, tipping, seating arrangement, paying bill

        3. Rest-room behavior: asking for location, washing, tipping

      c. Social gatherings

        1. Introducing self and other

        2. Appropriate conversation: beginning a conversation, typical topic, expressing interest in others

        3. Use of social skills: dancing, adult games, community singing

        4. Taking leave

        5. Organizing a gathering or picnic

      d. Commercial Situations

        1. What you need to know when buying items, i.e., size, quantity, price

        2. How to speak up if overlooked

        3. How to resist sales pressure

        4. How to order over the phone

        5. How to make an appointment

        6. How to call attention to incorrect change

e. Interpersonal Situations
1. Maintaining acquaintances: asking for or accepting a date, extending an invitation, entertaining at home, use of phone and letters
2. Forming acquaintances: places to meet others, club memberships (library, Y, church), on-the-job acquaintances
3. Appropriate dress, behavior, and conversation for a variety of situations: weddings, church, gatherings, funerals
4. Resolving interpersonal conflicts: problems with peers (other patients, fellow workers, roommates), problems with authorities (attendants, landlord, boss), expressing dissatisfaction, dealing with exploitation, prejudice, hostility

III Home Life
Goals:
a. To impart the experience and skills essential for basic maintenance in the community—nurture, shelter, and self-care
b. To provide the framework for the enjoyment of family-type leisure
Topics Discussed:
a. Food
1. Nutrition
2. Meal planning
3. Marketing and budgeting
4. Basic cooking: small quantity cooking, preparation of low-cost meals, variation in use of surplus food items
5. Table manners
6. Preparation of packed lunches with nutrition and variety
b. Clothing and Dress
1. Importance of being well groomed: appropriate dress for hospital, community, including different social situatons, i.e., movies, restaurants, indoor and outdoor dress, seasonal dress
2. Wardrobe
a. Where to buy, what to look for (used clothing stores, quality vs. price, comparative shopping, Army-Navy stores, specialty shops)
b. Maintenance and care: laundry, ironing (demonstration and practice), community resources (laundromats, automatic cleaners), basic sewing—patching, darning, but-

tons, hems, trouser cuffs (realistic sewing without aid of sewing machine)
    3. Purchase of clothing
        a. Where to buy: discount houses, thrift shops, Goodwill Industry, Salvation Army
        b. How to buy: economy, fit (knowing one's size and measurements), appropriate and becoming styles—current fashions
    c. Housekeeping and Home Decorations
        1. Repairs and maintenance: who is responsible for repairs in community living situations
        2. Cleanliness and sanitation: good housekeeping methods, new cleaning products on the market and their use, helpful household hints: spot remover, easy methods and short cuts to housekeeping, sanitation (trash and garbage disposal)
        3. Basic living requirements in different living situations: pros and cons of sharing room or apartment with someone, living alone or with others (boarding house or family)
        4. Decorating within a limited budget
            a. Colors
            b. Furniture arrangement
            c. Redecorating a room (group project): inexpensive places to buy: second-hand stores, Goodwill Industry, thrift shops, 5 & 10 (community trip to shop for items to be used in room); methods of refinishing or redecorating furniture: use of "safe" paint removers, contact paper, decals, quick-drying paints
        5. Entertainment
            a. Hobbies and solitary leisure-time activities
            b. Parlor games, card games with others
            c. Preparing snacks for group entertainment
            d. TV watching, how to be selective
            e. What to do with excessive spare time

IV   Project Group
     Goals:
        a. Provide patients the opportunity to participate in a group performance activity which is conducive to a variety of interactions

b. Involve the patients in decision-making, leadership, and co-operative behavior

Types of Projects:

a. Golf Course—Spring, Summer, Fall   (4 Months)

Each group works on one hole at a time. Plan hole and draw, design, and select such things as figures, water wheel, and other objects which are a part of the miniature golf course. Dig out holes with hand tools—blacktop job done by maintenance department. Group uses tools for cutting out wooden figures, constructing wooden objects, working with metal and paint. Modification and maintenance of golf course will also be an ongoing activity.

b. Puppet Show   (4 Months)

Plan, draw, design, and select types of puppets, costumes, stage, background, and scenery. Women work on dresses; men on stage and background. Make puppets with paper and glue, paint faces, cut out yarn for eyebrows and hair, cut out hands. Paint background and scenery. Write script deriving from group discussion. Can be presented at a Unit Social.

c. Project Display   (3–4 Months)

Christmas Scene, model of Philadelphia, or other display. Plan, draw, and select scene. Work with paper and water, use cardboard and wood cutouts, absorbent cotton, cloth, rocks, dirt, etc. Paint finished project and have as display for seasonal holiday or as educational-visual aid for a class. This project theme could also involve constructing pieces of furniture that would have utility for a section of the Rehabilitation Service, e.g. a bird cage for the S-3 Lobby.

d. Mosaics   (3–4 Months)

Make table, wall plaque, ashtray, etc. Use bathroom tile and appropriate paste and sealer. Design mosaic, select best design, trace design, break tile. Each patient is responsible for fitting a specific design or color.

e. Pantomime Theater   (4 Months)

Design and select appropriate costumes, masks, and background. Sew costumes; make and paint masks and background. Decide upon or write appropriate story. Use Aesop's

Fables or Pierrot and Pierrette as source material for stories. Presentation planned for monthly social.

f. Gardening (ground prepared by farmer)   (4 Months)
Early spring. Select appropriate vegetables and flowers to be planted, with specific attention to those that will reach full maturity within the time interval covered by the activity. Take care of garden; weeding, hoeing, watering; setting up fences; making a rock garden. Vegetables can be prepared and eaten in the home-life classes.

(4 Months)
Late summer and fall. This activity also includes preparing the ground for the spring season and taking care of the vegetables and flowers which have not completely bloomed by end of early gardening project.

g. Unit Fair   (4 Months)
Design, select, construct, and finish various games to be used on a special unit "Fair Day."

V   Music and Recreation
    Goals:
        a. Allow patients to interact in a relatively relaxed atmosphere
        b. Expose patients to a variety of recreational and socializing activities which may be of value during leisure time in the community
    Activities:
    Three different recreational programs were developed in accord with the age and interest limitations of the patient population.
        a. For all patients
            Social dancing
            Playreading
            Music appreciation
            Community sing
            Square dancing
            Shuffleboard
        b. For younger patients
            Basketball
            Volleyball
            Dodgeball
            Relays

      Calisthenics
      Table tennis
      Badminton
      Softball
  c. For older patients
      Card and table games
      Quiz and word games, e.g., Twenty Questions, Spelling Bees
      Musical games: tape recorder used for playback
      Discussion of radio and TV programs

VI   Personal Grooming
     Goals:
      Provide training in personal grooming, self-care, and care of living area
     Discussion and Demonstration Areas:

MEN	WOMEN
Personal cleanliness	Personal cleanliness and feminine
Health rules	hygiene
Shaving and hair grooming	Health rules
Bathing and use of deodorants	Cosmetics and depilatories
Posture	Bathing and use of deodorants
Nutrition	Hair grooming
Care of clothes	Posture
Safety rules and first aid	Nutrition
	Care of clothes
	Beauty and fashion tips
	Safety rules and first aid .

VII Electives
     Goals:
      a. To provide a variety of socializing activities from which patients can choose in accord with their personal interests
      b. To encourage the development of hobbies
     The following is a representative list of electives from which each patient is required to select two activities following approval for Town Pass:
        Arts, crafts, and ceramics
        Model railroad club
        Fashion club (women)

Creative sewing (women)
Bible discussion group
Hot-plate cooking
Unit newspaper
Woodworking (men)
*Art workshop
*Orchestra
*Chorus
*Seasonal sports

* Available to all hospital patients with ground privileges.

Bibliography

APPELBY, L. Evaluation of treatment methods for chronic schizophrenia. *Archives of General Psychiatry, 8* (1963), 8–21.

ATTY, L. Daytona Beach Junior College, Proposed curriculum for associate in science degree in mental health technology (Mimeographed). 1966.

AYLLON, T., and HAUGHTON, E. Control of the behavior of schizophrenic patients by food. *Journal of Experimental Analysis of Behavior, 5* (1962), 343–352.

BAKER, A. A., and THORPE, J. G. Deteriorated psychotic patients: their treatment and its assessment. *Journal of Mental Science, 102* (1956), 780–789.

BEARD, J. H., GOERTZEL, V., and PEARCE, A. J. The effectiveness of activity group therapy with chronically regressed adult schizophrenics. *International Journal of Group Psychotherapy, 8* (1958), 123–134.

319

BELKNAP, I. *Human problems of a state mental hospital.* New York: McGraw-Hill, 1956.

BELLAK, L. The schizophrenic syndrome. In L. Bellak (Ed.), *Schizophrenia: A review of the syndrome.* New York: Logos Press, 1958. Pp. 3–63.

BENNIS, W. G. Leadership theory and administrative behavior. In W. G. Bennis, K. D. Benne, and R. Chin (Eds.), *The planning of change.* New York: Holt, 1961. Pp. 259–301.

BETTELHEIM, B., and SYLVESTER, E. A therapeutic milieu. *American Journal of Orthopsychiatry, 18* (1948), 191–206.

BIERER, J. Group psychotherapy. *British Medical Journal, 1* (1942), 214–217.

BIERER, J., and HALDANE, F. R. A self-governed patients' social club in a public mental hospital. *Journal of Mental Science, 87* (1941), 419–426.

BORTNER, R. W. The relationship between age and measures of id, ego, and superego functioning. *Journal of Gerontology, 18* (1963), 286–289.

BUGENTAL, J. F. T., and ZELEN, S. L. Investigations into the self-concept. I. The W-A-Y techniques. *Journal of Personality, 18* (1950), 483–498.

CAMERON, N. *The psychology of behavior disorders.* Boston: Houghton Mifflin, 1947.

CAMERON, J. L., LAING, R. D., and MCGHIE, A. Patient and nurse: effects of environmental changes in the care of chronic schizophrenics. *Lancet, 28* (1955), 1384–1386.

CASTELLAN, N. J., JR. On the partitioning of contingency tables. *Psychological Bulletin, 64* (1965), 330–338.

CAUDILL, W. *The psychiatric hospital as a small society.* Cambridge: Harvard University Press, 1958.

CLARK, D. H., and HOY, R. M. Reform in the mental hospital: a critical study of a programme. *International Journal of Social Psychiatry, 3* (1957), 211–223.

COHEN, M. B. The therapeutic community and therapy. *Psychiatry, 20* (1957), 173–175.

CUMMING, E., and CUMMING, J. Some questions on community care. *Canada's Mental Health, 13* (1965), 7–12.

CUMMING, E., and HENRY, W. E. *Growing Old.* New York: Basic Books, 1961.

CUMMING, J. Discussion: part II. Hospitalized aspects of rehabilitation. In M. Greenblatt and B. Simon (Eds.), *Rehabilitation of the mentally ill*. Washington, D.C.: American Association for the Advancement of Science, 1959. Publication Number 58. Pp. 113–116.

CUMMING, J., and CUMMING, E. Social equilibrium and social change in the large mental hospital, In M. Greenblatt, D. J. Levinson, and R. H. Williams (Eds.), *The patient and the mental hospital*. Glencoe, Ill.: Free Press, 1957. Pp. 49–72.

CUMMING, J., and CUMMING, E. *Ego and Milieu.* New York: Atherton, 1962.

DAVIS, R. A., and HARRINGTON, R. N. The effect of stimulus class on problem-solving behavior. *Journal of Abnormal Sociology, 54* (1957), 126–128.

DEAN, L. R. Aging and the decline of affect. *Journal of Gerontology, 17* (1962), 440–446.

DEUTCH, M. An experimental study of the effects of cooperation and competition upon group process. *Human Relations, 2* (1949), 199–231.

DINITZ, S., AUGRIST, S., LEFTON, M., and PASAMANICK, B. The post-hospital functioning of former mental hospital patients. *Mental Hygiene, 45* (1961), 579–588.

DUBIN, R. Stability of human organizations. In M. Haire (Ed.), *Modern organization theory*. New York: Wiley, 1959. Pp. 218–253.

DUNN, W. L. Visual discrimination of schizophrenic subjects as a function of stimulus meaning. *Journal of Personality, 23* (1954), 48–64.

EHRENTHEIL, O. F. Behavioral changes of aging chronic psychotics. In R. Kastenbaum (Ed.), *New thoughts on old age*. New York: Springer, 1964. Pp. 99–115.

ELISEO, T. S. Figurative and literal misinterpretations of words by process and reactive schizophrenics. *Psychological Reports, 13* (1963), 871–877.

ELLSWORTH, R. B. *The psychiatric aide and the schizophrenic patient.* Paper presented at American Psychological Association, Philadelphia, August, 1963.

FAIRWEATHER, G. W. *Social psychology in treating mental illness: an experimental approach.* New York: Wiley, 1964.

FAIRWEATHER, G. W., SIMON, R., GEBHARD, M. E., WEINGARTEN, E., HOLLAND, J. L., SANDERS, R., STONE, G. B., and REAHL, J. E. *Relative effectiveness of psychotherapeutic programs: a multicriteria comparison of four programs for three different patient groups.* Psychological Monographs, General and Applied, Volume 74, Whole Number 492. Washington, D.C.: American Psychological Association, 1960.

FARIS, R. E. L. Ecological factors in human behavior. In J. McV. Hunt (Ed.), *Personality and the behavior disorders*. New York: Ronald Press, 1944. Volume 2, pp. 736–760.

FESTINGER, L. An analysis of compliant behavior. In M. Sherif and M. O. Wilson (Eds.), *Group relations at the crossroads*. New York: Harper, 1953. Pp. 232–256.

FORSYTHE, R. P., and FAIRWEATHER, G. W. Psychotherapeutic and other hospital treatment criteria: the dilemma. *Journal of Abnormal and Social Psychology, 62* (1961), 598–604.

FOURIEZOS, N. T., HUTT, M. L., and GUETZKOW, H. Measurement of self-oriented needs in discussion groups. *Journal of Abnormal and Social Psychology, 45* (1950), 682–690.

FREEMAN, H. E., and SIMMONS, O. G. Mental patients in the community: family settings and performance levels. *American Sociological Review, 23* (1958), 147–154.

FREEMAN, H. E., and SIMMONS, O. G. *The mental patient comes home.* New York: Wiley, 1963.

FREUD, S. *Psychoanalytic notes upon an autobiographical account of a case of paranoia (dementia paranoides)*, Collected Papers, Volume 3. London: Hogarth, 1948.

FREUD, S. *Totem and taboo.* New York: Moffat, 1918.

FULLER, R. G. Expectation of hospital life and outcome for mental patients on first admission. *Psychiatric Quarterly, 4* (1930), 295–323.

GALIONI, E. F. Evaluation of a treatment program for chronically ill schizophrenic patients: a six-year program. In L. Appelby, J. M. Scher, and J. Cumming (Eds.), *Chronic schizophrenia*. Glencoe, Ill.: Free Press, 1960. Pp. 303–325.

GALIONI, E. F., ADAMS, F. H., and TALLMAN, F. F. Intensive treatment of backward patients: a controlled pilot study. *American Journal of Psychiatry, 109* (1953), 576–583.

GARMEZY, N. Stimulus differentiation by schizophrenic and normal subjects under conditions of reward and punishment. *Journal of Personality, 20* (1952), 253–276.

GOFFMAN, E. On the characteristics of total institution. In *Symposium on preventive and social psychiatry*. Washington, D.C.: Walter Reed Army Institute of Research, 1957. Pp. 43–84.

GREENBLATT, M., LEVINSON, D. J., and WILLIAMS, R. H. (Eds.) *The patient and the mental hospital.* Glencoe, Ill.: The Free Press, 1957.

GREENBLATT, M., YORK, R. H., and BROWN, E. L. *From custodial to therapeutic patient care in mental hospitals.* New York: Russell Sage Foundation, 1955.

HARRIS, A., and METCALFE, M. Slowness in schizophrenia. *Journal of Neurological and Neurosurgical Psychiatry, 22* (1959), 239–242.

HENRY, J. The formal structure of a psychiatric hospital. *Psychiatry, 17* (1954), 139–151.

HINGTGEN, J. N., and TROST, F. C., JR. *Shaping cooperative responses in early childhood schizophrenics: II. Reinforcement of mutual physical contact and vocal responses.* Paper presented at American Psychological Association, Los Angeles, September, 1964.

HUNTER, G. F., GOLDMAN, A. R., and SMITH, R. S. *Mental health workers: selection, training and evaluation of recent college graduates serving as therapeutic technicians.* Paper presented at the American Psychological Association, New York, September, 1966.

HYDE, R. W. Factors in group motivation in a mental hospital. *Journal of Nervous and Mental Disorders, 117* (1953), 212–225.

HYDE, R. W., and SOLOMON, H. C. Patient government: a new form of group therapy. *Digest of Neurology and Psychiatry, 18* (1950), 207–218.

JENSEN, A. R. Personality. *Annual Review of Psychology, 9* (1958), 295–322.

Joint Commission on Mental Illness and Health. *Action for mental health.* New York: Basic Books, 1961.

Joint Information Service of the American Psychiatric Association and National Association for Mental Health. *Fact Sheet,* No. 5, March, 1958.

JONES, M. A passing glance at the therapeutic community in 1964. *International Journal of Group Psychotherapy, 15* (1965), 7.

JONES, M. *The therapeutic community.* New York: Basic Books, 1953.

KAMMAN, G. R., LUCERO, R. J., MEYER, B. T., and RECHTSCHAFFEN, A. Critical evaluation of a total push program for regressed schizophrenics in a state hospital. *Psychiatric Quarterly, 28* (1954), 650–667.

KANDLER, H. M., and HYDE, R. W. Socialization activity index for a mental hospital. *Nursing World, 125* (1951), 343–345.

KELLEY, H. H., and THIBAUT, J. W. Experimental studies of group problem solving and process. In G. Lindzey (Ed.), *Handbook of social psychology.* Cambridge, Mass.: Addison-Wesley, 1954. Vol. 2, pp. 735–785.

KEY, W. H. Coordination of the ancillary therapies. In M. Greenblatt and B. Simon (Eds.), *Rehabilitation of the mentally ill.* Washington, D.C.: American Association for the Advancement of Science, 1959. Pp. 89–102.

KING, H. E. *Psychomotor aspects of mental disease.* Cambridge: Harvard University Press, 1954.

KISSINGER, R. D. *The untherapeutic community: a team approach that failed.* Paper presented at the Eastern Psychological Association, New York, April, 1963.

KRAMER, M., GOLDSTEIN, H., ISRAEL, R. H., and JOHNSON, N. A. *Application of life table methodology to the study of mental hospital populations.* Washington, D.C.: American Psychiatric Association, 1956.

KRAUS, P. S. Considerations and problems of ward care for schizophrenic patients. *Psychiatry, 17* (1954), 283–292.

LEE, H. *Two rehabilitation programs for the chronic services.* Final Progress Report, Medfield State Hospital Project Grant OM-547, Harding, Mass., September, 1961–August, 1964.

LEHRMAN, N. S. A state hospital population five years after admission: a yardstick for evaluative comparison of follow-up studies. *Psychiatric Quarterly, 34* (1960), 365–373.

LEMKAU, P. V., and CROCETTI, G. M. Vital statistics of schizophrenia. In L. Bellak (Ed.), *Schizophrenia: a review of the syndrome.* New York: Logos Press, 1958. Pp. 64–81.

LEVINE, S. *Socialization through group interaction.* Paper presented at the American Psychological Association, Philadelphia, August, 1963.

LIKERT, R. *A motivation approach to a modern organization theory.* New York: Wiley, 1959.

LONG, R. C. Praise and censure as motivating variables in the motor behavior and learning of schizophrenics. *Journal of Abnormal and Social Psychology, 63* (1961), 283–288.

LORR, M., JENKINS, R. L., and HOLSOPPLE, J. Q. Multidimensional scale for rating psychiatric patients, hospital form. *U. S. Veterans Administration Technical Bulletin* 10-507. Washington, D.C., Veterans Administration, 1953.

MAIN, T. F. The hospital as a therapeutic institution. *Bulletin of the Menninger Clinic, 10* (1946), 66–76.

MALZBERG, B. Rates of discharge and rates of mortality among first admissions to the New York civil state hospitals. *Mental Hygiene, 36* (1952), 104–120.

MARKS, M. R. How to build better theories, tests, and therapies: The off-quadrant approach. *American Psychologist, 19* (1964), 793–798.

MEDNICK, S. A. A learning theory approach to research in schizophrenia. *Psychological Bulletin, 55* (1958), 316–327.

MERRY, J. An experiment in a chronic psychotic ward. *British Journal of Medical Psychology, 29* (1956), 287–293.

MILLER, D. The rehabilitation of chronic open ward neuropsychiatric patients. *Psychiatry, 17* (1954), 347–358.

MILLER, D. H., and CLANCY, J. An approach to the social rehabilitation of chronic psychotic patients. *Psychiatry, 15* (1952), 435–443.

MULDER, M. Power and satisfaction and task-oriented groups. *Acta Psychologica, 16* (1959), 178–225.

MYERSON, A. Theory and principles of total push in the treatment of chronic schizophrenia. *American Journal of Psychiatry, 95* (1939), 1197–1204.

NEUGARTEN, B. L., and GUTMANN, D. L. *Age-sex roles and personality in middle age: a thematic apperception study.* Psychological Monographs, General and Applied, Volume 72, Whole Number 470. Washington, D.C.: American Psychological Association, 1958.

OSGOOD, C. E., SUCI, G. J., and TANNENBAUM, P. H. *The measurement of meaning.* Urbana: University of Illinois Press, 1957.

PACE, R. E. Situational therapy. *Journal of Personality, 25* (1957), 578–588.

PARSONS, T. *The social system.* Glencoe, Ill.: Free Press, 1951.

PAUNCZ, A. Theory of the total push program in psychiatry. *American Journal of Psychotherapy, 8* (1954), 11–20.

PEARLIN, L. I. Sources of resistance to change in a mental hospital. *American Journal of Sociology, 68* (1962), 325–334.

PETERS, H. L., and JENKINS, R. L. Improvement of chronic schizophrenic patients with guided problem-solving motivated by hunger. *Psychiatry Quarterly Supplement, 28* (1954), 84–101.

POLAN, S., and SPARK, I. Group psychotherapy of schizophrenics in an out-patient clinic. *American Journal of Orthopsychiatry, 20* (1950), 382–396.

RABIN, A. J., KING, G. F., and EHRMANN, J. C. Vocabulary performance of short-term and long-term schizophrenics. *Journal of Abnormal and Social Psychology, 50* (1955), 255–258.

RAFI, A. A. Motor performance of certain categories of mental patients. *Perceptual Motor Skills, 10* (1960), 39–42.

RAPOPORT, R. N. *Community as doctor.* Springfield, Ill.: Charles C Thomas, 1960.

REES, T. P., and GLATT, M. M. The organization of a mental hospital on the basis of group participation. *International Journal of Group Psychotherapy, 5* (1955), 157–161.

RIECKEN, H. W., and HOMANS, G. C. Psychological aspects of social structure. In G. Lindzey (Ed.), *Handbook of Social Psychology.* Cambridge, Mass.: Addison Wesley, 1954, Vol. 2, pp. 786–832.

ROSEN, J., and NEUGARTEN, B. L. Ego functions in the middle and later years: a thematic apperception study of normal adults. *Journal of Gerontology, 15* (1960), 62–67.

SANDERS, R. New manpower for mental hospital service. In E. L. Cowen, M. Zax, and A. Gardner (Eds.), *Emergent approaches to mental health services.* New York: Appleton, 1967 (in press).

SARWER-FONER, G. J., OGLE, W., and DANCEY, T. E. A self-contained women's ward as a therapeutic community. In H. C. B. Denber (Ed.), *Research Conference on Therapeutic Community.* Springfield, Ill.: Charles C Thomas, 1960.

SCHAFER, R. *The clinical applications of psychological tests.* New York: International Universities Press, 1948.

SCHAW, L. C., and HENRY, W. E. A method for the comparison of groups: a study in thematic apperception. *Genetic Psychology Monographs, 54* (1956).

SCHER, J. M. The structured ward: research method and hypothesis in a total treatment setting for schizophrenia. *American Journal of Orthopsychiatry, 28* (1958), 291–299.

SCHNORE, M. M. Re-evaluation of our activity treatment programme with regressed schizophrenic patients. *Canadian Psychiatric Association, 6* (1961), 158–162.

SCHOOLER, C. Affiliation among schizophrenics: preferred characteristics of the other. *Journal of Nervous and Mental Disease, 37* (1963), 438–446.

SECORD, P. F., and BACHMAN, C. W. Personality theory and the problem of stability and change in individual behavior: an interpersonal approach. *Psychological Review, 68* (1961), 21–32.

SEMON, R. G., and GOLDSTEEN, N. The effectiveness of group psychotherapy with chronic schizophrenic patients and an evaluation of different therapeutic methods. *Journal of Consulting Psychology, 21* (1957), 317–322.

SHARTLE, C. L. *Executive performance and leadership.* Englewood Cliffs, N.J.: Prentice-Hall, 1956.

SHATIN, L. Psychological motivation of the geriatric patient. *American Archives of Rehabilitative Therapy, 6* (1958), 35–38.

SMITH, A., SANDERS, R., SMITH, R., WEINMAN, B., KENNY, J., and FITZ-GERALD, B. Predicting the outcome of social therapy with chronic psychotics. *Journal of Abnormal and Social Psychology, 66* (1963), 351–357.

SMITH, H. L. Mental hospital organization: challenge and response. *Mental Hospitals, 15* (1964), 67–71.

SMITH, R. J. The impact of an innovative treatment program on the structure and culture of a large state mental hospital. Unpublished report, addendum to the *Third Interim Report on Social Rehabilitation of the Chronic Mental Patient,* Philadelphia State Hospital Project Grant OM-126, March, 1961.

Southern Regional Educational Board. *The community college in mental health training: report of a conference to explore the role of the community college in training mental health workers.* Atlanta: Southern Regional Educational Board, 1966.

SPOHN, H. E. *The controlled test of a socio-environmental treatment program applied to chronic schizophrenics.* Paper presented at the Eastern Psychological Association, New York, April, 1963.

SPOHN, H. E., and WOLK, W. Effect of group problem-solving experience upon social withdrawal in chronic schizophrenics. *Journal of Abnormal and Social Psychology, 66* (1963), 187–190.

STANTON, A. H., and SCHWARTZ, M. S. *The mental hospital.* New York: Basic Books, 1954.

STOTLAND, E., and KOBLER, A. L. *Life and death of a mental hospital.* Seattle: University of Washington Press, 1965.

STRAUS, G. Some notes on power equalization. In H. J. Leavitt (Ed.), *The social science of organizations: four perspectives.* Englewood Cliffs, N.J.: Prentice-Hall, 1963. Pp. 39–84.

SULLIVAN, H. S. *Conceptions of modern psychiatry.* Washington, D.C.: William Alanson White Foundation, 1947.

SULLIVAN, H. S. Socio-psychiatric research: its implications for the schizophrenia problem and for mental hygiene. *American Journal of Psychiatry, 87* (1931), 977–991.

TORRANCE, E. P. Some consequences of power differences on decision making in permanent and temporary three-man groups. *Research Studies, Washington State College, 22* (1954), 130–140.

United States Department of Labor, Bureau of Employment Security. *Dictionary of occupational titles. Estimates of worker trade requirements for 4000 jobs.* Washington, D.C.: United States Government Printing Office.

United States Department of Labor, Bureau of Employment Security. *Dictionary of occupational titles, Volume I: Definition of titles.* Washington, D.C.: United States Government Printing Office, March, 1949.

United States Department of Labor, Bureau of Employment Security. *Dictionary of occupational titles, Volume II: Occupational classification.* Washington, D.C.: United States Government Printing Office, March, 1949.

Veterans' Administration Hospital Psychiatric Evaluation Project. *Patterns of mental patient post-hospital adjustment.* Intramural Report 65-1. Washington, D.C.: Veterans' Administration Hospital Psychiatric Evaluation Project, February, 1965.

Veterans' Administration Hospital Psychiatric Evaluation Project. *Release and community stay criteria in evaluating psychiatric treatment.* Intramural Report 63-3. Washington, D.C.: Veterans' Administration Hospital Psychiatric Evaluation Project, March, 1963.

Veterans' Administration Hospital Psychiatric Evaluation Project. *Release and community stay in chronic schizophrenia.* Intramural Report 64-4. Washington, D.C.: Veterans' Administration Hospital Psychiatric Evaluation Project, July, 1964.

WEBB, W. W. Conceptual ability of schizophrenics as a function of threat of failure. *Journal of Abnormal and Social Psychology, 50* (1955), 221–224.

WHITEMAN, M. The performance of schizophrenics on social concepts. *Journal of Abnormal and Social Psychology, 49* (1954), 266–271.

WILMER, H. A. Toward a definition of the therapeutic community. *American Journal of Psychiatry, 114* (1958), 824–834.

WILMER, H. A. *Social psychiatry in action.* Springfield, Ill.: Charles C Thomas, 1958.

WINER, B. J. *Statistical principles in experimental design.* New York: McGraw-Hill, 1962.

WING, J. K. Institutionalism in mental hospitals. *British Journal of Social and Clinical Psychology, 1* (1962), 38–51.

WING, J. K., and BROWN, G. W. Social treatment of chronic schizophrenia: a comparative survey of three mental hospitals. *Journal of Mental Science, 107* (1961), 847–861.

WYNNE, R. D. The influence of hospitalization on the verbal behavior of chronic schizophrenics. *British Journal of Psychiatry, 109* (1963), 380–389.

YORK, R., GREENBLATT, M., YORK, R. H., and BROWN, E. L. *From custodial to therapeutic patient care in mental hospitals.* New York: Russell Sage Foundation, 1955.

ZIGLER, E., and PHILLIPS, L. Social effectiveness and symptomatic behaviors. *Journal of Abnormal and Social Psychology, 61* (1960), 231–238.

ZOLIK, E. S., LANTZ, E. M., and BUSIEL, G. J. *New look in mental hospital programs as reflected in patient return rates.* Paper presented in symposium at American Psychological Association, Chicago, September, 1965.

ZUBIN, J. Role of prognostic indicators in the evaluation of therapy. In J. O. Cole, and R. W. Gerard (Eds.), *Psychopharmacology: problems in evaluation.* Washington, D.C.: National Research Council, 1959. Publication Number 583, pp. 343–355.

Name Index

331

Subject Index

335